CURRENT TOPICS IN

DEVELOPMENTAL BIOLOGY

VOLUME 8

CURRENT TOPICS IN
DEVELOPMENTAL BIOLOGY

EDITED BY

A. A. MOSCONA

DEPARTMENT OF BIOLOGY
THE UNIVERSITY OF CHICAGO
CHICAGO, ILLINOIS

ALBERTO MONROY

C.N.R. LABORATORY OF MOLECULAR EMBRYOLOGY
ARCO FELICE (NAPLES), ITALY

VOLUME 8
Gene Activity and Communication
in Differentiating Cell Populations

1974

ACADEMIC PRESS   New York • London

A Subsidiary of Harcourt Brace Jovanovich, Publishers

ACADEMIC PRESS, INC.
111 Fifth Avenue, New York, New York 10003

United Kingdom Edition published by
ACADEMIC PRESS, INC. (LONDON) LTD.
24/28 Oval Road, London NW1

LIBRARY OF CONGRESS CATALOG CARD NUMBER: 66-28604

PRINTED IN THE UNITED STATES OF AMERICA

CONTENTS

CHAPTER 4.   **Concepts and Mechanisms of Cartilage Differentiation**

DANIEL LEVITT AND ALBERT DORFMAN

CHAPTER 5.   **Cell Determination and Biochemical Differentiation
of the Early Mammalian Embryo**

M. C. HERBERT AND C. F. GRAHAM

CHAPTER 6.   **Differential Gene Activity in the Pre- and
Postimplantation Mammalian Embryo**

ROBERT B. CHURCH AND GILBERT A. SCHULTZ

CHAPTER 7. **Neuronal Specificity Revisited**

R. K. HUNT AND MARCUS JACOBSON

LIST OF CONTRIBUTORS

Numbers in parentheses indicate the pages on which the authors' contributions begin.

PETER J. BRYANT, *Center for Pathobiology, University of California, Irvine, California* (41)

ROBERT B. CHURCH, *Divisions of Medical Biochemistry and Biology, Faculty of Medicine, University of Calgary, Calgary, Alberta, Canada* (179)

ALBERT DORFMAN, *Department of Pediatrics, Biochemistry, and Biology, Joseph P. Kennedy, Jr., Mental Retardation Research Center, La Rabida Institute, Pritzker School of Medicine, University of Chicago, Chicago, Illinois* (103)

MICHAEL FELDMAN, *Department of Cell Biology, The Weizmann Institute of Science, Rehovot, Israel* (1)

CHARLOTTE FRIEND, *Center for Experimental Cell Biology, The Mollie B. Roth Laboratory, Mount Sinai School of Medicine, City University of New York, New York, New York* (81)

AMIELA GLOBERSON, *Department of Cell Biology, The Weizmann Institute of Science, Rehovot, Israel* (1)

C. F. GRAHAM, *Zoology Department, Oxford, United Kingdom* (151)

M. C. HERBERT, *Zoology Department, Oxford, United Kingdom* (151)

R. K. HUNT, *Department of Anatomy and the Institute of Neurological Sciences, University of Pennsylvania Medical School, Philadelphia, Pennsylvania* (203)

MARCUS JACOBSON,* *Thomas C. Jenkins Department of Biophysics, The Johns Hopkins University, Baltimore, Maryland* (203)

DANIEL LEVITT, *Department of Pediatrics, Biochemistry, and Biology, Joseph P. Kennedy, Jr., Mental Retardation Research Center, La Rabida Institute, Pritzker School of Medicine, University of Chicago, Chicago, Illinois* (103)

HARVEY D. PREISLER, *Department of Medicine, Mount Sinai School of Medicine, City University of New York, New York, New York* (81)

* Present address: Department of Physiology and Biophysics, University of Miami, School of Medicine, Miami, Florida.

WILLIAM SCHER, *Center for Experimental Cell Biology, The Mollie B. Roth Laboratory, Mount Sinai School of Medicine, City University of New York, New York, New York* (81)

GILBERT A. SCHULTZ, *Division of Medical Biochemistry, Faculty of Medicine, University of Calgary, Calgary, Alberta, Canada* (179)

PREFACE

The Editors wish to thank the contributors to Volume 8 for their cooperation in meeting the specific aims of *Current Topics in Developmental Biology*. We also thank the members of the Advisory Board and the staff of Academic Press for their continuous efforts to increase the usefulness of this publication and to maintain its high standards.

A. A. MOSCONA
ALBERTO MONROY

CONTENTS OF PREVIOUS VOLUMES

Volume 3

CURRENT TOPICS IN

DEVELOPMENTAL BIOLOGY

VOLUME 8

CHAPTER 1

RECEPTION OF IMMUNOGENIC SIGNALS BY LYMPHOCYTES

Michael Feldman and Amiela Globerson

DEPARTMENT OF CELL BIOLOGY
THE WEIZMANN INSTITUTE OF SCIENCE
REHOVOT, ISRAEL

I. Introduction

The process of cell differentiation usually comprises two distinct stages, both of which are responses to specific signals. In the first stage a "primitive" pluripotential cell is induced to become a "committed" cell. In the second stage the committed cell is induced to express its restricted potentiality. In analyzing the immune response as a developmental system, we will deal mainly with a model for the second stage.

In this model, lymphocytes committed to produce immunoglobulins of restricted specificities respond to antigenic signals by producing antibody. The restriction in specificity was originally inferred from studies that tested whether each individual cell produced antibodies to only one or to both of two simultaneously presented antigens (Nossal and Lederberg, 1958; White, 1958; Attardi *et al.*, 1959; Gershon *et al.*, 1968). Al-

1

though the results indicated a restricted specificity, they provided no evidence as to whether or not this was based on diversity among the antibody-forming cell precursors, before their exposure to antigen. A state of diversity in these precursor cells was demonstrated in experiments in which (*a*) a given antigen was shown to bind specifically to a restricted number of lymphocytes (Naor and Sulitzeanu, 1967; Byrt and Ada, 1969); (*b*) antigen-coated columns could specifically bind lymphocytes that were potentially reactive to those antigens (Wigzell and Andersson, 1969; Truffa-Bachi and Wofsy, 1970); and (*c*) following treatment with a highly readioactive form of an antigen, reactivity to that antigen was abolished, probably due to the elimination of lymphocytes that could recognize and react (i.e., they were committed to respond) to that same antigen (Ada and Byrt, 1969; Basten *et al.*, 1971). Thus, whatever its ontogenic origin, a state of commitment can be shown among precursors of antibody-producing cells.

The unique nature of the immune response, relative to other developmental systems, lies in two characteristics: (*a*) the inducer, i.e., the antigen, is a chemically defined molecule, unlike most, if not all morphogenetic inducers studied so far; (*b*) the differentiation of a small resting lymphocyte to an immunoglobulin-producing plasma cell is characterized by a specific and measurable molecular marker, the antibody. Furthermore, the antibody has a specific molecular affinity to the inducer antigen. Hence, the antibody response is more suitable for an analysis of the basic issues in the recognition of specific signals than are other developmental systems. To approach these issues we have developed an experimental system in which the immune response can be induced *in vitro* under controlled conditions, using chemically defined antigens (Segal *et al.*, 1970a). This system is based on the spleen organ culture used for the primary induction of antibody responses to more "complicated" and, hence, chemically less defined antigens such as red blood cells (Globerson and Auerbach, 1965, 1966) and bacterial antigens (Globerson and Feldman, 1969, 1970). The application of chemically defined haptenic determinants, 2, 4-dinitrophenyl (DNP), within an immunogenic molecule, i.e., DNP–rabbit serum albumin (RSA), DNP–hemocyanin-(Hcy), etc., or of chemically defined antigens, such as α-DNP–poly-L-lysine (PLL) (Segal *et al.*, 1970a) or 4-hydroxy-3-iodo-5-nitrophenacetyl (α-NIP)–PLL (Bernstein and Globerson, 1973a), made it possible to analyze in a direct way some of the crucial problems underlying the control of the differentiation of lymphocytes to antibody-producing cells. There is obviously nothing magical about immunogens comprising a defined haptenic determinant and a carrier molecule. However, whereas proteins have many undefined antigenic determinants, these conjugates have a "marked" immunodeterminant, the hapten, which by itself is not immunogenic. For this reason they serve as useful models for protein immunogens in general. It is generally known that immunogens are in most cases macromolecules, yet following. stimulation with the immunogen, antibodies are formed to various, relatively small, antigenic determinants on the immunogenic macromolecule. This gives rise to the obvious question: Does the precursor of the antibody-forming cell have to recognize the entire immunogen in order to produce antibodies to one determinant or does it recognize only the determinant against which it produces the specific antibodies?

Obviously, an analytical approach to this question involves the use of immunogens containing chemically defined haptenic groups, which would serve as "marked" determinants. Antibodies produced after the introduction of such immunogens are directed against the hapten as well as against other determinants of the carrier molecule. One could, therefore, ask whether or not production of antibodies to the haptenic determinant itself requires recognition of the carrier components. If so, which type of cell is equipped with receptors for the carrier? Is the mechanism for recognition of the hapten by the precursor of the antibody-producing cell similar to the recognition of the carrier, and are the cell receptors for carrier determinants similar in structure, specificity, and size to the receptors of the antibody-producing cells? Previous studies have indicated that the capacity of an organism to respond to an immunogenic molecule depends on the existance of cells originating in the bone marrow but "processed" in the thymus (T cells) (Davies et al., 1966; Miller and Mitchell, 1967) although antibodies are produced by cells deriving from the bone marrow (B cells) and not processed by the thymus (Davies et al., 1967; Nossal et al., 1968). If the T cell recognizes different components of the immunogen than does the B cell, we might be dealing with a developmental process in which B cells differentiate to antibody-producing cells, following T–B cell cooperation. Can this type of cell cooperation constitute a model for other known cases of cell interactions in embryogenesis? A simplified approach to this question would be to consider the immune response as a bicellular interaction. Yet, our recent observations of the capacity of certain B cells to recognize and react with carrier determinants (Kunin et al., 1973) suggest a more complex interaction. Furthermore, it is known that the first target cell for an immunogenic signal, be it a protein (Pribnow and Silverman, 1967; Mitchison, 1969) or a microorganism (Fishman, 1961; Gallily and Feldman, 1966, 1967), is the macrophage. The macrophage might thus be the cell presenting the antigen to the lymphoid system. Is the macrophage essential for signaling antibody production and, if so, what are its possible functions?

Antibody production is an expression of gene activity. Such expressions, in other developmental system were shown to be preceded, if not actually determined, by deoxyribonucleic acid (DNA) or cell replication (Turkington, 1968; Bischoff and Holtzer, 1969). In fact, it has been suggested that one critical replication determines cell differentiation in these cases (Turkington, 1968; Bischoff and Holtzer, 1969). However, since antibody-producing cells manifest a clonal pattern of cell proliferation (Burnet, 1959), the questions arise whether this clonal replication is a prerequisite for antibody production, whether there is only one critical replication in this system as in others, or whether replication, although augmenting antibody production, is not essential for the differentiation of B lymphocytes to antibody-producing plasma cells. Thus, the analysis of gene expression in antibody production is usually focused on the immuno-globulin-producing B cells. However, if the cooperation of T cells is required for the induction of B cells to differentiate and produce antibodies, it should be established whether their activity is also determined by cell replication.

All these questions are relevant to the immune response as a developmental process in the adult organism. It is generally accepted that the capacity to produce antibodies appears late during ontogeny (Solomon, 1971; Auerbach, 1972). The development of reactivity to antigenic stimuli in embryonic or fetal organs is, therefore, a question of interest not only with regard to general aspects of embryogenesis, but also to the understanding of the origin of the diversity of lymphocytes. Only evidence derived from a proper experimental approach will separate the numerous theories developed to account for the diversity of lymphocytes as a fundamental phenomenon in the immune system. The present review will summarize our approach to the questions we have outlined.

II. The Experimental System

In Vitro INDUCTION OF A PRIMARY RESPONSE TO A CHEMICALLY DEFINED DETERMINANT

In order to answer some of the questions raised in the foregoing, we have studied the induction of a primary immune response *in vitro*, namely in spleen organ cultures (Globerson and Auerbach, 1966). The antigen used was a chemically defined determinant, the DNP haptenic group, coupled to a protein or a synthetic polypeptide carrier (Segal *et al.*, 1970a). Antibodies were assayed by a sensitive technique based on the inactivation of chemically modified bacteriophages (Haimovich and Sela, 1966). Thus, spleens were taken from unimmunized mice and cultured in medium either with or without antigen. Antibody formation was assayed following stimulation *in vitro*, with DNP coupled either to a protein, Hcy or to the chemically defined synthetic carrier, PLL.

The results indicated that after treatment with antigen most of the cultures produced antibodies to DNP. The difference between the experimental (antigen-treated) and the control cultures was evident not only from the higher incidence of cultures forming antibodies after treatment with antigen but also from the extent of inactivation of DNP-T4 bacteriophage. Medium samples from most of the experimental cultures inactivated the phage to a significantly higher level than did those of the controls. In fact, the high levels of antibodies produced against DNP–PLL suggest that, in mice, this antigen is more immunogenic *in vitro* than *in vivo*. Other chemically defined synthetic antigens, α-NIP–PLL, DNP–poly-Glu^{19}Lys^{75}Tyr^6(TGL) containing 2.2% DNP groups (Sela *et al.*, 1970), poly (L-phe, L-Glu)–poly-DL-Ala- -poly-L-Lys[(Phe, G)–A- -L], have been recently shown in our laboratory to elicit primary immune responses in spleen organ cultures (Bernstein and Globerson, 1973a; Mozes and Globerson, unpublished).

The specificity of the antibodies produced was determined by the capacity of DNP–lysine to inhibit inactivation of DNP-T4 phage by the culture media. We found that the reaction was inhibited in the presence of DNP–lysine, although the extent of inhibition varied in different cultures (Segal *et al.*, 1970a). Thus, the antibodies produced *in vitro* are specific to DNP. *In vivo* the production of antibodies following immunization varies, as a function of time, from 2-mercaptoethanol (2-ME)-sensitive 19 S immunoglobulins to 2-ME-resistant 7 S antibodies. A similar sequential response was found *in vitro* in our organ cultures (Globerson and Auerbach, 1966; Segal *et al.*, 1970a). Initially, 2-ME-sensitive IgM antibodies are produced, followed by a second phase of 2-ME-resistant antibodies (Fig. 1), characterized in certain cases as IgG and in others as IgA antibodies (Nakamura *et al.*, 1973).

III. Cell Receptors for Immunogenic Signals

A. CELL RECEPTORS FOR HAPTENIC DETERMINANTS

Since spleen explants did produce specific antibodies to the DNP determinants of DNP–protein conjugates or DNP–PLL, we tested whether specific cell receptors for DNP determinants exist prior to the primary experimental exposure to the antigen. We used the synthetic DNP–PLL immunogen and assumed that if specific receptors for DNP exist as recognition sites on cells, then the nonimmunogenic hapten DNP–lysine(Lys) would compete with the DNP–PLL for the cell receptors for DNP, and thus decrease or prevent the production of antibodies triggered by DNP–PLL. A similar approach has been employed for studies of the secondary immune response (Dutton and Bulman, 1964; Brownstone *et al.*, 1966). We therefore measured the effect of different concentrations of the free

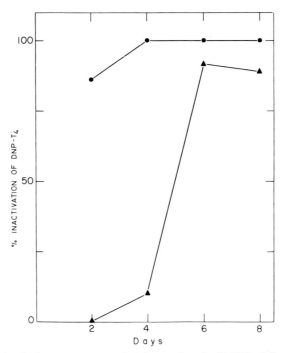

FIG. 1. Antibody response to 2,4-dinitrophenyl (DNP) following primary stimulation *in vitro* with α-DNP–poly-L-lysine (PLL). Medium samples were diluted 1:12 and assayed either following treatment with 2-mercaptoethanol (ME) (triangles) or without any treatment (dots).

hapten on the induction of the primary antibody response by DNP–PLL. It was found that DNP–Lys at a concentration of 5×10^{-4} M applied 3 hours before stimulation with 5×10^{-5} M DNP–PLL significantly inhibited the antibody response (Segal *et al.*, 1971a). When the same concentration of hapten was applied 3 hours after stimulation with the immunogen, no inhibition of antibody production was observed. Thus, specific cell receptors recognizing DNP do exist prior to the experimental exposure to the antigen. Antibody production to DNP seems to require binding of the DNP–carrier conjugate to the DNP receptors.

B.   CELL RECEPTORS FOR CARRIER DETERMINANTS

A further question arose: Do carrier determinants of the immunogenic molecule, which may not themselves induce antibody production, need to be recognized by cells in order to trigger a response to the hapten? Previous studies carried out *in vivo* have suggested that this may be the case (Salvin and Smith, 1960; Ovary and Benacerraf, 1963; Mitchison, 1966). These were concerned with the so-called carrier effect in the secondary immune response to a hapten following immunization with a hapten–carrier conjugate. It was observed that following immunization with DNP coupled to a given protein A, a secondary response to DNP was produced only if the second immunization was carried out with the hapten coupled to that same protein A. When the challenge was made with DNP coupled to another protein B, no secondary response to the DNP was produced. This carrier effect could be interpreted in either of the following ways.

1. Cells capable of producing anti-DNP antibodies have receptors that recognize in the DNP–carrier conjugate not the DNP alone, but the DNP and its carrier environment, i.e., they recognize the DNP and the polypeptide sequence adjacent to the hapten *as one recognizable unit*.

2. Cells capable of producing antihapten antibodies have receptors for the DNP, yet, in order to trigger antibody production to the hapten, the carrier determinants as well have to be recognized by *specific carrier receptors* located either on the same or on different cells.

To separate these possibilities, Mitchison (1967) immunized animals with a hapten–carrier conjugate, NIP–bovine serum albumin (BSA), and then tried to induce a secondary response to NIP, using as the secondary antigen NIP–BSA into which a spacer molecule had been inserted between the NIP and the BSA (NIP–(L-Ala)$_4$–BSA). If the crucial recognition is of the NIP–BSA environment, no secondary response to NIP would be expected to follow immunization with NIP–(L-Ala)$_4$–BSA; if, however, the carrier effect is due to recognition of carrier determinants by specific receptors to such determinants, then the spacer molecule would not prevent the production of a secondary response to NIP. In fact, a secondary response to NIP was produced and as a result, the carrier environment concept has been largely disregarded. However, the need remained for a more direct approach to the questions (*a*) whether, following *primary* immunization by a hapten–protein conjugate, the induction of production of antibodies to the hapten requires the recognition of carrier determinants and (*b*) whether hapten and carrier determinants are recognized by the same or by different cells.

To investigate these questions we have used the *in vitro* system already described. The working hypothesis was that carrier determinants have to be recognized for a primary response to the hapten and that the free carrier would, therefore, inhibit the production of antibodies following stimulation with hapten–carrier conjugates. Experiments were carried out to test whether PLL itself would inhibit induction of an anti-DNP response by DNP–PLL. The result was that cultures pretreated with the free carrier did not produce anti-DNP antibodies, but cultures that had first been treated with the conjugate immunogen and then with the free carrier were not affected (Segal *et al.*, 1971a). To test the specificity of the inhibitory effect of PLL, we measured the effect of (D-alanine)$_4$ on the production of antibodies to DNP–PLL. No inhibition was recorded. (D-alanine)$_4$ did, however, reduce the production of anti-DNP antibodies when applied prior to the administration of DNP–D-alanine–poly-L-lysine (DLPA) as an immunogen (Segal *et al.*, 1971a). These results indicate that a primary production of antibodies to DNP is determined by the binding of both the hapten and the carrier to their respective cell receptors.

To rule out the possibility that receptor reactivity to DNP and to PLL may be attributed to the existence of natural antibodies, we repeated these studies with 5-day-old mice. These animals do show immune reactivity *in vitro* but do not produce detectable background antibodies (Friedman *et al.*, 1971; Friedman, 1971). As shown in Fig. 2, both DNP–

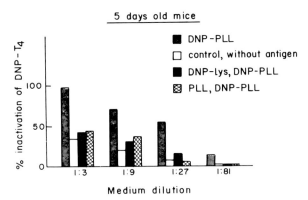

FIG. 2. Inhibition of the *in vitro* response to α-(DNP)–poly-L-lysine (PLL) in spleens of 5-day-old mice by either DNP–lysine or PLL. (Friedman, 1971.)

Lys and PLL inhibited the *in vitro* response to DNP when applied 3 hours before the immunogen DNP–PLL.

We could then pose the question whether such distinct receptors are located on the same or on different cells.

IV.   Cell Interactions

A.   One or Two Cells in a Primary Response?

The carrier effect was originally demonstrated by showing that, following immunization with DNP coupled to protein, a secondary response to DNP requires immunization with the hapten conjugate to the same protein (Salvin and Smith, 1960; Ovary and Benacerraf, 1963). Because the hapten and the carrier are individually recognized by specific receptors, the carrier effect could be operating through either of the following mechanisms: (a) stimulation of cells, each of which happens to possess receptors for both the carrier and the hapten and the response would thus depend on the interaction of the immunogen with both receptors on the same cells; (b) stimulation of cells that possess receptors either to the carrier or to the hapten, and, accordingly, a cell with receptors for the carrier has to cooperate or interact with a cell having receptors for the hapten in order to trigger the latter to produce antihapten antibodies. The incidence of each of these cells will determine the likelihood of cooperation, and thus the level of antibody response. Deficiency in one type of cell will limit cooperation and thus limit antibody production.

The DNP–PLL induced an excellent primary response to DNP *in vitro* as mentioned previously. On the other hand, DNP coupled to RSA was found to be a poor immunogen *in vitro*, since its primary application in culture did not result in antibody production to DNP (Segal *et al.,* 1971a). On the basis of the bicellular interaction, one could attribute this to the low incidence in the spleen of cells possessing receptors for RSA determinants since the response to DNP–PLL indicates that cells reacting to DNP do occur in sufficient quantities. If this interpretation is correct, then increasing the incidence of RSA-sensitive cells in the spleen should render its cell population reactive to DNP–RSA. Such an increase might be achieved by primary immunization with RSA. To test this concept, mice were immunized with RSA, and at various time intervals their spleens were removed and challenged *in vitro* with DNP–RSA. Such cultures were found to show a significant response to DNP (Segal *et al.,* 1970b, 1971a). In contrast, no response could be detected in spleens of unimmunized mice. The specificity of this carrier effect was tested in a number of experiments. Spleens of mice immunized with RSA were challenged *in vitro* with DNP coupled to either RSA or to various non-cross-reacting carriers, human serum albumin (HSA), guinea pig albumin (GPA), Hcy from *Calinectes sapidos,* and keyhole limpet hemocyanin (KLH). High levels of antibodies were obtained only in cultures challenged with DNP–RSA (Segal *et al.,* 1971a). Thus, preimmunization with the carrier itself led to a higher reactivity of the RSA recognizing cells in the spleen, making the spleen responsive to DNP–RSA conjugates. This indicates that the response to DNP–RSA involves the cooperation, probably via the antigen, of cells recognizing carrier determinants and cells recognizing haptenic determinants. Furthermore, it may be predicted from this that spleens from animals primed with RSA will not respond to DNP–RSA if treated simultaneously with free RSA, since the latter molecules will compete with the DNP–RSA for the cell receptors to RSA.

Indeed, the response to DNP–RSA was inhibited in the presence of free RSA (Fig. 3) (Segal *et al.*, 1971a). It appears, therefore, that the induction of an antibody response to protein immunogens involves a bicellular cooperation between cells recognizing certain determinants of the molecule against which they do not necessarily produce antibodies (i.e., carrier

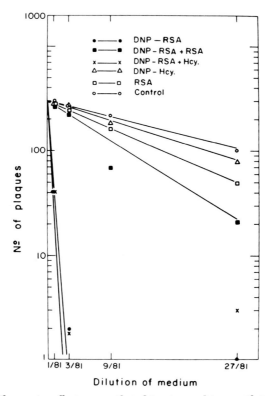

FIG. 3.   The carrier effect as manifested *in vitro* and its specificity. Cultures were prepared from spleens of mice injected with rabbit serum albumin (RSA) 14 days before explantation. Medium samples were assayed on the eighth day of culture for inactivation of 2,4-dinitrophenyl (DNP)–T4 bacteriophage. Hcy, hemocyanin. (Segal *et al.*, 1971a.)

determinants) and cells recognizing other determinants against which they do produce specific immunoglobulins.

B.   Identity of the Cooperating Cells

The notion that the induction of an antibody response is based on cooperation between two distinct cell types was originally suggested by experiments in which sheep red blood cells (SRBC) were used as immunogens. Claman *et al.* (1966) provided evidence for a synergistic effect when they showed that X-irradiated mice, repopulated with both thymus and bone marrow cells, gave a response that was significantly higher than the sum of the responses following reconstitution by either cell type alone. These studies as well as others employing a similar approach provided support for the bicellular concept (Claman and Chaperon, 1969; Davies, 1969; Miller and Mitchell, 1969; Taylor, 1969). Furthermore, functional differences between the thymus and the bone marrow-derived cells were demonstrated. Thus, antibody production was the function of bone marrow-derived lymphocytes, yet the latter had to interact with thymus-derived cells in order to produce antibodies (Davies *et al.*, 1967; Mitchell and Miller, 1968). Thymus-derived lymphocytes were incapable of antibody production, but they were shown to possess specific recognition capacity for SRBC antigens, since thymus-derived cells from the donors tolerant to SRBC could not effectively cooperate with bone marrow-derived cells (Gershon *et al.*, 1968; Miller and Mitchell, 1970).

These observations raised the obvious question of whether the production of antibodies to DNP–protein conjugates is similarly based on cooperation of thymus and bone marrow cells with thymus cells constituting the carrier-sensitive cells and bone marrow cells being those that recognize and produce antibodies to the DNP. To approach this question, we first tested whether the *in vitro* production of antibodies to DNP requires the cooperation of thymus and bone marrow-derived cells. Irradiated mice were divided into three groups: one was injected with thymus and bone marrow cells together, the second was injected with bone marrow, and the third with thymus cells only. All three groups were injected with RSA 24 hours after inoculation. The mice were sacrificed 10 days later, and cultures of their spleens were studied both with or without stimulation with DNP–RSA *in vitro*. Figure 4 demonstrates that a significant production of antibody to DNP was obtained only in cultures of spleens recolonized with both thymus and bone marrow cells and stimulated with the immunogen. Spleens colonized with either cell population alone and then immunized with RSA did not produce anti-DNP antibodies when stimulated *in vitro* with DNP–RSA (Kunin *et al.*, 1971).

To determine which of the two cell populations, thymus or bone marrow-derived, contains the carrier-sensitive cells (i.e., cells recognizing carrier determinants), we exposed one of these populations to the carrier before interaction with the second population could occur. Thus, irradiated mice were first inoculated either with thymus cells or with bone marrow cells. Twenty-four hours later they received RSA, and after 6 days the animals that had received thymus cells were injected with bone marrow, and those that had received bone marrow were injected with thymus

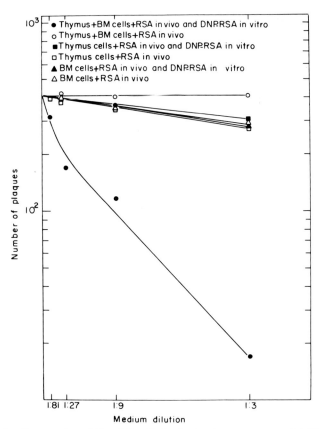

FIG. 4. Cooperation of T and B cells in the *in vitro* response to 2,4-dinitrophenyl (DNP)–rabbit serum albumin (RSA). Cultures were prepared from spleens of irradiated mice reconstituted with thymus and/or bone marrow (BM) cells. Medium samples were assayed on the eighth day of culture for inactivation of DNP–T4 bacteriophage. (Kunin *et al.*, 1971.)

cells. The mice were sacrificed 4 days later, and spleen organ cultures were made. The cultures from each spleen were divided into two groups: one was stimulated with DNP–RSA and the second served as an unstimulated control. The results (Fig. 5) show that only spleen cultures derived from donors that were first inoculated with thymocytes and RSA, and 6 days later with bone marrow cells, produced antibodies in response to stimulation with DNP–RSA *in vitro*. This experiment was repeated leaving an 8-day interval between the first and second inoculation of cells into the irradiated mice, and 2 days between the second inoculation and removal of spleens. The results were the same as those obtained in the previous experiment. The only explants that, after *in vitro* stimulation

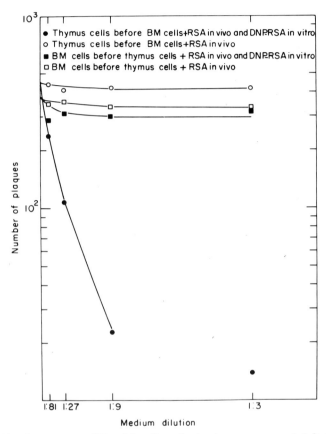

FIG. 5.   Cooperation of T and B cells in the *in vitro* response to 2,4-dinitrophenyl (DNP)–rabbit serum albumin (RSA). A two-step transfer experiment. BM, bone marrow cells. (Kunin *et al.*, 1971.)

with DNP–RSA responded by producing antibody to DNP, were those obtained from animals inoculated first with thymus and RSA and then with bone marrow. It was, therefore, deduced that the cells that interact with the carrier (RSA) determinants (i.e., the carrier-sensitive cells) are those derived from the thymus, the T cells. The antibody-producing cells might then be the lymphocytes derived from the bone marrow, the B cells, as demonstrated in the response to SRBC (Davies *et al.*, 1967; Nossal *et al.*, 1968).

C. THE CARRIER EFFECT: CELLULAR BASIS OF T-CELL ACTIVATION

We have demonstrated that preimmunization of normal mice with RSA rendered their spleens responsive to DNP–RSA. Similarly, enhancement of the response to a hapten by carrier preimmunization was reported by Katz et al. (1970). Our experiments in which the spleens of X-irradiated animals were first repopulated with thymus and then immunized with RSA suggested that it was the T cell that recognizes the carrier determinants. This conclusion was also derived from a variety of studies by elimination of cells carrying θ antigen (Raff, 1970; Mitchison et al., 1970).

Preimmunization against the carrier, which determined the in vitro reactivity toward hapten–carrier conjugates (Segal et al., 1970b; Segal et al., 1971a), could be explained in two distinct, although not mutually exclusive ways.

1. A priori, the incidence of T cells with receptors to RSA is low in the spleen. Therefore, in vitro, the spleen of an unimmunized mouse does not react to DNP–RSA. Immunization with the carrier molecule causes the RSA-reactive cells to migrate from the thymus to the spleen, can then react to this immunogen in vitro.

2. The spleens of untreated mice contain small numbers of cells reactive to RSA. Upon immunization with the carrier, they are induced to replicate, thus yielding either a higher number of cells or a population of cells that have differentiated during the replication phase to a stage of more effective reactivity to carrier determinants.

To test whether the first possibility explains the mechanism of the carrier effect, 9-day-old mice were thymectomized 24 hours before immunization with RSA. At this stage the mice are already competent to react to this antigen. It was expected that if the responsiveness of the spleen to DNP–RSA is, indeed, determined by an external supply (from the thymus) of RSA-specific T cells, then removal of the thymus prior to immunization would interfere with the subsequent response in vitro. The results, shown in Fig. 6, confirmed this hypothesis: spleens of these thymectomized mice did not react in vitro to DNP–RSA. On the other hand, thymectomy performed 3 days after injection of RSA had no effect on the response to DNP–RSA (Bernstein and Globerson, 1973b).

These results demonstrate that migration of RSA-reactive cells from the thymus into the spleen is triggered by immunization with RSA. However, this does not rule out the possibility that upon settling in the spleen the cells are stimulated by the antigen to replicate. We therefore attempted to find out whether cell replications are a prerequisite for the carrier effect.

An experiment was performed in which lymphoid cell replication was inhibited by vinblastine prior to, at the time of, or following immunization with the carrier protein. Mice were immunized with RSA and divided into four groups: one received vinblastine 24 hours before in-

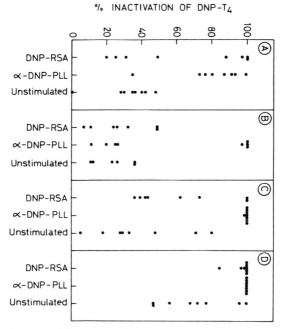

Fig. 6.   Inhibition of the carrier effect by thymectomy of 9-day-old mice. Rabbit serum albumin (RSA) was injected either before (A) or after thymectomy (B). Unoperated controls (C); cultures prepared from spleens of adult mice (D). Medium samples were collected on the seventh day of culture and diluted 1:9 before assay.

jection of RSA, the second at the same time as RSA, and the third 24 hours after injection of RSA; the fourth group received RSA with no vinblastine treatment. Five days after immunization the spleens were removed, cultured, and challenged *in vitro* with DNP–RSA. The results (Fig. 7) indicated that no significant levels of antibodies to DNP were produced by spleen cultures from animals treated simultaneously with RSA and vinblastine. On the other hand, spleens of mice treated with the drug just 24 hours after the injection of RSA responded to DNP–RSA with the production of high levels of antibodies (Segal *et al.*, 1971a). The very fact that vinblastine prevented immune reactivity when applied simultaneously with the carrier suggested that replication of carrier-recognizing cells is essential for the manifestation of the carrier effect. Yet, since its application 24 hours after the carrier did not suppress reactivity, it appears that a prolonged exponential proliferation of carrier-specific cells is not necessary. In order to test whether the replicating cells are indeed T cells, vinblastine was employed in an experiment using irradiated mice reconstituted with thymus cells and treated with RSA

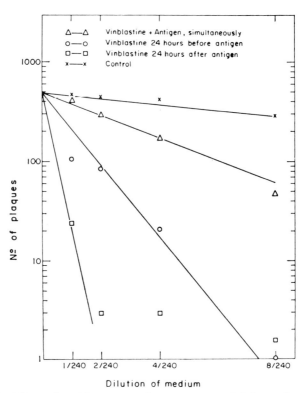

FIG. 7. Effect of vinblastine on the response to 2,4-dinitrophenyl (DNP)–rabbit serum albumin (RSA) by spleens of mice immunized with RSA. Medium samples were collected on the eighth day of culture and assayed for inactivation of DNP–T4 bacteriophage. (Segal *et al.*, 1971a.)

24 hours later. Bone marrow cells were administered 8 days after the thymocytes. Mice were injected with vinblastine either simultaneously with RSA or 4–7 days later. It was found that simultaneous treatment with vinblastine and RSA inhibited the subsequent *in vitro* response to DNP–RSA, whereas, when the application of vinblastine was delayed, the response was comparable to that of the control group that had received no vinblastine (Fig. 8) (Kunin, 1973). Thus, although replication of T cells is required for the establishment of the carrier effect, an exponential increase in the population of RSA-specific T cells is apparently not necessary. Rather there seems to be one critical cycle of replication essential for rendering T cells capable of cooperation with B cells. The single crucial replicating event of T cells triggered by the carrier molecule may determine a number of alternative molecular events. One could en-

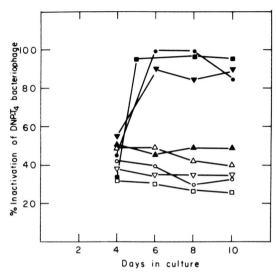

Fig. 8. Effect of vinblastine on T-cell activity. Irradiated mice were reconstituted with thymus cells, and 24 hours later injected with rabbit serum albumin (RSA). Mice were injected with vinblastine simultaneously with RSA (▲ △), 4 days later (▼ ▽) or 7 days later (■ □) or left uninjected (● ○). (▲ ▼ ■ ●) Spleen cultures stimulated with 2,3-dinitrophenyl (DNP)–RSA; (△ ▽ □ ○) Unstimulated controls. (Kunin, 1973.)

visage a crucial DNA replication as a requirement for the derepression of genes coding for the specific receptor molecules of T cells. Activation of carrier-sensitive T cells could then be based on the induction of T cells, each of which possesses an increased number of specific receptors. In this way, the increase in concentration of receptors per cell, rather than of the size of population, would increase the probability of a functional T–B cooperation via the hapten–carrier immunogen.

D. SPECIFIC BLOCKING OF T CELLS: TOLERANCE TO RABBIT SERUM ALBUMIN

We have demonstrated that the production of antibodies to DNP following immunization with a DNP–carrier conjugate involves cooperation between T cells recognizing antigenic determinants of the carrier and B cells recognizing the DNP. The induction of tolerance to carrier determinants (i.e., RSA) could then be expected to result in the loss of the capacity to produce antibody to DNP when the latter is coupled to RSA. To test this, tolerance to RSA was induced in adult mice (Greenberg-Ramon, 1969). Their spleens were cultured and stimulated in vitro with DNP–RSA. We found that such cultures did not respond to DNP

(Segal *et al.*, 1971b). We then tested whether the inability to produce anti-DNP antibodies in response to DNP–RSA is, indeed, derived from a specific unresponsiveness to RSA. Mice tolerant to RSA were immunized with Hcy. Their spleens were removed 5 days later and cultured in the presence of either DNP–Hcy or DNP–RSA. It was found (Segal *et al.*, 1971b) that cultures from RSA-tolerant mice stimulated *in vitro* with DNP–Hcy produced antibodies to DNP, whereas those challenged with DNP–RSA did not. Furthermore, spleen explants from mice tolerant to RSA responded *in vitro* to a primary challenge with DNP–PLL (Fig. 9).

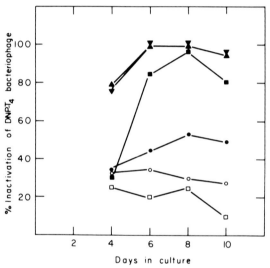

FIG. 9. *In vitro* response to 2,4-dinitrophenyl (DNP)–poly-L-lysine (PLL) by spleens of mice tolerant to rabbit serum albumin (RSA). (▲) Tolerant spleen, RSA *in vivo*, DNP–PLL *in vitro*; (●) tolerant spleen, RSA *in vivo*, DNP–RSA *in vitro*; (○) tolerant spleen, RSA *in vivo*; (▼) Normal spleen, RSA *in vivo*, DNP–PLL *in vitro*; (■) Normal spleen, RSA *in vivo*, DNP–RSA *in vitro*; (□) Normal spleen, RSA *in vivo*.

Thus, spleens tolerant to RSA do contain cells capable of recognizing and producing antibodies to DNP. In view of this it may be concluded that in order to produce anti-DNP antibodies in response to DNP–carrier conjugates, such cells have to interact with lymphocytes recognizing the specific carrier determinant, tolerance of which prevents interaction. Since the functional carrier-sensitive cells were shown to be T cells (Mitchison *et al.*, 1970; Raff, 1970; Kunin *et al.*, 1971), one might predict that the combination of tolerant T cells with normal B cells would not permit the necessary cooperation, and this was verified in the following experiment. Mice were exposed to 750 R total-body irradiation and inoculated with thymus cells from RSA-tolerant donors and bone marrow cells from normal donors. The controls were irradiated recipients inoculated with thymus and bone marrow cells, both from normal donors. Animals of both groups were immunized with RSA, their spleens were explanted, and the cultures were challenged with DNP–RSA. It was found that antibodies to DNP were produced only by spleen explants from mice colonized with thymus and bone marrow cells from normal donors. Antibodies were not produced in cultures of spleens repopulated with thymus cells from tolerant animals and bone marrow cells from normal donors (Kunin et al., 1973). These results confirm the basic prediction that carrier recognition is confined to the thymus, whereas the recognition of the hapten is a function of bone marrow cells.

On the basis of this deduction it would be expected that spleen cells from X-irradiated animals recolonized with thymus from normal donors and bone marrow from donors tolerant to RSA would respond to DNP–RSA. Yet, tests showed no antibody production to DNP in this case (Kunin et al., 1973). This suggests two alternative interpretations: (a) B cells from the tolerant animals suppress T cell–carrier interaction (Gershon et al., 1972) or produce blocking antibodies (Hellström et al., 1971; Zan-Bar et al., 1973) to the carrier determinants or bind the carrier to their cell receptors (Ada, 1969; Naor and Sulitzeanu, 1969; Sjöberg and Möller, 1970); (b) not only T cells but also B cells must recognize carrier determinants in order to trigger antibody production to the hapten.

To discover the correct interpretation, we delayed injection of the bone marrow so that the normal T cells were exposed to the carrier molecule 8 days before bone marrow cells from tolerant animals were inoculated. The spleens were then cultured and treated with DNP–RSA. Yet no antibodies to DNP were produced (Kunin et al., 1973). It appears, therefore, that tolerant bone marrow cells do not prevent the response to DNP–RSA by interfering with the reactivity of T cells. This was further confirmed by showing that the addition of tolerant B cells to explants of normal spleens immunized with RSA did not prevent the latter from responding to DNP–RSA in vitro (Kunin et al., 1973). Thus the T–B cooperation process might be more complicated than the simple bicellular concept implies.

Which are the cells in the bone marrow that recognize the carrier? To test the possibility of their being T cells (Burleson and Levey, 1972), we applied anti-θ antibodies (Schlesinger, 1970; Raff, 1971) to the bone marrow prior to inoculation. However, this treatment did not interfere with the response of normal bone marrow cells following inoculation of normal T cells (Kunin et al., 1973). Hence we suggest that the production of antibodies to an immunogen, such as DNP–RSA, involves carrier recognition by T and B cells as well as recognition of the hapten by B cells. This may be explained by either of the following models: (*a*) production of antibodies is based on a tricellular interaction system rather than on simple bicellular cooperation; (*b*) the response involves two phases that are sequentially related. An initial production of antibodies is determined by cooperation of B cells reacting with the carrier molecule and B cells producing antibodies to the hapten. Subsequently, the response is continued by interaction of T and B cells. So far, no experimental evidence is available to support or refute the first model. However, several observations favor the second model. Interaction between B cells was suggested from the recent studies of del Guercio (1972) and del Guercio and Leuchars (1972) showing that mice tolerant to the thymus-independent antigen, Levan, failed to react to DNP–Levan. Furthermore, it has been demonstrated that the response to thymus-independent antigens (i.e., *Pneumoccocus* polysacharide) involves antibodies of the IgM class (Howard *et al.*, 1971; Baker *et al.*, 1971; Howard, 1972). On the other hand, the response to conventional antigens involves an IgM response followed by production of IgG antibodies, the latter being more thymus-dependent than the former (Taylor and Wortis, 1968; Hunter and Munro, 1972). Accordingly, we suggest that the first IgM phase of a response to any antigen results from an initial B–B interaction, whereas the second phase manifested by IgG production is determined by the cooperation of T and B cells. Indeed, in our studies, the response of spleens of mice reconstituted with thymus and bone marrow cells showed the sequential production of 19 S and 7 S antibodies (Kunin, 1973). Furthermore, we found (Globerson, unpublished) that T-cell-deficient mice (nudes or neonatally thymectomized) did react *in vitro* to thymus-dependent antigens (i.e., DNP–TGL) (Karniely *et al.*, 1973) by producing 19 S antibodies. Their littermate controls, however, produced 7 S class antibodies in addition to these. Thus, thymus-independent antigens (Davies *et al.*, 1970; Feldmann and Basten, 1971; Andersson and Blomgren, 1971) may not be privileged antigens capable of interacting directly with B cells. It is, in fact, possible that every antigen is able to induce a phase of a thymus-independent response, but polymerized thymus-independent antigens cannot induce T cells to produce the subsequent IgG phase of the response.

E. Function of Macrophages

Macrophages represent the first target cell of an injected antigen. An obvious question therefore arises: Is the interaction between an antigen and a macrophage an essential step in the induction of antibody production? Fishman (1961), studying the primary induction of antibody to T2 phages, claimed that rat lymph node cells respond *in vitro* only if the antigen is applied in the presence of peritoneal exudate cells (PEC). Furthermore, analysis of this system led Fishman and Adler (1963) to suggest that interaction between macrophages and antigen results in the release of ribonucleic acid (RNA) which seems to trigger lymphocytes to produce antibodies. A specific immunogenic activity of RNA from macrophages or from spleen cells, as a result of interaction with antigen was further reported for T2 bacteriophage (Friedman *et al.*, 1965; Gottlieb *et al.*, 1967), Hcy (Askonas and Rhodes, 1965), and SRBC (Cohen and Parks, 1964; Abramoff and Brien, 1968). In some of these studies the RNA–antigen complex extracted from macrophages appeared to be involved (Fishman and Adler, 1963; Askonas and Rhodes, 1965; Friedman *et al.*, 1965). In more recent investigations, Adler *et al.* (1966) and Fishman and Adler (1967) reported that an active antigen-free RNA may be extracted from macrophages that have interacted with antigen. However, none of these studies indicated whether such informational RNA molecules, moving from one cell, possibly a macrophage, to another cell, possibly a lymphocyte, play a role in the normal *in vivo* processes of induction of antibody production.

We have tested whether macrophages are essential for antibody production by studying their ability to restore the immunosuppressive effect of total-body irradiation. Indeed, we found that normal macrophages that had interacted *in vitro* with *Shigella* could signal antibody production in mice that had been exposed to total-body irradiation (Gallily and Feldman, 1966, 1967; Feldman and Gallily, 1967). Such mice responded only lightly to the injection of the antigen alone. Hence, the impairment of the capacity of sublethally irradiated mice to produce antibodies to certain antigens is attributed to a defect in the immunogenic function of macrophages, which were thus shown to play a significant role in signaling antibody production. Mitchison (1969) extended the analysis of the role of macrophages to studies with protein antigens. These investigations, which followed those of Dixon and Weigle (1957) and of Pribnow and Silverman (1967), further indicated the importance of macrophage–antigen interaction in triggering lymphocytes to produce antibodies. After the more recent demonstration of the cooperation between T and B lymphocytes in the production of antibodies, the following question arose: Are macrophages required in addition to the T and B populations? A partial answer was inferred from the *in vitro* studies of Mosier (1967) showing that in addition to lymphocytes, adherent cells are essential for the response to SRBC. Analysis of the tissue origin of the cells demonstrated that the adherent cells originated in the bone marrow, whereas the lymphocytes were of both thymus and bone marrow popula-tions (Mosier et al., 1970). However, the identity of the adherent cells as macrophages required further analysis. The experiments of Shortman and Palmer (1971), Feldmann (1972), Gisler and Dukor (1972), and Leserman et al. (1972) produced further support for the idea that T–B interaction also involves macrophages. None of these studies answer the question whether or not the production of antibodies to one chemically defined antigenic determinant depends on interaction of all these cells. We therefore used the carrier effect to study this problem and performed experiments based on our previous observations that (a) priming with RSA in complete Freund's adjuvant (CFA) rendered the spleens of mice susceptible to a subsequent in vitro stimulation with DNP–carrier con-jugate (Segal et al., 1971a), (b) spleens of X-irradiated mice colonized with thymus and bone marrow cells manifested a similar carrier effect when immunized in vivo with RSA and tested in vitro with DNP–RSA (Kunin et al., 1971), and (c) by inoculating X-irradiated mice first with thymus cells and RSA, then with bone marrow cells, it was possible to demonstrate that the carrier-sensitive cells are thymus derived (Kunin et al., 1971). We subsequently used this system of activating thymus-derived carrier-sensitive cells to analyze the immunogenic function of macrophages in the production of antibodies to DNP–RSA.

We first tested the conditions of immunization with RSA necessary for conferring a carrier effect, i.e., for rendering spleens responsive to subsequent immunization with DNP–carrier conjugates. We found that in order to produce this effect, the RSA must be introduced in combination with CFA. The role of the adjuvant could be attributed to its capacity to stimulate macrophage activity (Munder et al., 1970). To test this, we immunized mice with RSA by inoculating them with PEC that had been incubated with RSA and then explanted the spleens and immunized them in culture with DNP–RSA. This resulted in the production of antibodies to DNP (Kunin et al., 1972). The same result was obtained when PEC incubated with RSA were injected to X-irradiated mice that had been reconstituted with thymus and bone marrow cells. A two-step experiment was then designed to test whether thymus or bone marrow cells serve as the target for the action of the PEC–RSA complex. Irradiated mice were injected with thymus cells and 24 hours later they were divided into two groups. One received RSA in CFA and the other PEC preincubated with RSA. After 8 days, the two groups were injected with bone marrow cells. The mice were sacrificed 2 days later and their spleens were cultured with DNP–RSA. Control groups were cultured without antigen. It was found that spleens of PEC-treated animals reacted to the DNP–RSA in the same way as the groups treated with RSA in adjuvant. On the other hand, when irradiated mice were first injected with bone marrow and PEC pretreated with RSA and the thymus cells were subsequently applied, no response to DNP–RSA stimulation *in vitro* could be detected (Kunin *et al.*, 1972).

The results obtained in these experiments could be attributed to either of two mechanisms: (1) macrophages present the antigen to specific T cells, and the activation of these T cells depends on their receiving the antigenic signal from macrophage-bound antigens; (2) macrophages can present the antigen directly to B cells, thus replacing T cells. To test the second possibility the following experiment was carried out. Irradiated mice reconstituted with bone marrow cells were injected with PEC incubated with RSA. A control group received thymus, bone marrow cells, and PEC incubated with RSA. Spleens were subsequently explanted and challenged *in vitro* with DNP–RSA. Cultures were set up in parallel with and without antigenic stimulation *in vitro*. Antibodies were detected in spleen cultures of bone marrow- and thymus-treated mice but not in those treated with bone marrow only (Kunin *et al.*, 1972). It was concluded that PEC cannot replace the T cells in this system. A similar conclusion was obtained by Unanue (1970) in studies with KLH.

Which cell population, then, do the macrophages interact with? It could be argued that the RSA macrophage complex acts on T cells and activates their functional cooperation with B cells. The nature of this T-cell activation is unknown, yet we suggest that the observations that induction of a carrier effect depends on a critical cell replication (Segal *et al.*, 1971a; Nakamura *et al.*, 1972) and that T-cell activation involves cell replication (Kunin, 1973) may be relevant to this discussion. A cinematographic analysis of omentum cells (Fischer *et al.*, 1970) showed that macrophage–lymphocytes interaction is associated with lymphocyte replication. It appears, therefore, that a cell replication critical for the initiation of an antibody response can be induced in T cells by a macrophage–complex but not by a soluble antigen. It is not yet known whether the induction is mediated by an antigen processed by the macrophage (Bainford and Black, 1972) by an interaction between the macrophage-bound antigen (Unanue and Cerottini, 1970) and the T cell or by an immunogenic RNA (Fishman and Adler, 1967).

In this context, the observation regarding the different RNA fractions active in the antibody response are of special interest. Fishman and Adler (1967, 1970) have shown that an RNA–antigen complex from the macrophages triggers the production of IgC antibodies, whereas RNA free of antigen induces IgM response. Accordingly, it may be assumed that the RNA–Ag complex induces the T-B response, whereas the RNA free of antigen reacts directly with B cells.

What do the T cells transfer to the B cells? Do they present the specific immunogen signal? Are macrophages active at this stage also?

Attempting to answer these questions, Feldmann and Basten (1972b, c) performed unique experiments in which flagellin was used as the immunogen. They suggested that macrophages transfer to B cells the receptor-immunoglobulin moiety from the T cells complexed with the antigen (Feldmann and Nossal, 1972). Before accepting this as the universal mechanism of T cell–macrophage interactions in the antibody response, further studies should be carried out to see just how general a phenomenon this is.

V.   Nature of Cell Receptors for Antigens

The production of antibodies is preceded by the recognition of antigenic determinants on the immunogenic molecule by two distinct cell types, the T and B lymphocytes. Using DNP–protein conjugates as immunogens, we demonstrated that different antigenic determinants of the same molecule are recognized by each of these cells. What then is the nature of the cell receptor?

Studies of the properties and structure of the cell receptors for antigens were based on an aesthetic rather than on rational considerations. It was assumed that evolution preferred economical pathways and, therefore, one cell should be incapable of synthesizing two distinct molecules, the antibody and the cell receptor each of which can recognize the same antigenic determinant. Hence, it was suggested that the cell receptors for antigens are antibodylike molecules. The fact that antibodies inhibit the induction of an immune response (Mitchison, 1967) was therefore not too surprising and was taken as an indication that the receptor is, indeed, an antibody entity. A more direct demonstration of the presence of immunoglobulins on lymphoid cell membranes was the observation that antibodies to immunoglobulins induce transformation in lymphoid cells (Sell, 1967a,b). To test whether antibodies indeed constitute the B-cell receptors, we designed experiments based on the assumption that the receptor for a hapten is identical to the antigen-binding site of the antibody to the same hapten. Suitable reagents that covalently bind to antibodies should then irreversibly block the receptors at the antibodylike recognition site. We used affinity labeling reagents of DNP that bind covalently with rabbit anti-DNP antibodies and lead to an accompanying loss of the activity of the antibody site (Weinstein et al., 1969). Two such reagents were applied α,N-bromoacetyl-ϵ,N-(2,4-dinitrophenyl)–lysine (BADL) and N-bromoacetyl-N'(2,4-dinitrophenyl)–ethylenediamine (BADE) prepared by introducing a reactive bromoacetyl group into homologous derivatives of the dinitrophenyl (DNP) hapten. It has been shown that the binding of these reagents to the antibodies to DNP can be inhibited by an excess of DNP–lysine; yet no binding was observed when the reagents were tested with normal rabbit IgG (Weinstein et al., 1969).

Studies were made on the effect of these affinity labeling reagents on the response to the 2,4-DNP determinant induced in vitro by DNP–protein conjugates. We used spleen explants originating in mice immunized 4–6 months before explantation with DNP–Hcy, DNP–RSA, or poly-DL-Ala–RSA. Each explant was incubated for 4 hours with either DNP–lysine or with BADL or BADE. The cultures were then washed and treated with antigens against which they had been immunized in vivo. The antigen containing medium was removed 48 hours later and replaced by antigen-free fresh medium. Culture medium samples were subsequently collected at 2-day intervals and were assayed for anti-DNP antibodies and antipoly-DL-Ala antibodies. The results indicated that treatment with BADL reduced the incidence of antibody-forming cultures (Segal et al., 1969b; Givol et al., 1970). Unlike DNP–lysine, BADL prevented antibody production even when the antigen was applied 44 hours after the removal of the affinity labeling reagent. Figure 10 shows that in fact DNP–lysine had a transient effect in inhibiting the induction of an antibody response to DNP by DNP–RSA, whereas BADL and BADE had a marked and lasting effect. To test the specificity of the inhibition obtained by BADL and BADE, the effect of these reagents on the response to a non-cross-reacting antigen was studied. Spleen explants were obtained from mice immunized with poly-DL-Ala–RSA. The capacity of BADL and BADE to inhibit antibody production to the poly-DL-alanine was tested. There was no inhibitory effect on the production of antibodies to this molecule, which does not cross-react with DNP. Thus, BADL and BADE specifically inhibit the production of anti-DNP antibodies, and the effect, unlike that of DNP–lysine, persists for at least 44 hours. Hence, it appears that these reagents become covalently bound to antibodylike molecules on the surface of spleen lymphocytes. In all probability, the binding of BADL and BADE takes place at the B-cell receptor to DNP resulting in the inhibition of antibody production to DNP. A similar experimental approach was applied by Plotz (1969) in studies of the secondary response to the NIP hapten. Since all these experiments involved the use of cells from preimmunized mice, it could be argued that the affinity labeling compounds bound to preformed antibodies, passively at-

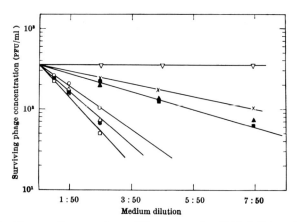

Fig. 10.   The   effect   of   α,N-bromoacetyl–ε,N-(2,4-dinitrophenyl)–lysine (BADL), N-bromoacetyl–N'-(2,4-dinitrophenyl)–ethylenediamine (BADE), and 2,4-dinitrophenyl (DNP)–lysine on antibody production *in vitro*. The curves show inactivation of DNP–T4 phage by medium from the spleen explants that were induced *in vitro* with DNP–rabbit serum albumin (RSA) for secondary response. Phage was incubated with medium samples for 2 hours. (▽) Explants from normal animals control; (×) explants from primed animals without *in vitro* stimulation with DNP–RSA; (▲) explants incubated with BADE before antigen; (■) explants incubated with BADL before antigen; (○) explants incubated with DNP–lysine before antigen; (●) explants incubated with phosphate buffered saline alone before antigen; (□) explants incubated with BADL 3 days after antigen; (△) explants incubated with BADE 3 days after antigen. (Segal *et al.*, 1969b.)

tached to the cells, rather than to cell receptors. We, therefore, attempted to repeat these studies on the primary immune response before any overt immunization to DNP could have occurred (Friedman *et al.*, 1971). As shown in Fig. 11, treatment with BADE of spleen explants from normal mice did inhibit the response to DNP–PLL *in vitro*. It thus appears that inhibition of the response by BADE results from binding to cell receptors rather than to antibodies passively attached to the cells.

Could the same approach be used to investigate the nature of the T-cell receptor? Here the situation is considerably more complex than that of the receptors for antigens on B cells. Actually, there is not unequivocal demonstration that immunoglobulins do exist as integral components of T-cell membranes. Some investigators have claimed to have extracted immunoglobulins from such cells (Marchalonis *et al.*, 1972). One of the main difficulties here is to distinguish between cell surface immunoglobulins that are actually synthesized by the T cells and might, therefore, represent the specific receptors and immunoglobulins that are present on T cells because they have been passively absorbed onto the cell

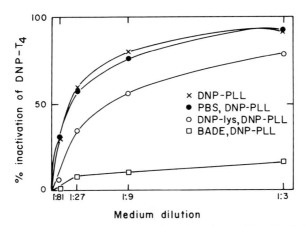

Fig. 11. The effect of N-bromoacetyl–N'-(2,4-dinitrophenyl)–ethylenediamine (BADE) and 2,4-dinitrophenyl (DNP)–lysine on the primary response to DNP–poly-L-lysine (PLL) *in vitro*. PBS, phosphate buffered saline. (Friedman, 1971.)

surface. The recent studies of Feldmann and Basten (1972c) indicate that macrophages take up antigen–immunoglobulin complexes from T cells and these might represent an antigen–T-cell receptor system. Yet, the origin and nature of these immunoglobulins remain unclear. In fact, carrier-specific "helper" cells of thymus origin were inactivated by rabbit antiserum against mouse kappa light chains (Lesley *et al.*, 1971). On the other hand, in experiments analyzing T-cell mediated immune reactions evoked *in vitro*, anti-immunoglobulin antibodies *did not* block the reactions (Feldman *et al.*, 1972). Hence, the possibility that T-cell receptors for antigens might be molecular entities different from the known immunoglobulins requires further analysis. Whatever the nature of the T-cell receptor, it appears that the capacity of T cells to recognize antigenic determinants is based on a different spectrum of specificities than that of the B cell. Thus, red blood cell antigens that do not cross-react at the level of B cells, i.e., at the level of antibodies, are cross recognized by T cells (Hartmann, 1971; Haritou and Argyris, 1972). This seems compatible with the notion that the molecular basis of recognition of antigens by T cells might be different from the molecular basis of recognition by B cells, i.e., from the immunoglobulin recognition. In principle we feel that one should not be alarmed at the possibility of the same inducer being recognized by two separate molecules. In *Escherichia coli* the lactose is recognized by at least three distinct molecules in the same cell—the permease, the repressor, and the β-galactosidase. Why cannot an antigen be recognized by two distinct receptor molecules produced by and located on different cells?

VI. Deoxyribonucleic Acid Replication as a Prerequisite for Antibody Production

The clonal proliferation of antibody-producing cells is a characteristic feature of the immune response. Yet the question of the necessity of replication of antibody-producing cells for the induction of the immune response merits special examination. Dutton and Mishell (1967) demonstrated that virtually all of the antibody-forming cells appearing in an *in vitro* primary response were direct progeny of cells that had been dividing at the initial period of the response. Studies in an *in vivo* system led to the same conclusion. It thus appeared that precursor cells divided to give rise to antibody-producing cells. Yet, Dutton and Mishell (1967) as well as Tannenberg (1967) suggested that at least some cells acquire the capacity to produce antibody without any cell division. In fact, subsequent investigations indicated that all antibody-producing cells, at least in some *in vitro* systems, developed without a prior stage of cell division (Bussard and Lurie, 1967; Saunders, 1969; Bussard *et al.*, 1970).

We therefore aimed at finding out whether cell replication actually determines the induction of a primary production of antibodies and, in particular, whether it is determined by DNA replication of the precursor of the antibody producing B cell. We tested the primary immune response induced *in vitro* by either DNP–PLL or DNP–RSA. For the inhibition of DNA synthesis *in vitro*, we used cytosine arabinoside (CA) which is an effective but reversible inhibitor (Chu and Fischer, 1962; Kihlman, 1966; Evans and Mengel, 1966) with little effect on RNA synthesis (Chu and Fischer, 1962). We found that (Nakamura *et al.*, 1972) when applied after antibody production had begun, $2 \times 10^{-5} M$ of CA inhibited DNA synthesis and cell proliferation, while leaving intact both synthesis and secretion of antibodies. Experiments were then designed to test for the existence of a phase of cell division essential for the induction of antibodies. Cytosine arabinoside was applied to cultures for periods of 24 hours starting at different times after treatment with the antigen. The result was that cultures exposed to the drug for the period between 24 and 48 hours failed to give rise to antibody-producing cells. Those treated with CA between 0 and 24 hours did not show any signs of suppression, whereas those exposed to CA between 48 and 72 hours showed only partial suppression. It was of interest to note that, following treatment with CA during the 24–48 hour period, immunocompetent cells were still viable. Their capacity to produce antibody is only revealed when the effect of CA is reversed by the addition of deoxycytidine hydrochloride (CdR) (Segal *et al.*, 1969a).

Since in all these experiments the antigen was given at the time of initiation of the culture, the observed lag of the first 24 hours during which CA had no inhibitory effect on antibody production might be attributed to the time required by the cells for adaptation to the new *in vitro* environmental conditions. To test this, a further experiment was carried out in which one group of cultures received antigen at time zero, whereas the other was treated with antigen 24 hours after explantation. The two groups were subjected to CA treatment as in the previous experiment. When the antigen was added after 24 hours, the cultures were apparently more sensitive to CA than when the antigen was added at time zero, yet the most sensitive period to CA was invariably between 48 and 72 hours. Thus in this group also, a lag of 24 hours of "CA insensitivity" was found. It seems, therefore, that this period is determined by the antigen rather than by culture conditions (Nakamura *et al.*, 1972). Hence it appears that the cell division critical for the induction of the response occurs during the period of 24 to 48 hours after the antigenic stimulation.

In order to find out the minimal number of cell replications required for a primary immune response, we carried out an additional experiment, applying CA for periods of 12 hours. Cultures were incubated with CA during the first to the sixth 12-hour period after antigenic stimulation (0–12, 12–24, 24–36, 36–48, 48–60 or 60–72 hours, respectively). It was found that in the group tested with CA in the 36–48 hour period the response was completely inhibited, whereas in the group treated during the 48–60 hour period antibodies were produced although at a lower level (Fig. 12).

It may, therefore, be concluded that the critical replications for the induction process occur within a 12–hour period and that there is, therefore, one critical replication essential for the induction of antibody production.

Does this critical replication occur in T or B cells? We have previously described experiments indicating that the carrier effect is most likely determined by a single replication of carrier-sensitive cells (Segal *et al.*, 1971a) of thymus origin (Kunin, 1973). Similarly, T-cell replication was shown by Miller *et al.* (1971) and by Feldmann and Basten (1972a). Hence the question arises whether the CA sensitivity described in the foregoing implies a critical cell division of (*a*) T-carrier-sensitive cells or of (*b*) precursors of antibody-producing B cells. In an attempt to answer this, mice were immunized with RSA and spleens were removed for culture 5 days later when the critical cell division on the part of carrier-sensitive cells had presumably already been completed. The CA sensitivity was then tested after stimulation with DNP–RSA (Nakamura *et al.*, 1972). The results, shown in Fig. 13, revealed the same pattern and the same degree of sensitivity to CA as had been with DNP–PLL, thereby suggest-

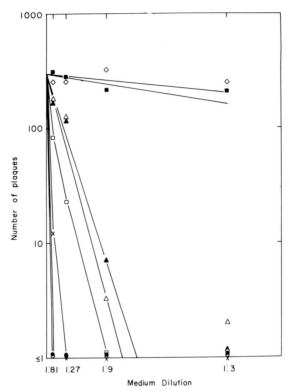

FIG. 12. Effect of pulse treatment with cytosine arabinoside (CA) on the antibody response to α-dinitrophenyl–poly-L-lysine. Controls were antigen stimulated cultures (×) and unstimulated cultures (◇). Experimental groups were stimulated with antigen and treated with CA for 0–12 hours (○), 12–24 hours (●), 24–36 hours (□), 36–48 hours (■), 48–60 hours (△), or 60–72 hours (▲). (Nakamura *et al.*, 1972.)

ing that the precursors of antibody-producing cells as well as the carrier-sensitive cells may require at least one cycle of division for the initiation of antibody production. However, no conclusive evidence is yet available as to whether the cells replicating *in vitro* following stimulation with DNP–RSA are precursors of B antibody-producing cells, B-carrier-sensitive cells (Kunin *et al.*, 1973), or whether another replication of the T cell must occur to ensure B-cell reactivity.

With regard to the critical replication of B cells, two alternatives should be considered (Fig. 14): (*a*) that DNA replication is required for the differentiation of precursors to antibody-producing cells (Fig. 14, I) and (*b*) that the differentiation of precursors to antibody-producing

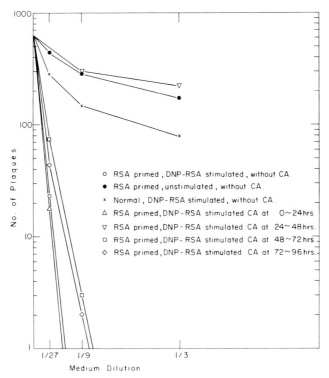

FIG. 13. Effect of pulse treatment with cytosine arabinoside (CA) on the *in vitro* response to 2,4-dinitrophenyl (DNP)–rabbit serum albumin (RSA) by spleens of mice immunized with RSA.

cells can take place without DNA replication but that multiplication is necessary for antibody-producing cells to reach a detectable number (Fig. 14, II).

The second possibility (Fig. 14, II) implies that some antibody-producing cells appear at 48 hours, even after CA treatment during the 24–48 hour period. These, however, might represent a population too small to be detected by our assay method. Yet, we have shown that cells that do produce antibodies continue to do so in the presence of CA and resume proliferation after removal of the inhibitor (Segal *et al.*, 1969a; Nakamura *et al.*, 1972). Had the inhibition of DNA synthesis between 24 to 48 hours prevented the replication of mature antibody producing cells, then the removal of the drug at 48 hours should have resulted in a detectable proliferation of such cells. This, however, was not the case. The same argument eliminates model III in Fig. 14, which is based on the assumption that antibody production results from the proliferation of

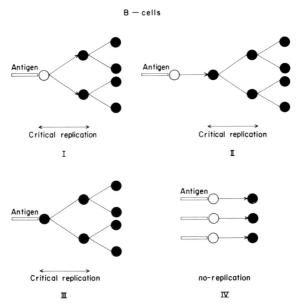

B — cells

Antigen

Critical replication

I

Antigen

Critical replication

II

Antigen

Critical replication

III

Antigen

no-replication

IV

FIG. 14. Possible models for "critical replications" of B cells. (Nakamura *et al.*, 1972.)

preexisting "background" antibody-producing cells. We, therefore, deduce that at least one cycle of DNA replication occurs prior to maturation and that this cycle of replication is essential for the differentiation of B-cell precursors into antibody-producing cells (Fig. 14, I).

Our previous studies have indicated that the carrier effect depends on one T-cell replication (Segal *et al.*, 1971a). From the current studies (Nakamura *et al.*, 1972) we deduce that antibody production requires the replication of a B precursor to an actual antibody-producing cell. Hence, antibody production, at least to hapten conjugates, may be determined by one critical replication of T cells and one critical replication of B cells. Figure 15 represents the combined model derived from these conclusions.

Although no experimental evidence from our study supports model IV of Fig. 14, the appearance of a small number of antibody-producing cells without a preceding phase of DNA replication has been observed in primary responses *in vitro* (Dutton and Mishell, 1967) and *in vivo* (Tannenberg, 1967). Yet it should be noted that in all of these studies the antigen used was SRBC. In view of the relatively frequent occurrence of anti-SRBC-producing cells in unsensitized animals, the possibility that they were derived from the stimulation of a cross-reacting antigen, and thus had completed the critical phase of DNA replication prior to the experimental stimulation with the antigen, cannot be ruled out. In any

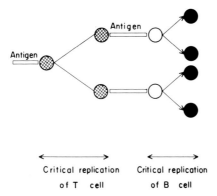

FIG. 15. Critical replication of T and B cells, in the induction of antibody to hapten–carrier conjugate (following preimmunization with the carrier). (Nakamura *et al.*, 1972.)

event, our *in vitro* experiments with SRBC did show dependency on DNA replication (Nakamura *et al.*, 1972) similar to that observed with DNP–carrier conjugates. On the other hand, Bussard and Lurie (1967) and Saunders (1969) have claimed that DNA synthesis is unnecessary for the *in vitro* induction of an anti-SRBC primary response. In the first study the cells in question were derived from peritoneal cells of which one out of ten cells became a hemolytic plaque producer within 24 hours of contact with the antigen (Bussard *et al.*, 1970). The plaque formers themselves did not multiply, and, thus, the behavior of the entire population of cells seemed to fit model IV. The fact that cells from other lymphoid organs responded only slightly to the antigen in the same *in vitro* system (Bussard *et al.*, 1970), however, makes it difficult to accept this phenomenon as a general feature of the immune response.

VII. Nature of Inducers for Immune Reactivity

We have already stated in the Introduction that the development of immune reactivity comes about in two stages and that only the second is induced by antigen. The first stage, which is antigen-independent, involves differentiation of immunocompetent cells. This process, which involves inductive interactions of thymus, bone marrow, and spleen (Auerbach, 1966; Globerson, 1966; Globerson and Auerbach, 1967) and is affected by thymus factors (Trainin *et al.*, 1969; Globerson *et al.*, 1973) is outside the scope of the present review. On the other hand, the complexity of the cell interactions triggered by antigen during the second phase of development has raised the questions whether activation of each of the individual cell types participating in the response is induced by a specific signal of the antigen and whether antigen is the sole inducer of differentiation of all the cell types. Early studies on the bicellular interactions envisaged an antigen bridge bringing the cells in contact and triggering B cells to produce antibodies (Mitchison, 1967; Rajewsky et al., 1969). This idea was based on the observation of the carrier effect in the secondary immune response. Salvin and Smith (1960) found that guinea pigs primed to hapten–carrier conjugates, i.e., p-aminobenzoic acid (PABA)- egg albumin, manifested a secondary response to the hapten only when challenged with the same immunogen. The hapten coupled to another carrier, bovine γ-globulin (BGG) did not elicit a secondary response. This phenomenon was later confirmed by others (Ovary and Benacerraf, 1963; Mitchison, 1967). Mitchison, in analyzing the mechanism underlying this observation found that irradiated mice repopulated with spleen cells primed to NIP–ovalbumin (OA) and spleen cells primed to BSA reacted to NIP–BSA. Furthermore, it was found that the carrier-active cells are from the T population (Mitchison, 1971a,b). The conclusion was that the antigen NIP–BSA, bridged the NIP-reactive cells and the BSA primed T cells, and that contact between these cells is essential for the response to the hapten. On a similar basis, Katz et al. (1971a) attempted to induce a response to DNP–BGG in guinea pigs primed to DNP–OA. Thus, guinea pigs of strain 13, primed to DNP–OA were inoculated with lymphoid cells from BGG-sensitized strain 2 donors, which are allogeneic to strain 13. They found quite unexpectedly that the animals inoculated with the allogeneic cells responded even if the cells were not sensitized to BGG. Thus, contact of T and B cells need not be established by the antigen toward which the antibodies will be produced. Rather, T cells and the allogeneic B cells can make contact via the cell membrane antigens and receptors to these antigens and this is sufficient to enhance the production of antibodies by the B cells. This phenomenon, termed "the allogeneic effect" (Katz et al., 1971b; Katz, 1972) has been extensively studied and confirmed in a variety of systems (Kreth and Williamson, 1971; Katz and Osborne, 1972; Schimpl and Wecker, 1971). Because T cells can be triggered without the immunogen to activate B cells, and only the latter need specific stimulation, it seems that, in addition to the antigens, factors released from the T cells are inducers for B cells (Dutton et al., 1971). Indeed, it has been shown that subcellular factors released from T cells upon allogeneic (Schimpl and Wecker, 1972; Britton, 1972; Sjöberg et al., 1972) or antigenic (Feldmann and Basten, 1972b, c, d) stimulation or even without any treatment (Doria et al., 1972; Gorczynski et al., 1972) could enhance the production of antibodies by B cells.

In most of the studies of the primary response the antibodies produced were of the IgM class. In view of the notion that in general the

IgG response is more T-dependent than the IgM (Taylor and Wortis, 1968; Hunter and Munro, 1972) and the observations that T cells can act via subcellular factors, it might be expected that T-cell factors will induce an IgG response if all their activity is, indeed, related to the nonspecific factors. Considering the fact that the *in vitro* techniques used for the studies of factors involved in the allogeneic effect do not permit production of antibodies other than IgM, it could be argued that the ability to produce IgG was induced by these factors, yet it was not manifested. Since the organ culture technique permits production of both 19 S and 7 S classes of antibodies following primary antigenic stimulation *in vitro* (Globerson and Auerbach, 1966; Segal *et al.*, 1970a), we tested whether the allogeneic effect does, indeed, lead to production of 7 S antibodies in the *in vitro* primary immune response. We induced an allogeneic effect *in vitro* in newborn spleen fragments; these fragments give only a slight response to DNP–PLL (Friedman *et al.*, 1971). The newborn spleen fragments were exposed to a short pulse of the antigen, DNP–PLL, for 30 minutes (Bernstein and Globerson, 1973a), washed in phosphate buffered saline, and overlayed with adult allogeneic spleen cells. It was found that these cultures showed an enhanced response to DNP, yet the antibodies produced were of the 19 S class only (Globerson, unpublished). It appears, therefore, that the factors released from T cells enhance the IgM response. Whether or not the T-cell activity in induction of IgG antibodies is also due to the release of nonspecific factors remains an open question.

The experimental approach of Feldmann and Basten (1972c) and Basten and Feldmann (1973) for testing the possible activity of T-cell factors showed a specific activation of T cells by the antigens. Such antigen-activated T cells liberated soluble factors that could pass by nucleopore membranes and stimulate B cells to produce antibodies. It was demonstrated that these factors differ in their specificity and molecular size from those released following allogeneic stimulation. Furthermore, they showed that the inducers for B cells were related to the T-cell receptors released and complexed to the antigen on the macrophage. In view of the common difficulties in demonstrating immunoglobulins on T cells, these results seem of utmost importance.

Finally, induction of both T and B cells may involve RNA molecules released by antigen-sensitized macrophages. Thus, antigen must first specifically interact with the macrophages which will then provide the signals for T and B cells. Further studies should be aimed at identifying and characterizing the inducers required for the differentiation of the various populations of immune reactive cells, since these may well provide a model for processes of differentiation in general and, as we have attempted to show, are readily available for study both *in vivo* and *in vitro*.

ACKNOWLEDGMENTS

Our studies reviewed in this paper were supported by a grant from the National Institutes of Health under agreement PL-480, Contract No. 06-005-1, and by the Max and Ida Hillson Foundation, New York.

The excellent technical assistance of Mrs. L. Abel, Mrs. M. Lev-Ran, Mrs. M. Shmerling, Mrs. H. Weinberg, and Mr. S. Leib in our experiments cited in this review is gratefully acknowledged.

REFERENCES

Abramoff, P., and Brien, N. B. (1968). *J. Immunol.* **10**, 1210.

Ada, G. L. (1969). *Transplant. Rev.* **5**, 105.

Ada, G. L., and Byrt, P. (1969). *Nature (London)* **222**, 1291.

Adler, F. L., Fishman, M., and Dray, S. (1966). *J. Immunol.* **97**, 554.

Andersson, B., and Blomgren, H. (1971). *Cell. Immunol.* **2**, 411.

Askonas, B. A., and Rhodes, J. M. (1965). *Nature (London)* **205**, 470.

Attardi, G., Cohn, M., Horibata, K., and Lennox, E. S. (1959). *Bacteriol. Rev.* **23**, 213.

Auerbach, R. (1966). *In* "The Thymus—Experimental and Clinical Studies" (G.E.W. Wolstenholme and R. R. Porter, eds.), pp. 39–49. Churchill, London.

Auerbach, R. (1972). *Curr. Top. Develop. Biol.* **7**, 257.

Bainford, D. R., and Black, S. (1972). *Cell. Immunol.* **4**, 175.

Baker, P. Z., Stashak, P. W., Amsbaugh, F., and Prescott, B. (1971). *Immunology* **20**, 469.

Basten, A., and Feldmann, M. (1973). *Advan. Exp. Med. Biol.* **29**, 171.

Basten, A., Miller, J. F. A. P., Warner, N. L., and Pyl, J. (1971). *Nature (London)* **231**, 104.

Bernstein, A., and Globerson, A. (1973a). *Cell. Immunol.* In press.

Bernstein, A., and Globerson, A. (1973b). *Joint Meet. European Soc. Immunol., Strasbourg* Abstracts.

Bischoff, R., and Holtzer, H. (1969). *J. Cell Biol.* **41**, 188.

Britton, S. (1972). *Scand. J. Immunol.* **1**, 89.

Brownstone, A., Mitchison, N. A., and Pitt-Rivers, R. (1966). *Immunology* **10**, 481.

Burleson, R., and Levey, R. H. (1972). *Cell. Immunol.* **4**, 305.

Burnet, M. (1959). "The Clonal Selection Theory of Acquired Immunity." Cambridge Univ. Press, London and New York.

Bussard, A. E., and Lurie, M. (1967). *J. Exp. Med.* **125**, 873.

Bussard, A. E., Nossal, G. J. V., Mazie, J. C., and Lewis, H. (1970). *J. Exp. Med.* **131**, 917.

Byrt, P., and Ada, G. L. (1969). *Immunology* **17**, 503.

Chu, M. Y., and Fischer, G. A. (1962). *Biochem. Pharmacol.* **11**, 423.

Claman, N. H., and Chaperon, E. A. (1969). *Transplant. Rev.* **1**, 92.

Claman, N. H., Chaperon, E. A., and Triplett, R. F. (1966). *J. Immunol.* **97**, 828.

Cohen, E. P., and Parks, J. J. (1964). *Science* **144**, 1012.

Davies, A. J. S. (1969). *Transplant. Rev.* **1**, 43.

Davies, A. J. S., Leuchars, E., Wallis, V., and Koller, P. C. (1966). *Transplantation* **4**, 438.

Davies, A. J. S., Leuchars, E., Wallis, V., Marchant, R., and Elliot, E. V. (1967). *Transplantation* **5**, 222.

Davies, A. J. S., Carter, R. L., Leuchars, E., Wallis, V., and Dietrich, F. M. (1970). *Immunology* **19**, 945.

del Guercio, P. (1972). *Nature (London), New Biol.* **238**, 213.

del Guercio, P., and Leuchars, E. (1972). *J. Immunol.* **109**, 951.

Diener, E., O'Callaghan, F. B., and Kraft, N. (1971). *J. Immunol.* **107**, 1512.

Dixon, E. J., and Weigle, W. O. (1957). *J. Exp. Med.* **105**, 75.

Doria, G., Agarossi, G., and Di Pietro, S. (1972). *J. Immunol.* **108**, 268.

Dutton, R. W., and Bulman, H. N. (1964). *Immunology* **7**, 54.

Dutton, R. W., and Mishell, R. I. (1967). *J. Exp. Med.* **126**, 443.

Dutton, R. W., Falkoff, R., Hirst, J. A., Hoffmann, M., Kappler, J. W., Kettman, J. R., Lesley, J. F., and Vann, D. (1971). *Progr. Immunol.* 355.

Evans, J. S., and Mengel, G. D. (1966). *Biochem. Pharmacol.* **13**, 989.

Feldman, M., and Gallily, R. (1967). *Cold Spring Harbor Symp. Quant. Biol.* **32**, 415.

Feldman, M., Cohen, I. R., and Wekerle, H. (1972). *Transplant. Rev.* **12**, 57.

Feldmann, M. (1972). *J. Exp. Med.* **135**, 1049.

Feldmann, M., and Basten, A. (1971). *J. Exp. Med.* **134**, 103.

Feldmann, M., and Basten, A. (1972a). *Eur. J. Immunol.* **2**, 213.

Feldmann, M., and Basten, A. (1972b). *J. Exp. Med.* **136**, 49.

Feldmann, M., and Basten, A. (1972c). *J. Exp. Med.* **136**, 722.

Feldmann, M., and Basten, A. (1972d). *Nature (London), New Biol.* **237**, 13.

Feldmann, M., and Nossal, G. J. V. (1972). *Transplant. Rev.* **13**, 3.

Fischer, H., Ax, W., Freund-Möbert, E., Holub, M., Krüssmann, W. F., and Matthes, M. L. (1970). *In* "Mononuclear Phagocytes" (R. van Furth, ed.), p. 528. Blackwell, Oxford.

Fishman, M. (1961). *J. Exp. Med.* **114**, 837.

Fishman, M., and Adler, F. L. (1963). *J. Exp. Med.* **117**, 595.

Fishman, M., and Adler, F. L. (1967). *Cold Spring Harbor Symp. Quant. Biol.* **32**, 343.

Fishman, M., and Adler, F. L. (1970). *In* "Mononuclear Phagocytes" (R. van Furth, ed.), p. 581. Blackwell, Oxford.

Friedman, D. (1971). M. Sc. Thesis, The Weizmann Institute of Science, Rehovot, Israel.

Friedman, D., Segal, S., Globerson, A., and Feldman, M. (1971). *Isr. J. Med. Sci.* **7**, 610.

Friedman, H. P., Stavitsky, A. B., and Solomon, J. M. (1965). *Science* **149**, 1106.

Gallily, R., and Feldman, M. (1966). *Isr. J. Med. Sci.* **2**, 358.

Gallily, R., and Feldman, M. (1967). *Immunology* **12**, 197.

Gershon, H., Bauminger, S., Sela, M., and Feldman, M. (1969). *J. Exp. Med.* **128**, 223.

Gershon, R. K., Cohen, P., Hencin, R., and Liebhaber, S. A. (1972). *J. Immunol.* **108**, 586.

Gershon, R. K., Wallis, V., Davies, A. J. S., and Leuchars, E. (1968). *Nature (London)* **218**, 380.

Gisler, R. H., and Dukor, P. (1972). *Cell. Immunol.* **4**, 341.

Givol, D., Haimovich, J., Segal, S., Globerson, A., and Feldman, M. (1970). *In* "Protides of the Biological Fluids, Proc. 17th Colloquium, Bruges, 1969" (H. Peeters, ed.), p. 59. Pergamon, Oxford.

Globerson, A. (1966). *J. Exp. Med.* **123**, 25.

Globerson, A., and Auerbach, R. (1965). *Science* **149**, 991.

Globerson, A., and Auerbach, R. (1966). *J. Exp. Med.* **124**, 1001.

Globerson, A., and Auerbach, R. (1967). *J. Exp. Med.* **126**, 223.

Globerson, A., and Feldman, M. (1969). In "Lymphatic Tissue and Germinal Centers in Immune Response" (L. Fiore-Donati and M. G. Hanna, eds.), pp. 407–414. Plenum, New York.

Globerson, A., and Feldman, M. (1970). In "Mononuclear Phagocytes" (R. van Furth, ed.), pp. 613–624. Blackwell, Oxford.

Globerson, A., Rotter, V., Nakamura, I., and Trainin, N. (1973). *Advan. Exp. Med. Biol.* **29**, 183.

Gorczynski, R. M., Miller, R. G., and Phillips, R. A. (1972). *J. Immunol.* **108**, 547.

Gottlieb, A. A., Glisin, V. R., and Doty, P. (1967). *Proc. Nat. Acad. Sci. U.S.* **57**, 1849.

Greenberg-Ramon, E. (1969). Ph.D. Thesis, The Weizmann Institute of Science, Rehovot, Israel.

Haimovich, J., and Sela, M. (1966). *J. Immunol.* **97**, 338.

Haritou, H., and Argyris, B. F. (1972). *Cell. Immunol.* **4**, 179.

Hartmann, K. U. (1971). *J. Exp. Med.* **133**, 1325.

Hellström, I., Hellström, K. E., and Allison, A. C. (1971). *Nature (London)* **230**, 49.

Howard, J. G. (1972). *Transplant. Rev.* **8**, 50.

Howard, J. G., Christie, G. H., and Courtenay, B. M. (1971). *Proc. Roy. Soc., Ser. B.* **178**, 417.

Hunter, P., and Munro, A. J. (1972). *Immunology* **23**, 69.

Karniely, Y., Mozes, E., Shearer, G. M., and Sela, M. (1973). *J. Exp. Med.* **137**, 183.

Katz, D. H. (1972). *Transplant. Rev.* **12**, 141.

Katz, D. H., and Osborne, D. P. (1972). *J. Exp. Med.* **136**, 455.

Katz, D. H., Paul, W. E., Goidl, E. A., and Benacerraf, B. (1970). *J. Exp. Med.* **132**, 261.

Katz, D. H., Paul, W. E., Goidl, E. A., and Benacerraf, B. (1971a). *J. Exp. Med.* **133**, 169.

Katz, D. H., Paul, W. E., and Benacerraf, B. (1971b). *J. Immunol.* **107**, 1319.

Kihlman, B. A. (1966). "Actions of Chemicals on Dividing Cells," p. 94. Prentice-Hall, Englewood Cliffs, New Jersey.

Kreth, H. W., and Williamson, A. R. (1971). *Nature (London)* **234**, 454.

Kunin, S. (1973). Ph.D. Thesis, The Weizmann Institute of Science, Rehovot, Israel.

Kunin, S., Shearer, G. M., Segal, S., Globerson, A., and Feldman, M. (1971). *Cell. Immunol.* **2**, 229.

Kunin, S., Shearer, G. M., Globerson, A., and Feldman, M. (1972). *Cell. Immunol.* **5**, 288.

Kunin, S., Shearer, G. M., Globerson, A., and Feldman, M. (1973). *Cell. Immunol.* **8**, 455.

Leserman, L. D., Cosenza, H., and Roseman, J. M. (1972). *J. Immunol.* **109**, 587.

Lesley, J. F., Kettman, J. R., and Dutton, R. W. (1971). *J. Exp. Med.* **134**, 618.

Marchalonis, J. J., Cone, R. E., and Atwell, J. L. (1972). *J. Exp. Med.* **135**, 956.

Miller, J. F. A. P., and Mitchell, G. F. (1967). *Nature (London)* **216**, 659.

Miller, J. F. A. P., and Mitchell, G. F. (1969). *Transplant. Rev.* **1**, 3.

Miller, J. F. A. P., and Mitchell, G. F. (1970). *J. Exp. Med.* **131**, 675.

Miller, J. F. A. P., Sprent, J., Basten, A., Warner, N. L., Breitner, J. S., Rowland, G., Hamilton, J., Silver, J., and Martin, W. J. (1971). *J. Exp. Med.* **134**, 1266.

Mitchell, G. F., and Miller, J. F. A. P. (1968). *J. Exp. Med.* **128**, 821.

Mitchison, N. A. (1966). *Progr. Biophys. Mol. Biol.* **16**, 3.

Mitchison, N. A. (1967). *Cold Spring Harbor Symp. Quant. Biol.* **32**, 431.

Mitchison, N. A. (1969). *Immunology* **16**, 1.

Mitchison, N. A. (1971a). *Eur. J. Immunol.* **1**, 10.

Mitchison, N. A. (1971b). *Eur. J. Immunol.* **1**, 18.

Mitchison, N. A., Rajewsky, K., and Taylor, R. B. (1970). *In* "Developmental Aspects of Antibody Formation and Structure" (J. Sterzl and I. Riha, eds.), p. 547. Academic Press, New York.

Mosier, D. E. (1967). *Science* **158**, 1573.

Mosier, D. E., Fitch, F. W., Rowley, D. A., and Davies, A. J. S. (1970). *Nature (London)* **225**, 276.

Munder, P. G., Modollel, M., Ferber, E., and Fischer, H. (1970). *In* "Mononuclear Phagocytes" (R. van Furth, ed.), p. 445. Blackwell, Oxford.

Nakamura, I., Segal, S., Globerson, A. and Feldman, M. (1972). *Cell. Immunol.* **4**, 351.

Nakamura, I., Ray, A., and Mäkela, O. (1973). *J. Exp. Med.* **138**, 974.

Naor, D., and Sulitzeanu, D. (1967). *Nature (London)* **214**, 687.

Naor, D., and Sulitzeanu, D. (1969). *Int. Arch. Allergy Appl. Immunol.* **36**, 112.

Nossal, G. J. V., and Lederberg, J. (1958). *Nature (London)* **181**, 1419.

Nossal, G. J. V., Cunningham, A., Mitchell, G. F., and Miller, J. F. A. P. (1968). *J. Exp. Med.* **128**, 839.

Ovary, Z., and Benacerraf, B. (1963). *Proc. Soc. Exp. Biol. Med.* **114**, 72.

Plotz, P. H. (1969). *Nature (London)* **223**, 1373.

Pribnow, J. F., and Silverman, M. S. (1967). *J. Immunol.* **98**, 225.

Raff, M. C. (1970). *Nature (London)* **226**, 1257.

Raff, M. C. (1971). *Transplant. Rev.* **6**, 52.

Rajewsky, K., Schirrmacher, V., Nase, S., and Jerne, N. K. (1969). *J. Exp. Med.* **129**, 1131.

Salvin, S. B., and Smith, R. T. (1960). *Proc. Soc. Exp. Biol. Med.* **104**, 584.

Saunders, G. C. (1969). *J. Exp. Med.* **130**, 543.

Schimpl, A., and Wecker, E. (1971). *Eur. J. Immunol.* **1**, 304.

Schimpl, A., and Wecker, E. (1972). *Nature (London), New Biol.* **237**, 15.

Schlesinger, M. (1970). *Nature (London)* **226**, 1254.

Segal, S., Globerson, A., and Feldman, M. (1969a). *Isr. J. Med. Sci.* **5**, 444.

Segal, S., Globerson, A., Feldman, M., Haimovich, J., and Givol, D. (1969b). *Nature (London)* **223**, 1374.

Segal, S., Globerson, A., Feldman, M., Haimovich, J., and Sela, M. (1970a). *J. Exp. Med.* **131**, 93.

Segal, S., Globerson, A., and Feldman, M. (1970b). *Isr. J. Med. Sci.* **6**, 445.

Segal, S., Globerson, A., and Feldman, M. (1971a). *Cell. Immunol.* **2**, 205.

Segal, S., Globerson, A., and Feldman, M. (1971b). *Cell. Immunol.* **2**, 222.

Sela, M., Mozes, E., Shearer, G. M., and Karniely, Y. (1970). *Proc. Nat. Acad. Sci. U.S.* **67**, 1288.

Sell, S. (1967a). *J. Exp. Med.* **125**, 289.

Sell, S. (1967b). *J. Exp. Med.* **125**, 393.

Shortman, K., and Palmer, J. (1971). *Cell. Immunol.* **2**, 399.

Sjöberg, O., and Möller, E. (1970). *Nature (London)* **228**, 780.

Sjöberg, O., Andersson, J., and Moller, G. (1972). *J. Immunol.* **109**, 1379.

Solomon, J. B. (1971). "Foetal and Neonatal Immunology." Elsevier, Amsterdam.

Tannenberg, W. J. K. (1967). *Nature (London)* **214**, 293.

Taylor, R. B. (1969). *Transplant. Rev.* **1**, 14.
Taylor, R. B., and Wortis, H. H. (1968). *Nature (London)* **220**, 927.
Trainin, N., Small, M., and Globerson, A. (1969). *J. Exp. Med.* **130**, 765.
Truffa-Bachi, P., and Wofsy, L. (1970). *Proc. Nat. Acad. Sci. U.S.* **66**, 765.
Turkington, R. W. (1968). *Curr. Top. Develop. Biol.* **3**, 199.
Unanue, E. R. (1970). *J. Immunol.* **105**, 1339.
Unanue, E. R., and Cerottini, J. C. (1970). *J. Exp. Med.* **131**, 711.
Weinstein, Y., Wilchek, M., and Givol, D. (1969). *Biochem. Biophys. Res. Commun.* **35**, 694.
White, R. G., (1958). *Nature (London)* **182**, 1383.
Wigzell, H., and Andersson, B. (1969). *J. Exp. Med.* **129**, 23.
Zan-Bar, I., Nachtigal, D., and Feldman, M. (1973). *Cell. Immunol.* (in press).

CHAPTER 2

DETERMINATION AND PATTERN FORMATION IN THE IMAGINAL DISCS OF *Drosophila*

Peter J. Bryant

CENTER FOR PATHOBIOLOGY
UNIVERSITY OF CALIFORNIA
IRVINE, CALIFORNIA

I. Introduction

During the development of an organism, there are many occasions when cells have to decide between various alternative developmental pathways, and each decision is followed by its implementation in terms of biochemical events that direct the subsequent behavior of the cells. Each decision is made with reference to a number of factors including the following: (1) the position of the cell within the developing system, which is assessed by some means not yet understood (see Wolpert, 1972); (2) the genotype of the cell, which causes developmental processes to be species-specific and also causes them to vary as a result of mutations; (3) the developmental history of the cell and of its somatic ancestors, that is, a cellular decision will often be conditioned by other decisions made earlier in development; and (4) the activities of other cells, as manifest in inductive and hormonal interactions.

The extent to which developmental decisions are inherited by the mitotic progeny of a cell is a crucial yet rarely considered parameter of developing systems. Although some comprehensive theories of development have been based on heritable cellular decisions (Baker, 1967; Mintz, 1971), there are undoubtedly many important decisions which are nonheritable. In this paper, I shall discuss the imaginal discs of *Drosophila* and show that both heritable and nonheritable cellular decisions are made in these systems. I shall refer to a heritable decision as an event of *determination* and to a decision that is nonheritable as an event of *specification*. Although specification itself is nonheritable and may change during cell division, there are rigid constraints on the possible changes of specification that can occur. I shall discuss these constraints as far as they are understood.

II.   General Features of Imaginal Discs

Imaginal discs present the following clear advantages for the study of cellular aspects of development: (1) they are physically isolated from each other and distinct from the remainder of the developing organism; (2) certain developmental decisions are widely separated in time from their implementation and can thus be studied separately; (3) cell lines can be cultured indefinitely and can be induced to differentiate at any time; (4) the cells undergo a wide variety of specializations in well-defined patterns; (5) mutants are available, some of which affect pattern formation and some of which can be used as genetic cell markers; and (6) several methods are available for making genetic mosaics and chimeras. Small size cannot be considered a disadvantage of this system, since pattern formation seems to occur on about the same size scale in a variety of systems (see Wolpert, 1972). Although a vast amount of experimental work has been done on imaginal discs (see Ursprung and Nöthiger, 1972), very few theoretical analyses of the data have so far been attempted (see, however, Hadorn, 1966b; Ouweneel, 1972; Kaufmann, 1973).

Imaginal discs can first be observed histologically in the late embryo (Laugé, 1967) or early larva (Auerbach, 1936), at which time they consist merely of thickenings of the epidermis. Later they became invaginated to give the basic saclike organization of the mature disc. The discs grow by cell division during the 4 days of larval life until in the mature larva they attain the appearance shown in Fig. 1. During metamorphosis,

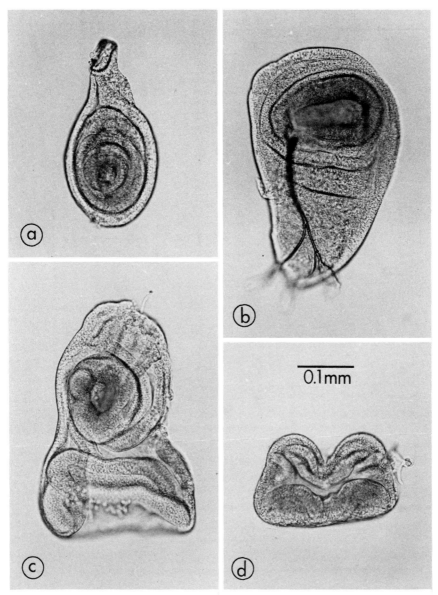

FIG. 1. Some of the major imaginal discs of *Drosophila melanogaster* (living, unstained whole mounts). (a) First leg disc; (b) wing disc; (c) eye-antenna disc; (d) genital disc.

each disc is known to give rise to a specific part of the integument of the adult fly. Thus the external parts of the adult head are formed from three pairs of imaginal discs: the labial discs, which produce the distal parts of the proboscis; the clypeolabrum discs, which produce the proximal parts of the proboscis; and the eye-antennal discs, which produce the remainder of the head. The integument of the thorax is made from six pairs of discs: the dorsal prothoracic discs, each of which produces a small sclerite called the humerus; the wing discs, which produce the dorsal part of the mesothorax and the wings; the haltere discs, which produce the dorsal metathorax and the halteres; and three ventral pairs of discs, which produce the three pairs of legs and the ventral parts of the thorax. The other major imaginal disc is the single genital disc, which produces the external and most of the internal genitalia. The abdominal integument of the adult is formed, not from imaginal discs as such, but from small, segmentally located nests of cells called *histoblasts,* which are contiguous with the larval epidermis (Fig. 2).

Each disc consists of a hollow epithelial sac attached to the larval epidermis by a stalk (Fig. 3). One side of the sac (the peripodial membrane) is made up of squamous cells that degenerate during metamorphosis, or perhaps contribute to the body wall. The other side is a highly

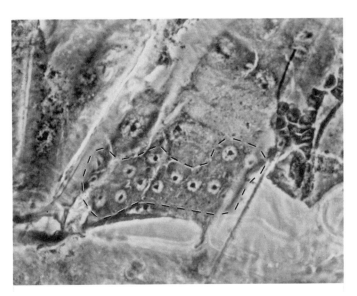

FIG. 2. An abdominal histoblast nest, the primordial cells for an abdominal tergite in *Drosophila melanogaster.* The small cells enclosed by the dashed line represent the histoblasts, and they are surrounded by large larval epidermal cells. (Courtesy of Mr. Craig Roseland.)

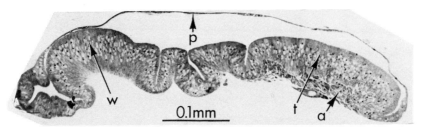

FIG. 3. Methylene blue-stained section of an imaginal wing disc. Large numbers of adepithelial cells (a) are associated with the presumptive thorax (t) but none with the presumptive wing blade (w). p, Peripodial membrane. (Courtesy of Dr. Clifton Poodry.)

columnar folded epithelium which is not visibly differentiated, but which, during metamorphosis, produces adult cuticle-bearing specializations such as bristles, hairs, and sensilla arranged in complex and almost unvarying patterns (Fig. 4). During metamorphosis and prior to differentiation, the epithelium undergoes an extensive morphogenetic movement known as eversion, which converts the folded epithelium of the disc into the extended integument of the adult insect. Accompanying eversion are changes in cell shape from highly columnar to squamous and alterations in the kinds of junctions present between cells (Poodry and Schneiderman, 1970). Some of the imaginal discs also contain presumptive muscle and nerve cells (Fig. 3), but this discussion will be restricted to the development of the epithelium.

One of the useful features of imaginal discs is that they can be caused to undergo differentiation at any time by transplanting them into host larvae that are about to undergo metamorphosis. The implanted disc responds to the hormonal conditions of the host and metamorphoses with it. Alternatively, these events can be stimulated *in vitro* by the addidition of an ecdysone to the culture medium (Mandaron, 1971). Thus it is possible to study the extent of pattern formation at various stages by causing the cells to differentiate. Furthermore, discs or disc tissue can be cultured either in an adult host in which the hormonal conditions do not induce metamorphosis of the implant but do allow it to grow, or in an adult host maintained on "sugar food," in which the tissue is unable either to grow or to differentiate (Garcia-Bellido, 1967).

III. Determination and the Origin of Imaginal Discs

A. EVIDENCE FOR DETERMINATION

During larval development, each imaginal disc grows in a specific manner, finally producing the mature disc with its characteristic mor-

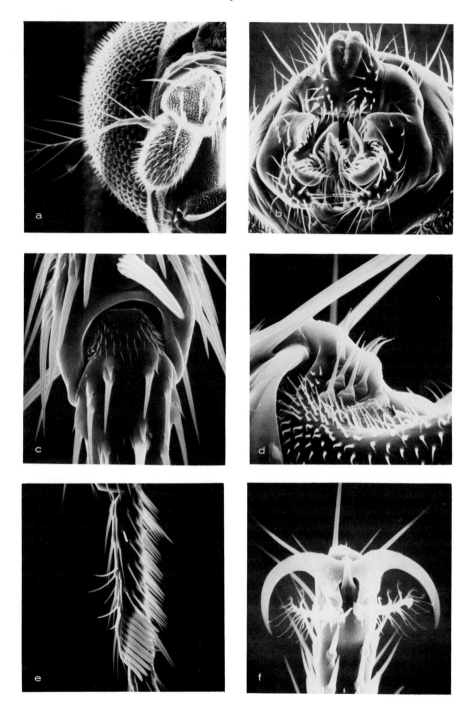

phology and folding pattern. When an individual disc from a third (last) instar larva is transplanted to a host larva for metamorphosis, only those structures appropriate to that disc will develop. Conversely, when a disc is extirpated from a larva, the adult develops without the corresponding part (Zalokar, 1943; Murphy, 1967). These experiments led to the conclusion that imaginal discs are determined for particular structures throughout larval life. Here the concept of determination is used in the sense of the retention of certain restricted developmental capabilities after isolation. But it has been shown that, in the case of disc determination ("legness," "wingness," etc.), the determined state has the additional feature of being retained during cell proliferation. Thus when a disc fragment is implanted into an adult host, it can be grown without differentiation and will give rise to a tissue line that can be subcultured for an indefinite period of time in a succession of adult hosts. When the subcultured tissue lines are tested by implanting test pieces into larval hosts for metamorphosis, it is often found that the tissue line has retained the determination of the disc which originated the tissue. Some tissue lines derived from a genital disc have retained their determination to produce anal plates during several years of culture (Hadorn, 1966a, b). Occasionally, the cells change their determined state to one which is characteristic of another disc. This phenomenon is known as transdetermination and has recently been reviewed by Gehring (1972). The inheritability of imaginal disc determination is an important feature which distinguishes it from other kinds of cellular commitments made later in the development of imaginal discs. It is an example of a "firm bias" as discussed by Schneiderman (1969).

A number of authors have suggested the possibility that the determined state is a property maintained by populations of contiguous cells rather than by individual cells. This possibility has been examined in experiments involving the dissociation and mixing of cells from different imaginal discs before metamorphosis (Nöthiger, 1964; Tobler, 1966; Poodry *et al.*, 1971). From these experiments one conclusion is clear: the determined state of cells is retained and not modified even by this intimate association with heteronomous cells. The "faulty mosaics" reported by Nöthiger (1964) illustrate this point very well—just a few genital disc cells trapped among a majority of wing disc cells will, nevertheless, produce a small island of genital structures. It therefore

---

FIG. 4. Scanning electron micrographs of various imaginal disc derivatives in *Drosophila*. (a) Eye and antenna; (b) male genitalia; (c) tibia-basitarsus joint; (d) a group of sensilla trichodea on the leg; (e) basitarsus with sex comb; (f) tarsal claw.

seems likely that the determined state could be maintained by isolated cells but definitive proof is still lacking.

B. DEFECT EXPERIMENTS

In order to understand the nature of cellular determination, it is important to know the precise stage of development at which it is initiated. Most of the available evidence suggests that imaginal disc determination may be established much earlier in the embryo than the time at which the structures become histologically identifiable.

The *Drosophila* embryo, like that of most insects, begins development as a syncytium (Rabinowitz, 1941). After fertilization, about eight nuclear divisions ("cleavage divisions") occur synchronously within the egg cytoplasm, and these are followed by migration of the nuclei to the cortex of the egg. Three more nuclear divisions occur in this preblastoderm (blastema) stage before the nuclei become separated from each other by cell membranes which grow down from the egg surface. This stage (about $2\frac{1}{2}$ hours after fertilization) is known as the blastoderm; it is followed by gastrulation and the remainder of embryogenesis, the time between fertilization and larval hatching being about 22 hours at 25°C.

In order to investigate the time of initiation of embryonic determination, several workers have produced defects in the embryo at various stages either by removal of cytoplasm with or without nuclei (Howland and Sonnenblick, 1936) by thermocautery (Bownes, 1973) or by localized ultraviolet radiation (Geigy, 1931b; Nöthiger and Strub, 1972). The conclusion from these experiments is that if the defects are made at the blastoderm stage or later, the positions of the resulting adult abnormalities correlate quite closely with the positions of the experimental defects. Geigy (1931b) found such a correlation using ultraviolet radiation in the 7-hour embryo; Howland and Child (1935) showed that puncturing postblastoderm embryos resulted in correlated defects in the surviving adults; and Bownes (1973) showed a precise correlation between the sites of cautery in the blastoderm and the locations of adult defects. On the other hand, it has proved more difficult to obtain such a correlation using embryos at the stage of nuclear multiplication. Geigy (1931b) found no abnormalities in the adults surviving from ultraviolet irradiation at this stage, and Nöthiger and Strub (1972) found no correlation between the site of ultraviolet irradiation of the embryo and the location of adult defects. Bownes (1973) did find such a correlation using thermocautery, but this could have been due to persistence in the embryo of cauterized tissue, which might have interfered with subsequent development. The implication, therefore, is that imaginal disc determination has not yet been established at the nuclear multiplication stage, or that complete regulation is possible. Hence, the defect experiments are consistent with the idea that imaginal disc determination is established at or shortly after the blastoderm stage.

C. TRANSPLANTATION EXPERIMENTS

An alternative technique for studying the onset of imaginal disc determination was developed by Hadorn *et al.* (1968) and Gateff (1971). These authors discovered that parts of embryos can be grown in the abdomens of adult flies and that these parts will continue to develop both larval structures and presumptive adult tissue under these conditions. When transplanted to a larval host, the presumptive adult tissue differentiates into recognizable cuticular structures. These experiments were extended by Schubiger *et al.* (1969), who mixed cells from genetically marked anterior and posterior halves of 10-hour embryos prior to the culture period. After metamorphosis of the test implants, it was found that head structures had arisen only from anterior halves and genital structures only from posterior halves. Legs, wings, halteres, and abdomens were found as chimeric structures, being derived from both anterior and posterior halves. More recently, Chan and Gehring (1971) have been able to carry out this type of analysis starting with blastoderm stage embryos. Genetically marked cells from anterior or posterior halves of blastoderm embryos were mixed with cells from whole embryos, and, after reaggregation, the tissue was cultured in adults for 10 to 14 days, then implanted into larvae for metamorphosis. These experiments showed that the anterior end of a blastoderm stage embryo will give rise to head and thoracic structures, and the posterior end will produce only thoracic and abdominal structures. They, therefore, constitute the most direct evidence for determination of imaginal disc precursors at the blastoderm stage.

Experiments such as those just described lend support to the theory that the cleavage nuclei are initially multipotent and that their developmental fates become determined when they enter the egg cortex, just prior to blastoderm formation. This determination might result from the presence, in the cortex, of localized determinative factors (see Counce, 1961). This idea has developed as a generalization from the well-documented example of localized determinants for germ cells in the "pole plasm" region of the cortex. Damage to the pole plasm region by ultraviolet light results in sterility of the resulting adult (Geigy, 1931a). The sterility can be prevented by the injection of pole plasm from unirradiated, fertilized eggs but not by the injection of cytoplasm from other regions (Okada *et al.*, 1973). Furthermore, pole plasm injected at the anterior pole can induce the formation of pole cells there, and these will develop into functional germ cells when transplanted into host embryos (Illmensee and Mahowald, 1973). The presence in the pole plasm of characteristic organelles, the polar granules, which become incorporated into the germ cells (Mahowald, 1971) provides an ultra-structural correlate for the determinants of germ cells, although there is as yet no evidence for the identity of polar granules with these determinants.

The fact that ultraviolet irradiation of other areas of the egg cortex does not produce correlated adult defects leads one to suspect that the pole plasm may be a special case, and the presence there of unique organelles reinforces this suspicion. On the other hand, it has been shown by Kalthoff (1971) that ultraviolet irradiation of the anterior pole of the egg of *Smittia* invariably produces "double-abdomen" embryos, lacking anterior structures. This suggests that ultraviolet-sensitive targets important for determination may not, in fact, be peculiar to germ cells.

Another line of evidence leading to the conclusion that the cleavage nuclei are multipotent comes from recent experiments involving trans-plantation of genetically marked nuclei from one embryo to another (Zalokar, 1971). Although the survival rate is not high, it is possible to make chimeric animals by this technique, and thus to follow the exact fate of the injected nuclei. Okada *et al.* (1973) have recently shown that nuclei withdrawn from near the anterior pole of a 256-nuclei embryo, can eventually give rise to either anterior or posterior structures when they are injected into a 32-nuclei embryo. Illmensee (1972) and Schubiger and Schneiderman (1971) have reported similar results from experiments in which nuclear transplantation was followed by culturing the parts of the resulting embryo in adults. The cultured tissue was then induced to metamorphose by transplanting it into host larvae. Illmensee has shown by this technique that cleavage nuclei, pole nuclei from preblastoderm embryos, or lateral nuclei from syncytial blastoderm embryos, can produce any of the adult structures normally derived from imaginal discs. These experiments demonstrate conclu-sively that the cleavage nuclei are multipotent and strengthen the argu-ments for a determinative role of the egg cortex, although, of course, they leave open the possibility that determination might occur some time after immigration of nuclei into the cortex.

D. Mutants Affecting the Origin of Imaginal Discs

If in the cortex of the egg there are localized determinants that direct early development, then it seems likely that these would be laid down during oogenesis and would, therefore, be under maternal genetic control. That this is the case for germ cell determinants is elegantly demonstrated by the mutant *grandchildless* of *Drosophila subobscura* (Fielding, 1967). Females homozygous for this mutation lay eggs in which the pole plasm degenerates and does not become populated by nuclei. As a result, no germ cells are formed in the embryos, and they develop into sterile adults.

If imaginal disc determinants, analogous to germ cell determinants, were also laid down in the egg cortex, then it should be possible to obtain maternal effect mutants that affect imaginal discs. Since imaginal discs are not necessary during larval life, the progeny of such mutants would either die as pupae or survive to produce abnormal adults. However, no such mutants have been reported in spite of special efforts to obtain them. There is some maternal influence on the expression of the homoeotic mutant *tumorous head* (Gardner, 1970; Postlethwait *et al.*, 1972), but it is difficult to evaluate its significance since the genome of the progeny is also involved and the mutant shows low and variable penetrance. The lack of clear-cut maternal effects on imaginal disc development does not, however, categorically deny the existence of cortical determinants. A possible explanation could be that imaginal disc determination is controlled by the same pattern-forming system as that determining larval structures. The reference points (Wolpert, 1972) for such a pattern-forming system could be laid down during oogenesis, but any defect in the system would lead to early death of the progeny rather than producing effects limited to imaginal discs. The mutant *bicaudal* (Bull, 1966) is relevant in this connection; this is a maternal-effect mutant in which the progeny of the homozygous female include some double-abdomen monsters that die as embryos. Unfortunately this mutant also shows very low penetrance.

In contrast to the foregoing results, it appears to be rather easy to obtain non-maternal-effect lethals that block the development of some or all of the imaginal discs. Thus, Shearn *et al.* (1971) isolated ten third-chromosome mutants in which no imaginal discs were produced, and fifty-three in which the development of some or all of the discs was abnormal. Stewart *et al.* (1972) collected sixteen first-chromosome mutants with various kinds of disc abnormalities. It is possible that some of these mutants affect the initial determinative events in imaginal discs (see Kaufmann, 1973). However, there are other possibilities; for example, the discs might become determined but fail to develop, or they might subsequently degenerate. The latter possibility seems rather plausible in view of the finding that several mutants of which parts of the adult are missing show cellular degeneration in the corresponding imaginal discs (Fristrom, 1969). In any case, the main conclusion from the genetic studies is that almost all aspects of imaginal disc development are under direct, rather than maternal, genetic control.

E. Homoeotic Mutants

One of the potentially most informative classes of mutants affecting imaginal discs in *Drosophila* comprises the homoeotic mutants, in which an organ develops structures characteristic of a different part of the insect. Many of the conceivable changes from one disc to another have been discovered, and these were reviewed recently by Gehring and Nöthiger (1973). The transformation almost always involves just part of a disc, although complete transformation from antenna to leg occurs sometimes in *Nasobemia* (Gehring, 1969). In the *bithorax* series, which transform parts of the mesothorax into parts of the metathorax or vice versa, complete transformation of a haltere disc into a wing disc can be achieved by the combination of two mutants, namely, *bithorax* and *postbithorax* (Lewis, 1964). In some cases, the area transformed by a homoeotic mutant varies greatly but in other cases it is very uniform. *Bithorax*, for instance, affects only the anterior half of the haltere and its allele, *postbithorax*, affects only the posterior half.

The explanation that suggests itself at first for homoeotic mutations is that they redirect the primary determinative event occurring in the imaginal disc precursors in the embryo. However, that this is not the case is convincingly demonstrated by the clonal analysis of *Antennapedia* by Postlethwait and Schneiderman (1969). These authors used X-ray induced somatic crossing over to produce clones of *yellow-singed* mutant cells in the homoeotic mutant *Antennapedia*, in which antennal structures are replaced by leg structures. When somatic crossing over was induced at any time up to 72 hours after oviposition, the resulting clones could embrace both antennal and leg structures (see Fig. 5). This demonstrates, then, that cells at stages up to 72 hours are not yet determined between the alternatives of leg or antenna. A similar conclusion follows from the work of Vogt (1946a) on a temperature-sensitive allele of *aristapedia*. She showed that the degree of homoeotic alteration can be modified as late as the third larval instar by the application of a temperature shock. Furthermore, small clones of *aristapedia* tissue, which are induced by somatic crossing over during the first larval stage, can, nevertheless, produce the homoeotic phenotype (Roberts, 1964). Evidently the homoeotic alteration does not take place in the early embryo. Either the homoeotic antennal disc contains a population of uncommitted cells up to a late stage, or some presumptive antennal cells undergo a transdetermination into presumptive leg during the larval stages.

An interesting model for homoeotic alterations has been put forward by Kobel (1968) and by Ouweneel (1969) on the basis of their work on

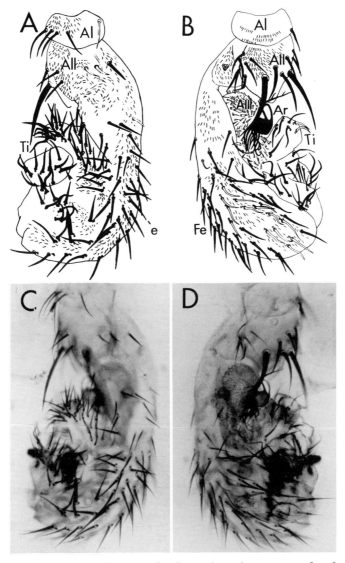

FIG. 5. A clone of *yellow-singed* cells resulting from X-ray-induced somatic crossing over in an *Antennapedia* antenna which in partially transformed into leg. (A and B) Camera lucida drawings from both sides; (C and D) photographs from both sides. The clone embraces some of the antennal structures and some of the leg structures. Since somatic crossing over was induced at 56 hours after oviposition, the cells at that time cannot be determined between leg and antenna. AI, AII, AIII, first, second, and third antennal segments; Ar, arista; Fe, femur; Ti, tibia. (From Postlethwait and Schneiderman, 1969.)

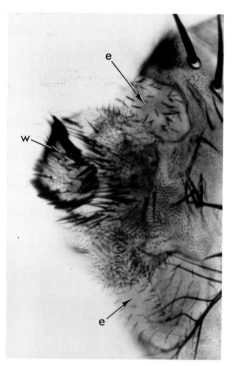

FIG. 6. Homoeotic wing tissue in the eye region of an *eyeless-ophthalmoptera* fly. w, Wing tissue; e, eye facets.

the mutation *ophthalmoptera,* in which some of the eye is replaced with wing tissue (Fig. 6). For the expression of this phenotype, two mutations are necessary: the homoeotic mutation itself and another mutation that reduces eye size, for example, *lobe* or *eyeless.* Since the latter is known to cause cell death in the eye disc, it is suggested that this is the primary defect and that the homoeotic alteration is in fact a transdetermination occurring during the compensatory growth of the remaining tissue. The role of the homoeotic mutation, then, would be to stimulate transdetermination and to encourage it to occur preferentially in the direction of wing during this compensatory growth.

This hypothesis seems quite feasible for those mutants in which the homoeotic tissue is markedly enlarged with respect to its normal counterpart, for example, *ophthalmoptera* or *Antennapedia.* Here the homoeotic tissue has evidently grown at an unusually high rate and this could have led to transdetermination. However, in many homoeotic mutants the altered tissue can be smaller than its normal counterpart (e.g., *contrabithorax;* Lewis, 1964; *tumorous head;* Postlethwait *et al.,*

1972). In these cases, an alternative explanation seems to be required. Furthermore, the complete autonomy of *bithorax* and *aristapedia* in genetic mosaics (Lewis, 1964; Roberts, 1964) seems to exclude the preceding hypothesis for these two cases.

F. GENETIC MOSAICS

Certain problems related to the origin of imaginal discs are amenable to indirect approaches utilizing genetic mosaicism. These problems concern, first, the number of cells in the disc at the time of its origin, and, second, the relative distances between imaginal discs at the time of their origin. Both of these procedures rely on the use of gynandromorphs—animals that are mosaics of male and female tissue, usually genetically marked with a mutation such as *yellow* or *singed* affecting the color or morphology of the bristles on the surface of the adult. In *Drosophila*, gynandromorphs usually arise by the loss of one X chromosome from one cell line in a zygote that is originally XX (female). Several stocks are available in which this loss occurs at high frequency, and in most cases the loss occurs at the first nuclear division, giving an embryo and eventually an adult which, on the average, consists of about half male and half female cells.

In a gynandromorph, then, the population of cells that will originate an imaginal disc must be a sample taken from the mixed embryo. The number of cells involved in the initiation of the disc can be estimated by studying the mosaicism patterns in the adult derivatives of that disc. For example, if the disc were to originate as a single cell, then the derivatives of that disc in the adult could be totally male or totally female but never mixed. This is not the case for any of the imaginal discs. If the disc originated as two cells, then it would be possible to find derivatives composed of 50% male and 50% female tissue. If the initial cell population were larger, then the number of classes of mosaic derivatives would be higher. Concomitantly, the minimum-sized patch of alternative sex that could be found in the mosaic derivatives would be smaller. Of course, these supposed classes of mosaic distribution would become obscured if there were heterogeneity of mitotic rate within imaginal discs, and this is an important reservation with these kinds of estimates. Using the gynandromorph technique, the number of cells involved in the initiation of imaginal discs has been estimated as eight to forty depending on the disc (see Nöthiger, 1972). Some of these estimates agree quite closely with initial cell numbers derived from mosaics produced by somatic crossing over (see Bryant and Schneiderman, 1969).

The primordial cell number estimated by these methods does not necessarily refer to the number of cells present when the imaginal disc precursor acquires determination in the sense of an intrinsic cellular commitment. It refers, rather, to the time at which the disc becomes clonally distinct from the remainder of the embryo; that is, the time after which no more cells will enter or leave the group whose fate is to produce the disc in question. Furthermore, the estimate refers only to those cells whose fate is to produce the epidermal part of the adult structure; the cells whose progeny might produce the adult muscles, for example, are not included in the estimates. The event resulting in clonal separation of a group of cells has been termed *allocation* by McLaren (1972, personal communication). Of course, it is conceivable that this event may sometimes coincide with a determinative event in the cells, but it could also be merely a reflection of the position of the group of cells at a certain stage in development; determination of these cells in the sense defined above might occur much later than allocation and cannot be demonstrated using these genetic mosaic techniques.

In a procedure originally devised by Sturtevant (1929) and later developed by Garcia-Bellido and Merriam (1969), gynandromorphs can be used to estimate the relative distances apart of imaginal disc precursors at the time of their allocation. This technique relies on the fact that the male-female borderline in gynandromorphs lies in various directions, due to the variable directions of nuclear division spindles in the early cleavage embryo (Parks, 1936). The frequency with which the borderline lies between any two imaginal disc precursors is, therefore, a function of their distance apart at the time of allocation. Hence these relative distances can be deduced from the relative frequencies with which the corresponding pairs of imaginal disc derivatives are of opposite sex in the adults. Using this method, Garcia-Bellido and Merriam have put forward a two-dimensional map of the relative locations of imaginal disc precursors in the embryo. They refer to this as a blastoderm fate map, in view of the evidence implicating the blastoderm stage as the probable time of determination of the imaginal disc precursors. A similar fate map constructed from our unpublished data is shown in Fig. 7.

The blastoderm fate map is almost completely congruent with the topography of the adult surface, indicating a lack of extensive tissue movements which might alter the relative positions of imaginal discs or their precursors. One exception to this is the rather surprising map position of the proboscis precursor between the eye and humerus; the proboscis is, of course, ventral to the eye in the adult. It seems likely that this reflects a rearrangement resulting from the involution of the

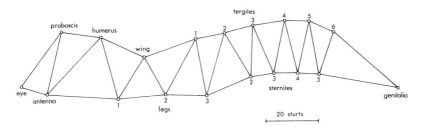

FIG. 7. Blastoderm fate map, derived from gynandromorph data as explained in the text. The unit of distance is the *sturt*, which is defined as a distance such that the boundary line in gynandromorphs passes between the derivatives in 1% of the cases. (Hotta and Benzer, 1972.)

larval head which occurs during embryonic development in the higher Diptera. Garcia-Bellido and Merriam (1969) attempted to correlate their blastoderm fate map with the embryonic fate map which was produced by Poulson (1950) using histological procedures. However, since the gynandromorph map refers to specific parts of the adult epidermis, which were not directly followed in Poulson's study, an exact correlation of the two maps was not possible. Hotta and Benzer (1972) have shown that various behavioral mutants can be used to place certain parts of the nervous system on the blastoderm fate map. In principle, lethal mutants could be used to map other organs although the difficulty of defining exactly the primary defect in lethal mutants makes this a rather tedious procedure. Mutants defective in particular enzymes can be used as histochemical markers for internal mosaicism and should increase the utility of this approach.

G. CONCLUSIONS ABOUT DETERMINATION IN IMAGINAL DISCS

It seems safe to conclude that determination of the imaginal disc precursors occurs very early in development, probably around the time of blastoderm formation. The determinative event for each disc occurs in a group of at least eight to forty cells and the determined state is transmitted to the somatic progeny of the primordial cells. The idea that imaginal disc determinants are built into the egg during oogenesis is not strongly supported by any of the experimental evidence. Homoeotic mutations appear to act not by redirecting the initial determinative event in the imaginal disc precursors, but rather by destabilizing the state of determination in subsequent development.

IV. Specification and Pattern Formation in Imaginal Discs

A. DIFFERENCES BETWEEN DETERMINATION AND SPECIFICATION

The mature imaginal disc is by no means merely a disc; it is a layer of cells with a specific morphology and regular folding pattern. The pattern of folds, specific patterns of cell death (Fristrom, 1969; Spreij, 1971), and regional differences in mitotic rate (Postlethwait and Schneiderman, 1971a) indicate that important differences already exist between cells in different parts of a disc. However, this point is more definitely established by the results of experiments in which specific parts of imaginal discs are transplanted into host larvae for metamorphosis. It has been shown many times that different disc fragments will metamorphose into different parts of the adult structure, as identified by particular bristles, sensilla groups, etc. Hence a fate map of the disc can be constructed, where in some cases even individual bristles and sensilla can be accurately mapped (see, for example, Schubiger, 1968).

The possibility of making accurate fate maps in this way indicates that the cells of an imaginal disc differ from one another according to their positions in the cell population as a whole; that is, specification of positional information (Wolpert, 1972) has occurred, giving the cells different positional values. For reasons which I shall discuss, it seems desirable to make a clear distinction between these events (or states) of specification and events (or states) of determination. There are well-defined differences between the two, and it is likely that specification occurs independently of the determined state of the cells, since different imaginal discs appear to have identical patterns of specification. Specification must, therefore, be interpreted differently by cells that have different determined states, resulting in disc-specific patterns of differentiation.

The main difference between determination and specification is that, whereas the former is a commitment propagated by cell heredity, the latter is nonheritable; it is a "transitory bias" (Schneiderman, 1969). This has become clear in recent experiments on the development of imaginal disc fragments. The most extensive experiments were by Schubiger (1971) who tested the developmental capacities of leg disc fragments after they had been allowed to grow for several days in adult abdomens before being transplanted to host larvae for metamorphosis. He found that upper or medial halves of the disc were able to regenerate the missing half, but that lower or lateral halves produced a duplication, in mirror-image symmetry, of the structures normally produced by those fragments. Similar results were obtained when the fragments were given the extra culture time in a larval host instead of an adult host. Furthermore, it was shown (Bryant, 1971) that operations *in situ* on imaginal leg discs of young larvae evoked the same response; bisection of the leg disc across the upper–lower axis (corresponding to dorsoventral in the adult) resulted in regeneration from the upper half and duplication from the lower fragment (Fig. 8).

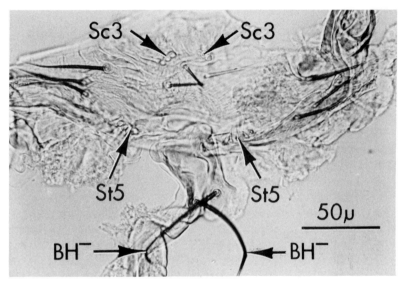

FIG. 8. Mirror-image pattern duplication of part of the coxa and part of the trochanter, produced by bisection of the leg disc *in situ* at 96 hours after oviposition. Sc3; Group of three sensilla campaniformia; St5; group of five sensilla trichodea; BH⁻, bristle on hairy island. (From Bryant, 1971.)

If specification were an inheritable state similar in nature to general imaginal disc determination, then it might be expected that extra culture time before metamorphosis would result in clusters of identically specified cells and that after metamorphosis these would produce clusters of identical structures. Although this effect is sometimes observed ("multiplication of units"; Schubiger, 1971) there are many cases of regeneration and of duplication where it does not occur (Bryant, 1971; Schubiger, 1971). It could, of course, be argued that sister cells with identical specified states could migrate away from one another and that this might provide an explanation of mirror-image pattern duplication in imaginal discs. This is the "cell-by-cell replication" hypothesis of pattern duplication, and it has been tested by the use of genetic mosaics. If this hypothesis were true, then, during the process of pattern duplication, any clones of genetically marked cells that were present in the original fragment would be precisely copied in the duplicate. This was not found to be the case (Postlethwait et al., 1971; Nöthiger, 1972); in fact, Ulrich (1971) found that a clone representing a small fraction of the original fragment could give rise to a much larger fraction of the duplicate. These results therefore exclude the cell-by-cell replication hypothesis and further indicate that the duplicate pattern might arise from a small fraction of the cells in the original fragment. Thus, the experiments on pattern duplication provide no support for the idea of heritability of the specified states in the mature imaginal disc. The fact that some disc fragments can regenerate also argues strongly against this idea, unless the process of regeneration involves recruitment of reserve cells, as suggested by Schubiger (1971).

The second difference between specified states and determined states in imaginal discs is in the number of cells involved in the initiation of those states. As we have already discussed, the allocation of cells to imaginal discs involves groups of eight to forty cells, so that the determinative events that establish discs must involve groups of cells at least this large. It is of interest that changes in this determined state in transdeterminations and in homoeotic mutants have also been shown to occur in groups of cells rather than in individual cells (Gehring, 1972; Postlethwait and Schneiderman, 1969). On the other hand, specification in imaginal discs need only involve single cells, since many of the structures for which it has been demonstrated are, in fact, made from individual cells or their immediate progeny (Lees and Waddington, 1942).

Because the specified states in the mature disc are nonheritable, therefore at least one of the daughter cells alters its specification during cell division. An attractive hypothesis, which has been suggested for other systems (Lawrence, 1971), is that positional information is respecified at every cell division during development. Thus, a pattern of specified states could exist in the developing tissue at all times, but the particular cell that carries a certain specification may change from time to time. It has been shown that cell division is necessary for either regeneration or duplication to occur in imaginal disc fragments (Wildermuth, 1968; Schubiger, 1973); hence it is likely that cell division is a prerequisite for change of specification in these cases. In this sense, imaginal discs are epimorphic systems rather than morphallactic ones.

B. Independence of Specification from Determination

Several studies on homoeotic mutants led to the important conclusion that the mechanism of specification may be the same in different imaginal discs. The most detailed study was that of Postlethwait and Schneiderman (1971b) on the mutant *Antennapedia*, where various parts of the antenna are transformed into leg structures. It was shown that the replacement of structures was absolutely position-specific; that is, a given part of the antenna, if transformed, would always produce a specific part of the leg. Hence, a correspondence map of the two structures could be drawn (Fig. 9), and this is interpreted to mean that

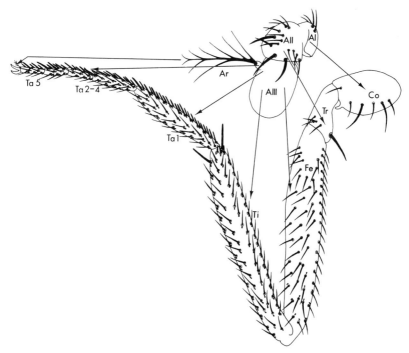

FIG. 9. The correspondence between antennal and leg structures, based on position-specific transformations in homoeotic antennae of *Antennapedia*. AI, AII, AIII, first, second, and third antennal segments; Ar, arista; Co, coxa; Tr, trochanter; Fe, femur; Ti, tibia; Ta 1–5, first to fifth tarsal segments. (From Postlethwait and Schneiderman, 1971b.)

presumptive leg cells can become specified according to their position in an antennal disc and can respond to that specification by differentiating in a particular direction. The mechanism for specification of positional information must, therefore, be the same in the antennal and leg discs. The difference between leg cells and antenna cells must be in their response to specification, and these differences in response must be the manifestation of the different determined states established in the embryo and inherited during disc development. It is tempting to generalize from these results and to propose that the mechanism for specification may be the same in all of the discs. Although they have not been studied in detail from this standpoint, the phenotypes of the other homoeotic mutants are consistent with this view. In any case, there is abundant evidence from other systems (Wolpert, 1972) to support the idea of universality of the mechanism for positional information specification.

C. GRADIENTS OF DEVELOPMENTAL CAPACITY

The finding that regeneration and duplication occur from the complementary halves of an imaginal disc seems to indicate a general property of these structures. In the leg discs, upper halves regenerate the lost portion while lower halves duplicate themselves; medial halves regenerate while lateral halves duplicate; and proximal parts regenerate but distal parts do not (Schubiger, 1971; Bryant, 1971). In the wing disc, presumptive wing can give rise to thorax tissue (Hadorn, 1966b), whereas the presumptive thorax region of the wing disc only shows duplication (Gehring, 1966; Bryant, unpublished). In the haltere disc "$\frac{3}{4}$ anterior" fragments regenerate whereas "$\frac{1}{4}$ posterior" fragments duplicate (Ouweneel and van der Meer, 1973). The eye region of the eye-antennal disc can regenerate the antenna, but the antennal and palpus regions duplicate (Vogt, 1946b; Gehring, 1966). A "$\frac{3}{4}$ fragment" of a male genital disc can replace the missing part, but the "$\frac{1}{4}$ fragment" begins by duplicating the anlagen present (Lüönd, 1961). Data are difficult to obtain for the abdominal histoblasts due to their small size, but surgical interventions do often result in tergites showing mirror-image duplications (Löbbecke, 1958; SantaMaria and Garcia-Bellido, 1972).

It was suggested (Bryant, 1971) that the finding of regeneration and duplication in the two fragments formed by bisection of an imaginal disc could be explained in terms of a gradient of developmental capacity in the disc. A surgical bisection of an imaginal disc would result in the formation of a "blastema" at each cut surface, which would give rise to all of the cells in the regenerate or the duplicate. During the growth of this blastema, cells could only give rise to lower levels of the postulated gradient. In Fig. 10, the cut is at level C, and the blastema which initially contains cells of level C can produce cells of levels D and E but not A and B. When levels D and E are added to the ABC fragment, this would constitute regeneration but when they are added to the CDE fragment the result would be mirror-image duplication. Thus, with this interpretation, regeneration and duplication are regarded as identical phenomena, the two processes differing only in the topological relation-

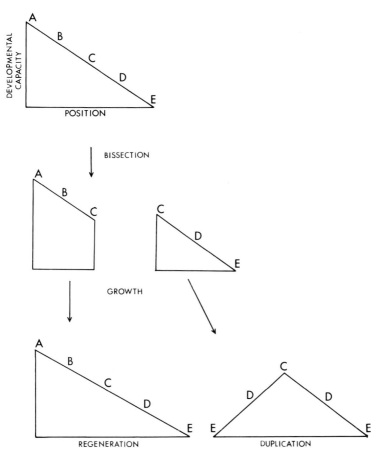

Fɪɢ. 10. The postulated gradient of developmental capacity and its response to bisection. (From Bryant, 1971.)

ships of the new parts to the old. Bohn (1965a,b) has proposed a similar model to account for leg regeneration in cockroaches, and Rose's (1962) "rule of distal transformation" for vertebrate limb regeneration is essentially identical. In Wolpert's (1972) terminology, we are proposing that cells can, during epimorphic development, change their positional information to lower but not to higher values within the gradient.

It would be of considerable interest to know whether during regeneration or duplication, the additional levels of the postulated gradient are added in sequence and if so what that sequence is. The data of Ursprung (1959) and Lüönd (1961) on duplication of genital disc fragments and of Schubiger (1971) on regeneration in leg disc fragments indicate that the levels nearest the cut are produced first and that these are followed by the more distant levels. If this is the case, then the phenomena can be explained by assuming that cellular specifications can change during cell division but that they can only change to a minimal degree and only in the direction corresponding to lower levels in the postulated gradient. Presumably this process is terminated in some way when the lowest gradient level is reached.

There are several mutations known in *Drosophila* which cause variable amounts of cell death in imaginal discs, and it is of considerable interest that many of these mutants show mirror-image duplication of some of the remaining parts. In *vestigial* there is extensive cellular degeneration in the presumptive wing blade region of the disc (Fristrom, 1968), and the thorax region sometimes shows duplications (Waddington, 1953). A similar phenomenon occurs frequently in the mutant *scalloped* (Fig. 11). This is consistent with the finding that the pre-

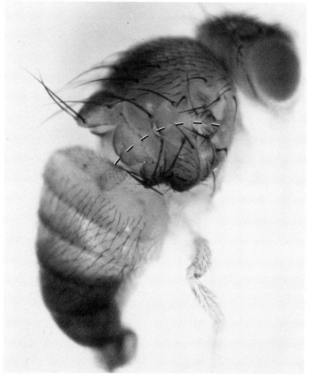

FIG. 11. A *scalloped* fly showing complete absence of the wing associated with duplication of thoracic structures on the right side. The dashed line indicates the line of mirror-image symmetry of the duplication. (Courtesy of Mr. Anthony James.)

sumptive thorax region of the wing disc undergoes duplication when the presumptive wing is removed (Gehring, 1966). Similarly, in *eyeless* there is cell death in the eye region of the disc (Fristrom, 1969) and this is associated with antennal duplications (Sang and Burnet, 1963) as might be expected from the surgical experiments (Gehring, 1966; Fristrom, 1970).

A phenomenon which might be similar or identical to the duplication of imaginal disc fragments occurs in a lethal mutant of *Drosophila* (*lethal (2) giant discs*) which we recently analyzed (Bryant and Schubiger, 1971). The phenotype of this mutant is a much prolonged larval phase which leads to tremendous overgrowth of the imaginal discs (Fig. 12). In the leg disc this overgrowth seems to occur preferentially in one region, and an extra pattern of concentric folds appears (Fig. 13) that after metamorphosis produces an extra leg. It is intriguing that this

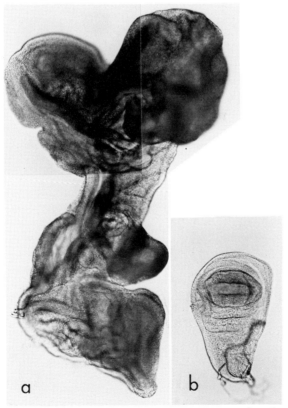

a   b

FIG. 12. (a) Giant wing disc from a *lethal (2) giant discs* larva which had spent 13 days in the larval stage instead of the usual 4. (b) Mature normal wing disc at the same magnification. (From Bryant and Schubiger, 1971.)

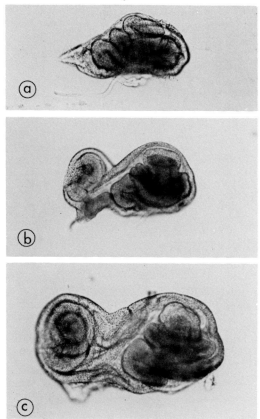

FIG. 13. (a) Mature normal third-leg disc. (b and c) *Lethal* (2) *giant disc* third-leg discs, 7 and 9 days after oviposition. (From Bryant and Schubiger, 1971.)

region is the one that we would predict from surgical experiments on normal leg discs to lie at the high point of the postulated gradient of developmental capacity. A similar kind of abnormality is found in the mutant *facet-notchoid* (Kroeger, 1960a). Here for some reason the male genital disc appears to grow abnormally and produce duplicate structures. These duplications appear first in the midline region of the genitalia; again, this is the region which would be expected from the surgical experiments to be at the highest level of the gradient. In both of these cases, the mutant seems to be eliciting a kind of regenerative behavior in the disc in the absence of the usual stimulus from the removal of parts.

D. ORIGIN OF SPECIFICATION

A recurring problem in the study of imaginal discs has been the origin of what I have called the specified states in the mature disc. An intriguing possibility, for example, is that patterns in normal development are built up in sequence as appears to be the case in regeneration and duplication. This kind of sequential pattern formation is the basis of Kroeger's (1960b) model for the genesis of symmetrical patterns, and the "determination waves" postulated by earlier workers (Kühn and von Engelhardt, 1933) also involve a sequential mechanism.

With imaginal discs, a number of approaches to this problem have been tried, but the answer is not yet known. Several authors (Gateff, 1971; Mindek, 1972; Schubiger, 1973, personal communication) have reported experiments in which young discs are caused to metamorphose prematurely, by transplanting them into mature larvae. These studies have shown that cells in very young discs have not yet acquired the competence to metamorphose, and this creates difficulties in assessing their specified states. At a later stage, competence is acquired, but at different times in different regions of the disc. In the eye–antennal disc, for instance, competence seems to be acquired first in the ommatidial region, later in the presumptive head, and then in a proximodistal sequence in the antenna (Gateff, 1971). In the leg disc, competence is acquired first in the presumptive proximal and distal regions, and later in between (Schubiger, 1973, personal communication). It has been shown that the acquisition of competence seems to proceed autonomously in the imaginal disc, independently of the hormones of the host, since it can occur in a metamorphosing host (Mindek, 1972) or an adult host (Hadorn *et al.*, 1968).

The foregoing experiments were conducted using whole imaginal discs; hence they are not really informative with respect to the specified states of the cells concerned. The appropriate experiment for that purpose was performed by Vogt (1946b) who transplanted fragments of eye-antennal discs from late second instar larvae into host larvae of the same age. She showed that the posterior part of the disc gave rise to eye facets, the central part produced eye facets, ocelli, arista, and palpus, and the anterior part produced arista, palpus, and chitinous spheres. Hence the basic specification of pattern appears to have been established in the disc at this time. Our *in situ* experiments (Bryant, 1971) also demonstrate that in the 72-hour larva there are differences between parts of the disc; one-half is able to regenerate but the other half duplicates. Furthermore, Postlethwait and Schneiderman (1973) have shown that duplications, which are similar to those produced surgically in the aforementioned experiments, can be produced by X-irradiating the 24-hour embryo (Fig. 14). This is interpreted as resulting from the killing of part of the disc where the remainder is only able to duplicate. Killing of a part of the disc where the remainder can regenerate would, of course, not be detectable since a normal leg would be formed. Similarly, Geigy (1931a)

FIG. 14. A partially duplicated leg produced by X-irradiation of a 24-hour embryo. (Courtesy of Dr. John H. Postlethwait.)

interpreted leg duplications induced by ultraviolet irradiation of embryos as resulting from partial destruction of the disc. If this interpretation is correct, then we can conclude that there are already regional differences established in the discs at 24 hours after oviposition.

Another kind of information relevant to the problem of the origin of specification comes from clonal analyses of imaginal disc development. When somatic crossing over is induced in an imaginal disc cell at some stage of development, the resulting clone of cells in the adult indicates the fate of the progeny of the ancestor cell. If the progeny of a given cell participate in the development of two different structures, then we can conclude that the ancestor cell was not determined to produce either one of those structures. Thus, clones induced at 72 hours or earlier, often encompass parts of two leg segments, for example, femur and tibia (Bryant and Schneiderman, 1969). The ancestor of the clone can, therefore, not have been determined as to leg segment. Similar results have been obtained for other structures, such as the antennal segments (Postlethwait and Schneiderman, 1971a). But the limitation of this conclusion is that it applies only to heritable determination for leg segments (for which there is no evidence), and we can make no conclusion about possible commitments which are nonheritable, such as the specified states in the mature disc. Indeed, none of the evidence available excludes the possibility that the imaginal disc at all stages of development is an assemblage of cells in specified states, which are modified at each cell division (see also Fristrom, 1970). In other words, positional information might be continually assessed by cells during imaginal disc development, and only interpreted in terms of differentiation when the disc is exposed to the conditions appropriate for metamorphosis. But the information may be interpreted by the cells in other ways; the specific folding patterns and regional differences of mitotic rate may be a reflection of such interpretations.

E. PATTERN RECONSTRUCTION BY DISSOCIATED IMAGINAL DISCS

Another method of studying specification is to disrupt experimentally the arrangement of cells in an imaginal disc before inducing metamorphosis, and to examine the effects of such disruption on pattern formation. In these experiments, cells of similar origin (e.g., leg discs) but different genotype (e.g., *yellow* bristles vs. *brown* bristles) are dissociated and reaggregated together, cultured for some time and then caused to metamorphose. The cells of the two genotypes can cooperate together in reconstructing recognizable patterns such as rows of sex-comb teeth (from the leg disc); rows of marginal bristles (from the wing disc), and others (Hadorn et al., 1959; Ursprung and Hadorn, 1962; Nöthiger, 1964; Tobler, 1966; Garcia-Bellido, 1966a; Poodry et al., 1971). These new patterns can contain cells of the two original genotypes, demonstrating that the pattern is actually reconstructed and that this reconstruction involves the establishment of new intercellular relationships. It has been shown (Nöthiger, 1964; Tobler, 1966; Garcia-Bellido, 1966a,b, 1968) that, whereas cells from homonomous imaginal discs (e.g., leg and leg) can cooperate in this way to form integrated patterns, cells from heteronomous discs (e.g., leg and wing) do not. This is perhaps not surprising since cells retain their determination during reaggregation and a mixture of leg and wing structures, however intimate, would not be regarded as an integrated pattern. However, several of the aforementioned authors have concluded that heteronomous cells sort out from each other and that the separated cell types independently reconstruct their patterns.

Two possible mechanisms were originally proposed to account for pattern reconstruction: Hadorn et al (1959) and Ursprung and Hadorn (1962) suggested that during reconstruction a new pattern of differentiation was imposed upon the randomly aggregated cells by a repetition of the normal process of pattern formation as it occurs in developing imaginal discs *in situ*. This would involve a change in the cellular specifications during reconstruction. On the other hand, Garcia-Bellido (1966a,b) proposed that cells are "determined to differentiate their cell specific structures" (equivalent to specified as used in this paper) and can "move about and choose their definite position in the pattern." This would, of course, involve the retention of cellular specification during pattern reconstruction.

We recently reexamined this question by dissociating and reaggregating two genetically different types of leg disc cells in the presence of varying amounts of wing disc cells (Poodry et al., 1971). After culturing for 3 to 5 days in adult abdomens, the implants were transferred to larvae for metamorphosis. A typical metamorphosed implant consisted of a hollow vesicle of wing tissue with islands of leg tissue contiguous with the wing tissue. The islands of leg tissue were either chimeric (containing the two genotypes of leg cells) or monotypic (containing only one of the two genotypes). In many cases, the islands showed typically reconstructed patterns that sometimes contained the two leg genotypes.

This experimental procedure provided a convenient method for studying the cellular dynamics of the reconstruction process. Thus, the frequency with which leg islands were chimeric could be used to estimate the average number of cells or cell clumps in the original cell suspension whose fate was to produce a leg island. In most experiments this average number was calculated to be less than 6. That is, a leg island containing up to several hundred cells is not produced by an equivalent number of cells in the suspension which cooperate to form the pattern, but it is the final result of a considerable amount of growth from a very small initial cell population. In many of the implants there were large monotypic patches, again indicating that considerable growth occurs in the aggregate.

Since such an extensive growth period intervenes between reaggregation of the cells and metamorphosis, the process of pattern reconstruction cannot be explained simply by the migration of each individual cell to its unique position in the pattern. Although our data do not exclude the possibility of some cell migration, we prefer to assume that the cells are reaggregated at random and that they change their specifications (perhaps during growth and cell division) in such a way as to reestablish spatial patterns. The degree to which the cells can change their specifications is limited, as has been shown by Garcia-Bellido (1966a) and Tobler (1966). The latter author mixed presumptive proximal leg tissue with presumptive distal leg tissue and found that this degree of restriction was retained during the mixing, culture, and metamorphosis. Chimeric patterns were only found in the middle leg segments. Garcia-Bellido (1966a) demonstrated the same thing for presumptive proximal versus distal, and anterior versus posterior, wing disc cells. A more extended culture period, of course, might have resulted in a change in these specifications as is indicated, for instance, by Schubiger's (1971) experiments showing that proximal leg tissue can regenerate the distal parts.

If our interpretation of pattern reconstruction is correct, then it emphasizes the role of intercellular communication in pattern formation. For pattern formation in imaginal discs *in situ* and for regeneration and duplication of imaginal disc fragments, the intercellular communication is not so obvious. It is possible, for instance, in those cases to consider seriously models involving ordered changes of specification which proceed autonomously in cell lines during growth and cell division. But for the reconstruction of a pattern by cells originating in two separate organisms there has to be some communication of positional information between the cells involved. The idea of positional information being encoded in the concentration of a diffusible morphogenetic substance would be adequate to account in principle for the process of pattern reconstruction.

F. EVIDENCE FOR AN INTERMEDIATE CELLULAR DECISION

Up to this point we have considered two decisions made by imaginal disc cells—the initial determination of the disc as a whole and the later, nonheritable decision (specification) made by individual cells of the disc. But several authors have suggested that there might be another decision interposed between these two, resulting in a subdivision of the disc into several differently determined areas ("regional blastemas" or "organ districts") (see Hadorn, 1966b; Ouweneel, 1972).

Some indications for a subdivision of discs come from studies of cell lineage during development *in situ* and during culture of fragments. Thus Ulrich (1971) has shown that in the female genital disc, the primordia for anal structures are clonally distinct from those for genital structures during all stages of normal development as well as during mirror-image duplication of a half-disc. The same appears to be true for the male genital disc (Nöthiger, 1972). Furthermore, Hadorn (1966a,b) has shown that during long-term culture of genital disc tissue, there is sometimes a tendency for "monoculturing" of anal plate material; that is, the successive removal of fragments from the tissue line for use as "test pieces" sometimes leaves only presumptive anal plate material in the tissue. These results have been interpreted as showing that a determinative event separates presumptive anal structures from presumptive genital structures at some time during development, and this idea leads to the concept of "stepwise" determination, or progressive restriction of potencies in imaginal discs. However, as pointed out by Nöthiger

(1972) the anal and genital structures arise from different body segments and even from separate imaginal discs in other Diptera (Dubendorfer, 1971). It seems likely, then, that the two primordia are separately
determined at the outset and represent a special case of fusion of imaginal
discs.

Clonal separations have been observed in the development of other
imaginal discs where the above explanation cannot hold. In the wing
disc Bryant (1970) and Garcia-Bellido and Merriam (1971) have shown
that the presumptive upper and lower wing surfaces are clonally distinct
from one another and probably from the presumptive mesonotum after
about 24 hours following oviposition. That this represents a real developmental distinction rather than a chance separation of lineages is indicated by the fact that clonal borderlines often coincide exactly with the
wing edge over long distances (Fig. 15). It was suggested (Bryant, 1970;
Garcia-Bellido and Merriam, 1971) that this clonal distinction may be
a result of a determinative event in the disc which separates it into
several primordia. But other interpretations are possible; for instance,
a zone of cell death between the presumptive upper and lower wing
surfaces would also lead to the preceding results.

The wing disc has provided another example of a tendency to "monoculture" during *in vivo* subculturing, in that the lines often become restricted to making mesonotal structures and lose the capacity to form
the wing blade. This might be regarded as evidence for two differently
determined cell populations in the wing disc, but a different explanation
is suggested by the recent findings on regenerative and duplicative
capacities of disc fragments. Thus certain parts of discs cannot regenerate removed parts but rather undergo duplication. It was shown by
Gehring (1966) that the presumptive mesonotum of the wing disc is of
this kind so that we might expect it to show a tendency to monoculture.
This tendency can, therefore, be understood as a reflection of graded
developmental capacities in the disc rather than an indication of cell
populations separated by a special determinative event. Hence none of
the preceding experiments provide convincing evidence for a determinative subdivision of imaginal discs prior to final pattern formation.

A different kind of evidence on this point comes from the work of
Poodry and Schneiderman (1973) on the tarsal bristle pattern in the
mutants *eyeless-dominant* and *shibire^{ts}*. In both of these mutants, there
are often gaps in the intersegmental membrane separating the first and
second tarsal segments, and in close proximity to these gaps are many
bristles that have abnormal or reversed polarity. This is taken to indicate
that bristle polarity is controlled by a segmentally repeating morphogenetic gradient, similar to that deduced from grafting experiments on

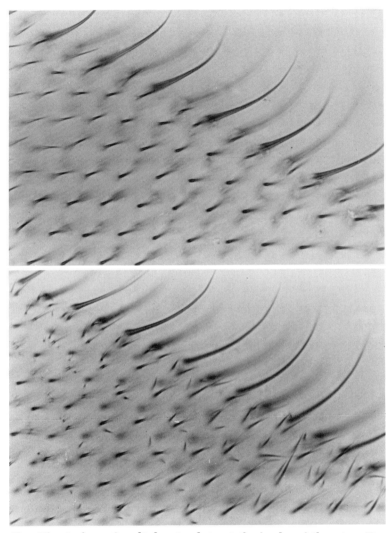

FIG. 15. A clone of *multiple wing hairs* at the border of the wing. Top and bottom photographs cover the same area at different levels of focus, to show the upper and lower wing surfaces. The borderline of the clone coincides with the edge of the wing over a long distance.

the legs and abdomen of hemimetabolous insects (see Bohn, 1965a,b; Lawrence, 1970). The intersegmental membrane is thought to separate the high point of one such gradient from the low point of the next. Hence, if the gradient can flow to a certain extent, a gap in the segment boundary would lead to local abnormalities of gradient profile. The results can be explained by assuming that bristle cell polarity coincides with the direction of maximum slope of the gradient at that site. Furthermore, the abnormalities of bristle distribution around the boundary gap can be explained on the same basis—flow of the morphogenetic gradient through the gap would result in some gradient levels being duplicated and others missing. This then provides an explanation for the duplication of the sex comb area found in the basitarsus of these mutants.

Although these findings point to the existence of a subdivision of the leg into segmental morphogenetic fields, it should be emphasized that this does not have to involve a determinative event separating the cell populations. Indeed, experiments by Schubiger (1971) clearly rule out this idea. He showed that, after the removal of the end knob (presumptive tarsus) from a leg disc, it can be regenerated by the remaining piece. Since cell lines must change their presumptive segment nature during this process, the separation of the leg into segments cannot be regarded as a determinative event in the sense used in this paper. Rather, it may be that specification in the leg disc proceeds in two steps: first, the establishment of leg segments and, second, the establishment of patterns of specification within those segments. The defect in *eyeless-dominant* and *shibire*[ts] would then be the failure of some cells to set up segment boundaries in response to the first specification, resulting in the gradient anomalies during the second step of pattern formation.

G. PREPATTERNS, MOSAICS, AND INHIBITORY FIELDS

In *Drosophila* there are many mutations known which modify the bristle pattern on the adult surface. Specific bristles or groups of bristles are missing, added, or changed in position in different strains. Stern (1954, 1968) has proposed that pattern formation in *Drosophila* is based on two factors: an underlying "prepattern" that specifies the ordering in space of different cellular activities, and, secondary to this, the responses of the cells to the prepattern, involving differentiation in particular directions. The concept of prepattern is an alternative to the idea of the specification of positional values, and it has some different connotations (see Wolpert, 1972; Poodry and Schneiderman, 1973).

Stern (1954, 1968) has pointed out that mutant bristle patterns could in theory result from one of two actions: a modification of the prepattern itself or of the response of certain cells to an invariant prepattern. These two alternatives can be distinguished by the use of animals that are genetically mosaic for normal and mutant tissue; a mutant in which cellular response is modified will behave completely autonomously in a mosaic, but a mutation affecting prepattern might be expected to modify the pattern in both the mutant cells and the adjacent, genetically normal cells. In the extensive work which has been done along these lines, it has been shown that the mutant tissue almost always develops autonomously and produces no pattern defects in adjacent wild-type tissue; neither does wild-type tissue impose a normal pattern on genetically mutant tissue. Hence the mutants seem to be affecting the cells' response to the prepattern rather than the prepattern itself. Alternatively, these results can be discussed in terms of positional information (Wolpert, 1972). Thus the mutations would appear to modify the cells' response to positional information, rather than the mechanism for positional information specification. Wolpert (1972) has discussed how the lack of nonautonomous pattern mutants might be explained in terms of the universality of the mechanism responsible for positional specification; any disruption in such a universal system would cause multiple abnormalities in development, and such a mutation would be expected to be lethal. Lethal mutants, however, have not been extensively studied from this point of view. An exception to the rule of autonomy in mosaics was found in the case of *eyeless-dominant* (Stern and Tokunaga, 1967). We have already seen how this case can be interpreted in terms of disruptions of a segmentally repeating morphogenetic gradient in the leg.

There are some other exceptions to the rule of antonomy of bristle pattern mutants; these exceptions have often been ignored but they may be rather informative with respect to the mechanism of specification. The first case is *achaete*, which was one of the first pattern mutants to be analyzed by Stern (1954) using mosaics and which was later studied by Claxton (1969). This mutation results in a lack of the anterior dorsocentral bristle (*adc*) of the thorax, and it generally behaves autonomously in mosaics. The interesting mosaics are those in which the normal site of the *adc* is occupied by a small patch of *achaete* tissue in a predominantly non*achaete* thorax. In accordance with its autonomous nature, the *achaete* tissue lacks an *adc* bristle but both Stern and Claxton discovered that this bristle was then often produced at an ectopic site in the adjacent non*achaete* tissue. Both authors interpreted this result to mean that, in normal development, a cell that begins to form an *adc* inhibits nearby cells from initiating the same differentiation. Blockage of normal *adc* development, as by a patch of *achaete* tissue, will relieve this inhibition and allow nearby cells to substitute. The existence of such a "fine-tuning" mechanism would be very important in pattern formation, since it would lessen the degree of accuracy required in positional specification. Only a general area, and not a specific cell, would need to attain the specification corresponding to *adc*.

A similar case is seen in the work of Gottlieb (1964) on the *Hairy-wing* mutant, which has the effect of producing extra bristles in the region of the dorsocentrals. Gottlieb made mosaics where homozygous Hw/Hw patches existed adjacent to homozygous Hw^+/Hw^+ patches (marked with y/y) in a background of heterozygous tissue. He found that extra bristles were formed not only in the Hw/Hw patch, but also in the adjacent Hw^+/Hw^+ patch. He explained this apparently non-autonomous development as resulting from the spread of a "chaetogenic substance" from the Hw/Hw tissue into the Hw^+/Hw^+ tissue. An alternative explanation would be that the effect of *Hairywing* is to block the fine-tuning inhibition which was postulated in the *achaete* case. This would then allow extra bristles to be produced in Hw/Hw flies, as well as in normal tissue adjacent to Hw/Hw tissue in mosaics. A prediction from this model might, of course, be that the extra y/y bristle might inhibit the formation of bristles in the Hw/Hw patch, and such a tendency is, in fact, seen in the data of Gottlieb.

Some of the surgical experiments on imaginal discs lend support to the idea that inhibitory fields play a role in bristle cell specification. Schubiger (1968) showed that if an imaginal leg disc from a late third instar was divided in half and the halves caused to metamorphose, then there were no cases where the edge bristle of the trochanter was formed in both fragments. On the other hand, when the experiment was begun with a leg disc from a young third instar larva, this bristle was formed in both fragments in 41% of cases. A possible explanation could be that the inhibitory field for the edge bristle had not been established in a young third instar larva, but it was in effect in the late third instar larva.

If the idea of inhibitory fields is a valid conclusion from these experiments, then some interesting questions arise. The most important of these is the degree of specificity of the inhibitory fields. Are they specific for each bristle type or is the same inhibitory influence used by cells with different specifications? If mutants such as *Hairywing* do, indeed, block inhibitory fields then they can be used to investigate this question.

H. CONCLUSIONS ABOUT SPECIFICATION IN IMAGINAL DISCS

The cells of a mature imaginal disc are in a determined state which is inherited from the primordial cells for that disc, and, in addition their positional values have become specified, such that they will produce particular parts of the derivative of the disc. Specification of positional value differs from determination in that it is established in individual cells rather than groups of cells and is nonheritable. It seems that the mechanism for specification is the same in different discs and that cells from different discs differ in the way they respond, at the time of differentiation, to their specification. These differences in response must be a reflection of their different determined states. I have suggested that there are certain restrictions on the degree and direction of the respecification that can take place during cell division. These restrictions result in gradients of developmental capacity in imaginal discs, which can account for the occurrence of regeneration and duplication from complementary imaginal disc fragments. Specification may be associated with a fine-tuning mechanism, whereby a specified cell inhibits nearby cells from attaining identical specification. The nature of the molecular events leading to the establishment and maintenance of both determined and specified states in cells remains to be elucidated.

ACKNOWLEDGMENTS

The comments of Drs. Howard Schneiderman, Susan Bryant, Richard Campbell, and Mr. John Haynie are gratefully acknowledged.

The author's investigations are supported by Grants GB 29561 from the National Science Foundation and HD 06082-02 from the National Institutes of Health.

REFERENCES

Auerbach, C. (1936). *Trans. Roy. Soc. Edinburgh* **58,** 787.

Baker, W. K. (1967). *Develop. Biol.* **16,** 1.

Bohn, H. (1965a). *Wilhelm Roux' Arch. Entwicklungsmech. Organismen* **156,** 49.

Bohn, H. (1965b). *Wilhelm Roux' Arch. Entwicklungsmech. Organismen* **156,** 449.

Bownes, M. (1973). Ph.D. Thesis, University of Sussex.

Bryant, P. J. (1970). *Develop. Biol.* **22,** 389.

Bryant P. J. (1971). *Develop. Biol.* **26,** 637.

Bryant, P. J., and Schneiderman, H. A. (1969). *Develop. Biol.* **20,** 263.

Bryant, P. J. and Schubiger, G. (1971). *Develop. Biol.* **24,** 233.

Bull, A. L. (1966). *J. Exp. Zool.* **161,** 221.

Chan, L.-N., and Gehring, W. (1971). *Proc. Nat. Acad. Sci. U.S.* **68,** 2217.

Claxton, J. H. (1969). *Genetics* **63,** 883.

Counce, S. J. (1961). *Annu. Rev. Entomol.* **6,** 295.

Dubendorfer, A. (1971). *Wilhelm Roux' Arch. Entwicklungsmech. Organismen* **168,** 142.

Fielding, C. J. (1967). *J. Embryol. Exp. Morphol.* **17,** 375.

Fristrom, D. (1968). *J. Cell Biol.* **39,** 488.

Fristrom, D. (1969). *Mol. Gen. Genet.* **103,** 363.

Fristrom, J. W. (1970). *Annu. Rev. Genet.* **4,** 325.

Garcia-Bellido, A. (1966a). *Develop. Biol.* **14,** 278.

Garcia-Bellido, A. (1966b). *Exp. Cell Res.* **44,** 382.

Garcia-Bellido, A. (1967). *Wilhelm Roux' Arch. Entwicklungsmech. Organismen* **158,** 212.

Garcia-Bellido, A. (1968). *Genetics* **59,** 487.

Garcia-Bellido, A., and Merriam, J. R. (1969). *J. Exp. Zool.* **170,** 61.

Garcia-Bellido, A., and Merriam, J. R. (1971). *Develop. Biol.* **24,** 61.

Gardner, E. J. (1970). *Advan. Genet.* **15,** 116.

Gateff, E. (1971). Ph.D. Thesis, University of California, Irvine.

Gehring, W. (1966). *J. Embryol. Exp. Morphol.* **15,** 77.

Gehring, W. (1969). In "Problems in Biology: RNA in Development" (E. W. Hanly, ed.), p. 231. Univ. of Utah Press, Salt Lake City, Utah.

Gehring, W. (1972). In "The Biology of Imaginal Discs" (H. Ursprung and R. Nöthiger, eds.), p. 35. Springer-Verlag, Berlin and New York.

Gehring, W., and Nöthiger, R. (1973). In "Developmental Systems. Insects" (C. H. Waddington and S. J. Counce, eds.), Vol. 2, p. 212. Academic Press, New York.

Geigy, R. (1931a). Rev. Suisse Zool. 38, 187.

Geigy, R. (1931b). Wilhelm Roux' Arch. Entwicklungsmech. Organismen 125, 406.

Gottlieb, F. J. (1964). Genetics 49, 739.

Hadorn, E. (1966a). Develop. Biol. 13, 424.

Hadorn, E. (1966b). Symp. Soc. Develop. Biol. 25, 85.

Hadorn, E., Anders, G., and Ursprung, H. (1959). J. Exp. Zool. 142, 159.

Hadorn, E., Hurlimann, R., Mindek, G., Schubiger, G., and Staub, M. (1968). Rev. Suisse Zool. 75, 557.

Hotta, Y., and Benzer, S. (1972). Nature (London) 240, 527.

Howland, R. B., and Child, G. P. (1935). J. Exp. Zool. 70, 415.

Howland, R. B. and Sonnenblick, B. P. (1936). J. Exp. Zool. 73, 109.

Illmensee, K. (1972). Wilhelm Roux' Arch. Entwicklungsmech. Organismen 170, 267.

Illmensee, K., and Mahowald, A. P. (1973). J. Cell Biol. 59, 154a.

Kalthoff, K. (1971). Wilhelm Roux' Arch. Entwicklungsmech. Organismen 168, 63.

Kaufman, S. (1973). Science 181, 310.

Kobel, H. R. (1968). Genetica 39, 329.

Kroeger, H. (1960a). J. Morphol. 107, 227.

Kroeger, H. (1960b). Naturwissenschaften 47, 148.

Kühn, A., and von Engelhardt, M. (1933). Wilhelm Roux' Arch. Entwicklungsmech. Organismen 130, 660.

Laugé, G. (1967). C. R. Acad. Sci. Paris 265, 814.

Lawrence, P. A. (1970). Advan. Insect Physiol. 7, 197.

Lawrence, P. A. (1971). Symp. Soc. Exp. Biol. 25, 379.

Lees, A. D., and Waddington, C. H. (1942). Proc. Royal Soc. Edinburgh Sect. B 131, 87.

Lewis, E. B. (1964). In "The Role of Chromosomes in Development" (M. Locke, ed.), p. 231. Academic Press, New York.

Löbbecke, E. A. (1958). Biol. Zentralbl. 77, 209.

Lüönd, H. (1961). Develop. Biol. 3, 615.

Mahowald, A. P. (1971). In "Origin and Continuity of Cell Organelles" (J. Reinert and H. Ursprung, eds.), p. 158. Springer-Verlag, Berlin and New York.

Mandaron, P. (1971). Develop. Biol. 25, 581.

Mindek, G. (1972). Wilhelm. Roux' Arch. Entwicklungsmech. Organismen 169, 353.

Mintz, B. (1971). Symp. Soc. Exp. Biol. 25, 345.

Murphy, C. (1967). Develop. Biol. 15, 368.

Nöthiger, R. (1964). Wilhelm Roux' Arch. Entwicklungsmech. Organismen 155, 269.

Nöthiger, R. (1972). In "The Biology of Imaginal Discs" (H. Ursprung and R. Nöthiger, eds.), p. 1. Springer-Verlag, Berlin and New York.

Nöthiger, R., and Strub, S. (1972). Rev. Suisse Zool. 79, 267.

Okada, M. Kleinman, I., and Schneiderman, H. A. (1973). Develop. Biol. (in press).

Ouweneel, W. J. (1969). *Wilhelm Roux' Arch. Entwicklungsmech. Organismen* **164**, 1.

Ouweneel, W. J. (1972). *Acta Biotheor.* **21**, 115.

Ouweneel, W. J., and van der Meer, J. M. (1973). *Drosophila Inform. Serv.* **49**, 88.

Parks, H. B. (1936). *Ann. Entomol. Soc. Amer.* **29**, 350.

Poodry, C. A., and Schneiderman, H. A. (1970). *Wilhelm Roux' Arch. Entwicklungsmech. Organismen* **166**, 1.

Poodry, C. A., and Schneiderman, H. A. (1973). *Develop. Biol.* (in press).

Poodry, C. A., Bryant, P., and Schneiderman, H. A. (1971). *Develop. Biol.* **26**, 464.

Postlethwait, J. H., and Schneiderman, H. A. (1969). *Proc. Nat. Acad. Sci. U.S.* **64**, 176.

Postlethwait, J. H., and Schneiderman, H. A. (1971a). *Develop. Biol.* **24**, 477.

Postlethwait, J. H., and Schneiderman, H. A. (1971b). *Develop. Biol.* **25**, 606.

Postlethwait, J. H., and Schneiderman, H. A. (1973). *Develop. Biol.* **32**, 345.

Postlethwait, J. H., Poodry, C. A., and Schneiderman, H. A. (1971). *Develop. Biol.* **26**, 125.

Postlethwait, J. H., Bryant, P. J., and Schubiger, G. (1972). *Develop. Biol.* **29**, 337.

Poulson, D. F. (1950). In "Biology of *Drosophila*" (M. Demerec, ed.), p. 168. Wiley, New York.

Rabinowitz, M. (1941). *J. Morphol.* **69**, 1.

Roberts, P. (1964). *Genetics* **49**, 593.

Rose, S. M. (1962). *Symp. Soc. Study Develop. Growth* **20**, 153.

Sang, J. H., and Burnet, B. (1963). *Genetics* **48**, 1683.

SantaMaria, P., and Garcia-Bellido, A. (1972). *J. Embryol. Exp. Morphol.* **28**, 397.

Schneiderman, H. A. (1969). In "Biology and the Physical Sciences" (S. Devons, ed.), p. 186. Columbia Univ. Press, New York.

Schubiger, G. (1968). *Wilhelm Roux' Arch. Entwicklungsmech. Organismen* **160**, 9.

Schubiger, G. (1971). *Develop. Biol.* **26**, 277.

Schubiger, G. (1973). *Experientia* **29**, 631.

Schubiger, M., and Schneiderman, H. A. (1971). *Nature (London)* **230**, 185.

Schubiger, G., Schubiger-Staub, M., and Hadorn, E. (1969). *Wilhelm Roux' Arch. Antwicklungsmech. Organismen* **163**, 33.

Shearn, A., Rice, T., Garen, A., and Gehring, W. (1971). *Proc. Nat. Acad. Sci. U.S.* **68**, 2594.

Spreij, T. E. (1971). *Neth. J. Zool.* **21**, 221.

Stern, C. (1954). *Proc. Int. Congr. Genet., 1953* **6**, 355.

Stern, C. (1968). "Genetic Mosaics and Other Essays." Harvard Univ. Press, Cambridge.

Stern, C., and Tokunaga, C. (1967). *Proc. Nat. Acad. Sci. U.S.* **57**, 658.

Stewart, M., Murphy, C., and Fristrom, J. W. (1972). *Develop. Biol.* **27**, 71.

Sturtevant, A. H. (1929). *Z. Wiss. Zool.* **135**, 323.

Tobler, H. (1966). *J. Embryol. Exp. Morphol.* **16**, 609.

Ulrich, E. (1971). *Wilhelm Roux' Arch. Entwicklungsmech. Organismen* **167**, 64.

Ursprung, H. (1959). *Wilhelm Roux' Arch. Entwicklungsmech. Organismen* **151**, 504.

Ursprung, H., and Hadorn, E. (1962). *Develop. Biol.* **4**, 40.

Ursprung, H., and Nöthiger, R. (1972). "The Biology of Imaginal Discs." Springer-Verlag, Berlin and New York.

Vogt, M. (1946a). *Biol. Zentralbl.* **65**, 238.

Vogt, M. (1946b). *Biol. Zentralbl.* **65**, 223.

Waddington, C. H. (1953). *J. Genet.* **51**, 243.

Wildermuth, H. R. (1968). *Wilhelm Roux' Arch. Entwicklungsmech. Organismen* **160**, 41.

Wolpert. L. (1972). *Curr. Top. Develop. Biol.* **6**, 183.

Zalokar, M. (1943). *Rev. Suisse Zool.* **50**, 232.

Zalokar, M. (1971). *Proc. Nat. Acad. Sci. U.S.* **68**, 1539.

CHAPTER 3

STUDIES ON THE CONTROL OF DIFFERENTIATION OF MURINE VIRUS-INDUCED ERYTHROLEUKEMIC CELLS*

Charlotte Friend, Harvey D. Preisler,† and William Scher

CENTER FOR EXPERIMENTAL CELL BIOLOGY, THE MOLLIE B. ROTH LABORATORY, AND
DEPARTMENT OF MEDICINE, MOUNT SINAI SCHOOL OF MEDICINE
CITY UNIVERSITY OF NEW YORK
NEW YORK, NEW YORK

I. Introduction

One of the properties that characterize malignant cells is a decreased ability to mature. Normal cells generally follow a programmed pattern of development which leads to a final stage where deoxyribonucleic acid (DNA) synthesis and cell division cease. In contrast, malignant cells remain relatively immature and continue to divide. It is in this context that an understanding of the mechanisms that regulate growth and maturation is fundamental to the understanding and ultimately to the

* This work supported in part by National Cancer Institute grants CA 10,000, CA 13,047, and CA 12,737.
† Scholar of the Leukemia Society of New York.

control of neoplastic processes. The reader is referred to the papers of Braun (1969, 1972), Pierce (1970), Pierce and Johnson (1971), Markert (1968), and Fiala (1968) which consider the evidence that the regulatory mechanisms controlling differentiation and neoplastic growth are similar. This chapter will be limited to a discussion of our studies on a murine virus-induced leukemia (FLV) (Friend, 1957) which is serving as a model system for exploring the relationship between differentiation and malignancy. The cells of this virus-induced leukemia (FLC) differentiate along the erythroid pathway *in vitro* (Friend *et al.* 1966; Patuleia and Friend, 1967; and Friend and Rossi, 1969) and, under special conditions, *in vivo* as well (Rossi and Friend, 1967).

II. Historical Background

A. DISTINGUISHING FEATURES OF FRIEND VIRUS-INDUCED LEUKEMIA

The inoculation of the virus into young or adult mice of susceptible strains is followed by a short incubation period of 1 to 2 weeks (Friend, 1957). The early phase of the disease is characterized by erythroblastosis accompanied by enlargement of the spleen and liver. Terminally, the spleen, liver, and bone marrow are massively infiltrated with immature cells which almost completely replace the normal cells of these tissues. Lymph nodes remain unaffected. Although some of the animals die within a few weeks, the average survival time of the leukemic mice is about 2 months. Neither splenectomy nor thymectomy affect the course of this erythroleukemia. Mice immunized with formalin-inactivated virus are solidly protected against challenge with active virus preparations (Friend, 1959) or leukemic cells (Friend and Rossi, 1968; Friend, 1973).

B. DEVELOPMENT OF TRANSPLANTABLE TUMORS

The normal architecture of the spleen and liver are almost completely replaced by primitive hematopoietic cells in the advanced stages of leukemia. Subcutaneous implantation of fragments of these organs into recipient syngeneic mice results in tumor formation at the site of inoculation (Friend and Haddad, 1960). These tumors, which are serially transplantable, resemble reticulum cell sarcomas. They are devoid of recognizable erythroid elements and consist of a uniform population of primitive cells chronically infected with virus. When, however, the tumor cells are assayed in lethally irradiated mice, spleen colonies composed of the characteristic neoplastic cells as well as cells that are indistinguishable from proerythroblasts and normoblasts develop (Rossi and Friend, 1967).

C. ESTABLISHMENT OF TISSUE CULTURE LINES

The technique of Jensen *et al.* (1964) was utilized to establish tissue culture lines from fragments of the transplantable tumors described above (Friend *et al.*, 1966). The leukemic cells shed from these tumors grow in suspension and are maintained in continuous culture in Eagle's basal medium supplemented with 15% fetal calf serum. The potential of the leukemic cells to differentiate is apparent in that a small percentage of these cells are capable of performing specific functions characteristic of their normal erythrocytic counterparts, i.e., differentiation to the level of orthochromatophilic normoblast and synthesis of hemoglobin (Scher *et al.*, 1971; Friend *et al.*, 1971; Boyer *et al.*, 1972). About 1% of the cells of the mass cultures generally stain benzidine-positive (B+). The ratio of primitive cells to proerythroblasts and erythroblasts varies both among different cell lines and different passages of each line, which may be a reflection of the response to individual lots of serum or medium. Since an abnormal erythropoietic response is characteristic of the murine virus-induced leukemia from which the *in vitro* lines were developed, this system offers the opportunity to explore the possibility that leukemia is a disease caused by a maturation defect.

Of further interest is the fact that, although these leukemic cell lines exhibit a limited ability to mature *in vitro*, they retain their neoplastic properties and produce tumors that are histologically identical to those from which the culture lines were derived. When these tumors are explanted and returned to the tissue culture milieu, the cells again show maturation along the erythrocytic line.

III. Properties of Cloned Cell Lines

Single cells of the mass cultures have been repeatedly cloned in semisolid agar medium (Patuleia and Friend, 1967; Friend *et al.*, 1971), and the progeny of each clone were found to exhibit the same pleomorphism observed in the parent cultures; that is, each cell gave rise to a colony containing undifferentiated cells and cells of varying sizes and levels of erythroid maturity. The percentage of B+ cells varied from clone to clone, from less than 1–15%.

Other than the difference in the baseline level of B+ cells, the cloned lines are identical to the parent cultures in regard to growth rate and malignancy when implanted subcutaneously into syngeneic hosts.

IV. Iron Metabolism and Hemoglobin Synthesis

The differences in the degree of spontaneous differentiation are also reflected in differences in iron metabolism (Scher *et al.*, 1971). The amount of iron accumulated by the cells of the mass culture (in which approximately 1% of the cells are B+) increased only for the first 40 hours after seeding and then leveled off. On the other hand, cells of clone 707, with a baseline of 5% B+ cells, accumulated iron for the entire 96 hours of the culture period. The amount of iron incorporated into heme also differed between these cell lines. Although the amount of heme per cell in the mass culture did not increase after the twentieth hour of growth, in the cells of clone 707 the amount of heme was much greater by the fortieth hour and continued to increase during the 96 hours of observation.

Further biochemical analysis demonstrated that these cells were synthesizing hemoglobin identical to that of DBA/2J mice, the strain of origin of the cells (Scher *et al.*, 1971; Boyer *et al.*, 1972). Acrylamide gel electrophoretic analysis of cell lysates from clone 707 revealed three protein bands that contained iron, stained B+, and whose R_f values were identical with the R_f's of hemoglobin derived from DBA/2J erythrocytes. However, the amount of hemoglobin in cells of clone 692, in which B+ cells were very rare (<1%), was below the limits of detectability using these procedures. Thus the percentage of B+ cells correlated well with the amount of hemoglobin synthesized by the various clonal lines.

V.   Enhancement of Erythroid Differentiation

A.   Effect of Dimethyl Sulfoxide

When dimethyl sulfoxide (DMSO), which has a wide range of biological activities (Leake, 1967; Jacob *et al.*, 1971), was added to the medium, the number of differentiating cells markedly increased (Friend *et al.*, 1971). The percentage of B+ cells observed after 4 to 5 days of culture in medium containing 2% DMSO was generally about 85% (Fig. 1). At this concentration of DMSO, despite the fact that there was a 24-hour lag before logarithmic growth occurred, cell densities approximated those of the control cells by the fourth day of culture.

Dimethyl sulfoxide did not affect all of the cells. Approximately 10–15% of the cells, which morphologically appeared quite primitive, remained benzidine-negative (B−). When DMSO-treated cells were transferred to DMSO-free medium, the cell population produced was morphologically identical to that found in previously untreated cultures. Despite alternate passages in DMSO-supplemented and DMSO-free medium, the cells did not develop resistance to DMSO stimulation.

The degree of response to DMSO stimulation, however, varied among individual clones so that a range of lines from high inducibility to low or imperceptible inducibility was obtained. In general, the prog-

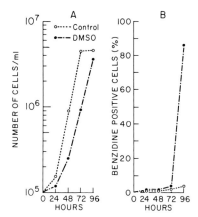

Fig. 1. Effect of dimethyl sulfoxide (DMSO) on the growth (A) and differentiation (B) of murine leukemia cells *in vitro*. The cells were grown in the absence or in the presence of 2.0% DMSO. (Friend *et al.*, 1973.)

eny of the highly inducible cell lines gave rise to clones that were predominantly inducible, whereas the progeny of the cells that were negligibly inducible were, for the most part, noninducible. However, even noninducible cell lines yielded some clones that were significantly stimulated by DMSO.

1. Morphological Changes

When cells seeded in DMSO-supplemented medium were observed daily for 7 days after seeding, no definitive morphological alterations were noted until the third day when there was a slight rise in the percentage of small cells that stained B+. By the fourth day, a marked change was apparent and the number of B+ cells was greatly increased. When aliquots of the DMSO-treated cultures were centrifuged daily during the course of the experiment, a change in the color of the cell pellet was apparent within 1 day. With continued culture, the pellet color gradually deepened and was red by day 4, indicating the presence of hemoglobin. In contrast, the control cell pellet remained almost colorless throughout the period of study. After 7 days of growth, the primitive cells characteristic of the leukemic cell line were most prominent in the control cultures, whereas most of the treated cells had decreased nuclear to cytoplasmic ratios, were B+, and resembled orthochromatophilic normoblasts (Friend *et al.*, 1971). Control and DMSO-treated cells after 6 days of growth are seen in Fig. 2.

When the cells were examined under the electron microscope (Sato *et al.*, 1971), several ultrastructural changes were observed. There were

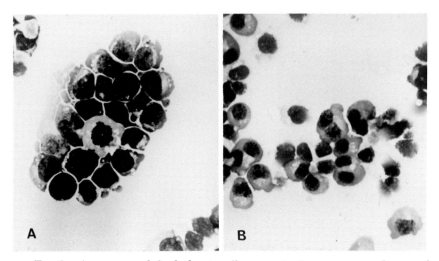

Fig. 2. Appearance of the leukemic cells grown in the presence or absence of dimethyl sulfoxide (DMSO) for 6 days. (A) Control cells; (B) DMSO-treated. All of the cells in the field are benzidine positive. Note the reduced nuclear:cytoplasmic ratio as compared to the control cells. × 625.

complex vacuolar structures containing numerous viruses in the DMSO-treated cells. These cells also had an increased number of viruses budding from their membranes. In addition, ribosomes, which were numerous in the control cells were decreased in number in the treated cells. Whereas the control cells contained so many ribosomes that it was difficult to discern polysomes, ribosomes in the DMSO-treated cells were arranged in clusters of 2 to 4. In further experiments, described in the following, these findings were extended by biochemical analysis.

2. Alterations in Malignant Potential

One of the most significant alterations in the DMSO-treated cells appeared to be the decrease in malignancy (Friend et al., 1971). The cells from the cultures were bioassayed daily for 4 days by subcutaneous inoculation into syngeneic DBA/2J mice. Although there was little variation in the time of appearance of the tumors in mice inoculated with untreated cells or cells growing in DMSO for up to 48 hours, mice inoculated with cells exposed to DMSO for 72 hours lived longer and had slower growing tumors than mice injected with untreated control cells. The tumors arising from both treated and untreated cells were morphologically identical. This difference was more marked when the mice were inoculated with cells that had been growing in the DMSO-supplemented medium for 96 hours. The mean survival time of mice injected with 5×10^5 treated cells was 56 days as compared to 38 days for mice that had received an equal number of untreated control cells. It was necessary to inject 10 times more treated cells to approximate the survival time of mice receiving the control cells, i.e., mice receiving 5×10^5 DMSO-treated cells lived as long as mice injected with 5×10^4 control cells. Our preliminary results using spleen colony assays in lethally irradiated mice confirmed these findings in that there was a significant loss in the colonizing ability which correlated with the length of time the cells were grown in the presence of DMSO.

It is yet to be determined whether the normoblasts in the DMSO-treated cultures have indeed lost their malignant potential. It is possible that the 15% of the cells in the preparation used which had remained blastic and B— despite 4 days of DMSO treatment were responsible for the tumors and spleen colonies that had arisen in the mice inoculated with these preparations. These cells may be more primitive and, for the most part, uncommitted, whereas the cells that are inducible may already be committed to proceed along the erythroid pathway.

3. Effect on Macromolecular Synthesis

a. *Heme and Hemoglobin.* In the DMSO-treated cultures, the great increase in the number of B+ cells was accompanied by an equivalent increase in the synthesis of hemoglobin (Friend et al., 1971). Cells grown in the presence of DMSO accumulated more iron and incorporated more iron into heme and hemoglobin than did control cultures. A detectable stimulation of heme synthesis was noted after 2 days of culture and by the third day hemoglobin synthesis was enhanced. For example, the amount of heme synthesized after 4 days of culture was 60 times greater and the amount of hemoglobin synthesized was 40 times greater in DMSO-treated cells than in the corresponding control cells. Recent experiments using polyacrylamide gel electrophoresis have detected globin synthesis as early as the second day.

In one of the clones, designated 745A, which we have used extensively in recent studies, approximately one-ninth of the total proteins synthesized during 4 days of culture in DMSO-supplemented medium was globin (Boyer et al., 1972). The amount of hemoglobin per cell was determined using two different techniques. As estimated by immunodiffusion with New World spider monkey antihemoglobin A, each differentiating cell contained an average of 8.5 pg of hemoglobin after 100 hours of growth. When the amount of radiolysine incorporated into globin by the entire cell population during a 17-hour incubation was determined, in cells that had been grown for three days in DMSO, the average amount of hemoglobin produced per cell was 4 pg.

A comparison of the globin chains synthesized by the differentiating erythroleukemic cells with those present in the red cells of the DBA/2J mouse, the strain of origin, was also carried out. The α- and β-globins synthesized by the leukemic cells cochromatographed with those of adult DBA/2J mouse reticulocytes. Tryptic peptide analysis of the α- and β-globin chains revealed no differences between the globins isolated from differentiating erythroleukemic cells and those of adult mouse reticulocytes. Furthermore, embryonic globins could not be detected in these cells.

b. *Deoxyribonucleic Acid, Ribonucleic Acid, and Protein.* As seen in Fig. 1, addition of DMSO to the culture medium resulted in a lag in cell growth, i.e., the number of cells in the culture did not begin to increase until the second day after seeding. This delay in the onset of cell replication was reflected in the overall rates of precursor incorporation (thymidine, uridine, or leucine, respectively) into DNA, RNA, and protein (Friend *et al.*, 1973). The maximum rates of precursor incorporation occurred after 48 hours in the cells of DMSO-treated cultures as compared to 24 hours in the cells of the control cultures where cell proliferation began almost immediately after seeding. Throughout the entire period of culture, the absolute amount of labeled precursor incorporated into macromolecules was less in the DMSO-supplemented cultures than in the controls. Since the total number of cells after 4 days of growth is not appreciably different in the DMSO and control cultures, this may be a reflection of differences in the rate of uptake of the precursors and/or in the pool sizes of the precursors.

4. Polysome Patterns and RNA Synthesis

Biochemical studies revealed the development of a significant difference between the polysome configurations of control and DMSO-treated cells (Preisler *et al.*, 1973a). Aliquots of control and treated cells were processed daily for 4 days. Differences in the polysome profiles of control and DMSO-treated cells were detectable as early as the second day of culture but were most pronounced on the fourth day of culture when the majority of polysomes in the DMSO-treated cells consisted of 3 to 5 ribosomes (Fig. 3). In addition, while the number of ribosomes per cell was greater in control cells than in DMSO-treated cells, the monosome:polysome ratio in DMSO-treated cells was greater than in control cells. Thus, the polyribosome profile of the DMSO-treated cells resembled that of mouse reticulocytes (Williamson *et al.*, 1969).

Acrylamide gel electrophoretic analysis of polysome-associated RNA revealed a variety of RNA species (Fig. 4). The molecular weights of these have been calculated. The series of RNA peaks which began at

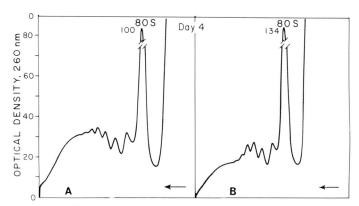

Fig. 3.   The polysome profiles of control (A) and dimethyl sulfoxide-treated (B) cells after 4 days of growth. (Preisler *et al.*, 1973.)

9 S and extended into the 18 S region are similar to those detected in other replicating tissue culture lines (Schochetman and Perry, 1972). The 4 S RNA is probably transfer RNA (tRNA) with perhaps a small component of FLV RNA. Although the 5, 5.5, 18, and 28 S RNA's are probably ribosomal RNA's (rRNA's), a 7 S RNA has been detected in some oncogenic viruses (Bishop *et al.*, 1970) as well as in reticulocytes (Labrie, 1969; Williamson *et al.*, 1969).

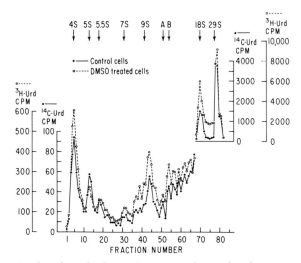

Fig. 4.   Acrylamide gel electrophoretic analysis of polysome-associated ribonucleic acid from 2-day control and dimethyl sulfoxide-treated cells labeled *in vitro* for 3 hours either with ^{14}C- or ^{3}H-uridine (Urd), respectively. (Preisler *et al.*, 1973.)

Under the conditions employed in our studies, it does not appear likely that 9 S RNA is the messenger RNA (mRNA) for globin. The molecular weight of the 9 S RNA is $1.45-1.55 \times 10^5$ which is similar to that for histone mRNA (Kedes and Gross, 1969; Gallwitz and Mueller, 1969; Schochetman and Perry, 1972) but considerably less than that of reticulocyte globin mRNA which has an S value of 10 as determined by acrylamide gel electrophoresis (Gaskill and Kabat, 1971). Coelectrophoresis of uridine-^{3}H-labeled polysome-associated RNA with ^{32}P-labeled RNA from reticulocytes revealed that the 9 S RNA did not coelectrophorese with globin mRNA (Preisler et al., 1973a). The synthesis of 9 S RNA appeared to be closely associated with cell replication since the decrease in DNA synthesis occurring on the fourth day of culture was accompanied by a decrease in 9 S synthesis. Similarly, inhibition of DNA synthesis during the second day by hydroxyurea resulted in a decrease in the synthesis of 9 S RNA (Fig. 5). Based on size and association with DNA synthesis, it appears that 9 S RNA is the mRNA for histone.

Gel electrophoretic analysis of polysome-associated RNA failed to reveal any significant qualitative differences in types of RNA's synthe-

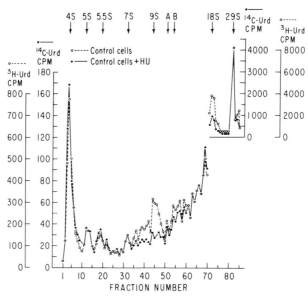

FIG. 5. Analysis of polysome-associated RNA isolated from a mixture of 2-day control cells and 2-day control cells preincubated with hydroxyurea (HU) at a concentration of 500 μg/ml for 30 minutes and then incubated with isotope for 3 hours. Urd, uridine (Preisler et al., 1973.)

sized in control and DMSO-treated cells. Even though both control and DMSO-treated cells synthesized RNA with the same electrophoretic mobility as that of reticulocyte globin mRNA, this does not necessarily mean that it is globin mRNA. These nucleated cells are in the course of active replication and are synthesizing other protein, the size of which is similar to that of globin (Preisler *et al.*, 1973c). In any event, it was not possible to distinguish qualitatively between control and DMSO-treated cells on the basis of gel electrophoretic analysis of their polysome-associated RNA's.

5. Detection of Globin mRNA

Since the erythroleukemic cells possess the genetic information necessary for synthesizing globin, the important question is whether the block in the utilization of this information in these cells is at the level of transcription or of translation. Although no differences were found in the number and type of RNA species in treated and untreated cultures, the technique of DNA–RNA hybridization did detect substantial amounts of globin mRNA only in DMSO-stimulated cells.

Deoxyribonucleic acid that is complementary to 9 S globin mRNA (cDNA) has been synthesized using avian myeloblastosis virus (AMV) reverse transcriptase (Ross *et al.*, 1972a; Verma *et al.*, 1972; Kacian *et al.*, 1972). This cDNA was used to detect mRNA's that have base sequences complementary to cDNA. The cells treated with DMSO (clone 745) for 4 days were found to contain at least 100 times the amount of globin mRNA present in control cells (Table I). These studies indicated that of the total cell RNA at least 0.14% was globin mRNA and that this RNA had an S value of 9 as determined by sucrose gradient centrifugation (Preisler *et al.*, 1973b).

TABLE I

EFFECT OF DMSO AND BUdR ON GLOBIN mRNA CONTENT OF FLC[a]

| | % Total cell RNA that hybridizes with cDNA | | | |
Experiment No.	Control	BUdR (3 µg/ml)	DMSO (2%)	DMSO (2%) + BUdR (3 µg/ml)
1	0.0003	0.0015	0.149	0.041
2	0.0002	0.0007	0.144	0.036

[a] Cells were grown in the absence or presence of BUdR, DSMO, or BUdR + DMSO for 4 days. Total cell RNA was extracted and used in hybridization experiments with cDNA.

There are still questions that remain to be answered. Is globin mRNA synthesized by control cells but rapidly degraded and hence never accumulates to a level comparable to that of DMSO-treated cells? Do control cells possess an RNA that interferes with DNA–RNA hybridization? We are currently exploring these possibilities.

B. INFLUENCE OF OTHER FACTORS

Dimethylformamide (DMF), which has a structure similar to and shares some of the biological properties of DMSO, induced comparable, although less marked changes in the cells, i.e., differentiation and stimulation of hemoglobin synthesis (Scher *et al.*, 1973; Sato *et al.*, 1972).

Among the compounds thus far examined, DMSO and DMF have been the most effective in inducing erythroid maturation in our leukemic cell lines. A slight but significant increase in B+ cells has been observed when testosterone or cortisone was added to the medium. The conditions of growth may also influence differentiation. After cells, which had been maintained for 4 days in serumless medium (Neuman and Tytell), were transferred to complete serum-containing medium, the production of B+ cells was 10 times greater than that of the control cells (Friend *et al.*, 1971).

VI. Inhibition of Dimethylformamide- and Dimethyl Sulfoxide-Induced Differentiation by Bromodeoxyuridine

Bromodeoxyuridine (BUdR), a halogenated pyrimidine, has been demonstrated to inhibit differentiation in several systems including erythroid differentiation in developing chick embryos (Miura and Wilt, 1971). Addition of BUdR at a concentration of 3 µg/ml to cells cultured with DMSO or with DMF resulted in a significant inhibition of differentiation (Scher *et al.*, 1973; Friend *et al.*, 1973). The DMSO- and DMF-induced stimulation of heme synthesis was inhibited by an average of 70% as was the development of benzidine positivity. As in other systems, BUdR was incorporated into DNA of FLC and its inhibitory effects were prevented by the simultaneous addition of thymidine to the culture medium. It also appeared that BUdR must be present during cell replication, when DNA synthesis is maximal, for its inhibitory effects to be manifested.

It was also found that the inhibition of DMSO-induced differentiation by BUdR correlated with a decrease in the globin mRNA content of these cultures (Preisler *et al.*, 1973b). The amount of globin mRNA present in the cultures 4 days after seeding was determined by hybridization of whole cell RNA with cDNA. Table I gives the results of two separate experiments in which whole cell RNA from (1) control cells, (2) cells exposed to DMSO, (3) cells exposed to BUdR, or (4) cells exposed to both DMSO and BUdR was hybridized with cDNA. It can be seen that the amount of globin mRNA present in BUdR–DMSO-treated cultures was less than half of that present in cultures treated with DMSO alone. Of interest was the slight increase in globin mRNA content of cells cultured with BUdR alone as compared to control cells.

VII. Properties of the Virus Synthesized in Tissue Culture

Although the virus synthesized by these established lines of erythroleukemic cells has lost its leukemogenic potential, as do most murine leukemia viruses in culture, it can be assayed on X-C cells, using the mixed culture cytopathogenicity test (Klement *et al.*, 1969). The tissue culture-attenuated virus, however, has maintained its ability to immunize susceptible mice against active virus as efficiently as does the vaccine prepared from formalin-inactivated virus from leukemic spleen filtrates (Friend and Rossi, 1968; Friend, 1973).

A. EFFECT OF DIMETHYL SULFOXIDE, DIMETHYLFORMAMIDE, AND BROMODEOXYURIDINE

Treatment with either DMSO, DMF, or BUdR did not alter the structure of the virions or the proportion of enveloped type A or type C virus particles found in the pellets prepared from the tissue culture supernatant fluid. An increase in the number of budding viruses, however, was observed on cells treated with 2% DMSO or 1% DMF, alone or in combination with BUdR (Sato *et al.*, 1971, 1972). The number of budding viruses observed after 4 days of treatment with BUdR at concentrations of 3 or 20 µg/ml was comparable to that observed in cells treated with DMSO or DMF for the same period of time. Although no further change was noted in the cells exposed to BUdR alone for 7 days, the number of budding viruses observed at that time from both DMF and DMSO cultures had continued to increase. When either DMSO or DMF was added to the medium in combination with BUdR, the level of increase after 4 and 7 days was enhanced as compared to that observed after treatment with the individual compounds for those intervals. Although these compounds in combination were somewhat cytotoxic, the number of budding viruses per cell was increased more than 5 times over the untreated controls. It is yet to be determined whether the increase in the number of budding viruses on the surfaces of these treated cells is due to a stimulation of viral synthesis or to some inhibition in the process of virus assembly or release, resulting in the accumulation of partially completed budding particles. Experiments using the X-C assay to compare the virus titers from control and treated cells are in progress. Other workers (Ikawa *et al.*, 1973), studying a different line of FLC with a much lower level of endogenous virus production, have reported a 100-fold increase in the virus titer from DMSO-treated cells over that of the corresponding control cells.

B. REVERSE TRANSCRIPTASE OF VIRUS FROM CONTROL AND DIMETHYL SULFOXIDE-TREATED CELLS

Studies on the reverse transcriptase activity of virus produced in tissue culture in the presence or absence of 2% DMSO were carried out, using reaction conditions similar to those described by Temin and

TABLE II

RNA- AND DNA-DEPENDENT DNA POLYMERASE ACTIVITIES OF FLV
FROM CONTROL AND DMSO-TREATED CULTURES[a]

Days in culture	Reaction condition	Control[b]	DMSO-treated[b]
3	—	14.0	13.0
	+DNA	47.0	33.0
4	—	15.0	24.0
	+DNA	33.0	63.0
5	—	18.0	21.0
	+DNA	26.0	29.0
6	—	19.0	23.0
	+DNA	74.0	75.0
7	—	19.0	28.0
	+DNA	36.0	45.0

[a] Pellets from the tissue culture medium were resuspended in 0.01 M Tris-HCl buffer, pH 7.8, and centrifuged at 30,000 rpm for 20 minutes in an SW 39L rotor. The pellets were then resuspended in 0.25 ml of the same buffer; 0.1 ml were used for the DNA polymerase assays and 0.05 ml for determination of protein (Lowry's). From 10–20 μg viral protein in 250 μl of 0.01 M Tris-HCl buffer, pH 8, 10 mM MgCl$_2$ with 0.5% NP$_{40}$ [Nonidet P-40 (non-ionic detergent) Shell Chemical Co., New York], 0.25% 2-β-mercaptoethanol, 1 μmole each of deoxyguanosine triphosphate, deoxycytidine triphosphate and 2 μmoles deoxyadenosine triphosphate, and 0.3 μmole of ^{3}H-thymidine triphosphate (^{3}H-TTP) (specific activity 20 μCi/μmole) were incubated at 37° C for 90 minutes. Calf thymus DNA, 10 μg, was added when specified. The reaction was stopped by adding 5.0 ml of 10% trichloroacetic acid with 0.05 M Na pyrophosphate at 4°C. The precipitates were collected on Millipore filters, washed with 15 ml of cold 10% TCA, and counted in a Beckman scintillation counter with 35% efficiency.

[b] nmoles TTP/mg protein per 90 minutes.

Mizutani (1970) (Pogo and Friend, 1973). The results of a series of experiments comparing the activities of RNA-dependent and DNA-dependent DNA polymerases of virus produced after the designated days in tissue culture are shown in Table II. In virus obtained from untreated cultures, the RNA-dependent DNA polymerase activity remained constant with a slight increase on day 5, whereas the DNA-dependent activity showed an increase on day 6. On the other hand, the virus from the DMSO-treated cultures always showed a slightly higher activity than the controls in both enzymatic activities, except on day 3. These small increases can be explained by a possible protective effect of the DMSO on the enzymes. The addition of up to 5% DMSO added directly to the assay mixture, however, did not affect the enzymatic activities, for there was no difference in the kinetics of the reactions of both enzymes from the viruses produced either by the control or DMSO-treated cells. Furthermore, the activities of the virus harvested from the supernatant fluid of each of a number of different clones of the erythroleukemic cells and from the plasma of leukemic mice were similar.

The sensitivity of the reverse transcriptase reaction to different inhibitors was also tested with virus synthesized in the presence or absence of DMSO (Table III). The reaction was completely inhibited by deoxyribonuclease (DNase), which attacks the product, and was less inhibited by ribonuclease (RNase), which destroys the template. Furthermore, actinomycin D was not inhibitory, since the reverse transcriptase reaction does not depend on a DNA template. Stimulation,

TABLE III

EFFECT OF INHIBITORS ON REVERSE TRANSCRIPTASE ACTIVITY OF FLV[a]
FROM CONTROL AND DMSO-TREATED CULTURES[b]

| | Control | | DMSO-treated | |
Reaction conditions	Protein (nmoles/mg)	%	Protein (nmoles/mg)	%
Complete	15.0	100	25.0	100
+DNase (20 μg)	0	0	0	0
+Pancreatic RNase (DNase-inactivated) (20 μg)	0.40	2.7	0.90	3.6
+Actinomycin D (20 μg)	14.0	93	23.0	90
+Calf thymus DNA (10 μg)	27.0	130	40.0	160

[a] Assayed on the fifth day of culture.
[b] Conditions of reaction as noted in Table II.

however, was observed with added DNA as was to be expected since the virion also contains DNA-dependent DNA polymerase activity.

VIII. Discussion

In recent years, evidence as accumulated to support the hypothesis that some, if not all, malignant diseases may be disorders of cell differentiation. Reports on differentiation of tumor cells *in vitro* have included studies of human and murine neuroblastoma cells (Goldstein *et al.*, 1964; Tumilowicz *et al.*, 1970; and Kleinsmith and Pierce, 1964) as well as of human leukemic cells (Nowell, 1960; Farnes and Trobaugh, 1961; Clarkson *et al.*, 1967; and Golde and Cline, 1973) and murine leukemic cells (Metcalf *et al.*, 1969; Ichikawa, 1969). These findings would suggest that malignancy, like differentiation, may be reversible. Recent studies on virus-transformed cells that phenotypically revert to normal lend support to this idea. For example, cells transformed at the permissive temperature by temperature-sensitive mutants of avian sarcoma virus (Bader and Brown, 1971; Kawai and Hanafusa, 1971; and Toyoshima and Vogt, 1969) and murine sarcoma virus (Scolnick *et al.*, 1972) became morphologically normal when placed at nonpermissive temperatures. Even though in some instances the revertant cells retained the gs antigen found in the transformed cells, there was a decrease in tumorigenicity (Stephenson *et al.*, 1973). Further evidence for the reversibility of the malignant state is found in the observation that the nuclei of the Lucké frog renal adenocarcinoma cells are able to program normal tadpole development when transplanted into enucleate eggs (McKinnell and Ellis, 1972).

The studies described here also point to the fact that malignant cells possess at least some of the genetic information that controls the growth and fate of their normal counterparts. Since maturation was accompanied by a decrease in malignancy, the possibility exists that means may be found to release the block preventing the expression of the information necessary to instruct the cell to mature. Similarly, recent studies on human acute lymphoblastic leukemia cells have demonstrated the presence of terminal deoxynucleotidyl transferase, an enzyme found only in normal thymus cells, indicating that in some human leukemic cells there is a retention of certain specific genetic information of the tissue of origin (Baltimore, personal communication).

Although a number of compounds have been found to influence the maturation of the leukemic cells under study, differentiation beyond the level of orthochromatophilic erythroblast has not as yet been observed.

The studies completed to date suggest that the block in maturation of FLC is prior to translation, at least for the synthesis of globin mRNA. These experiments have principally relied upon hybridization techniques in *in vitro* studies with total cellular RNA in which the globin mRNA content in FLC cultures was very low prior to DMSO stimulation, but progressively rose during growth in DMSO-supplemented medium (Ross *et al.*, 1972b; Preisler *et al.*, 1973a, b). On the other hand, no qualitative difference in the polysome-associated RNA's of control and DMSO-stimulated FLC could be detected by polyacrylamide gel electrophoresis (Preisler *et al.*, 1973a; J. Paul, personal communication). Although it has recently been reported that DMSO-stimulated differentiation in another line of FLC was accompanied by the synthesis of a cytoplasmic 9 S RNA (Ostertag *et al.*, 1972), our results indicate that 9 S RNA is synthesized by both control and treated FLC and appears to be the mRNA for histone rather than for globin.

While DMSO has been effective in stimulating the synthesis of globin mRNA, it may be that the synthesis of other mRNA's essential for directing the leukemic cells to proceed to the final mature enucleate erythrocyte stage is not affected. It is yet to be determined whether enucleation in this system depends on forces extrinsic [as suggested by Tavassoli and Crosby (1973)] or intrinsic to the cell.

Bromodeoxyuridine, which has been shown to inhibit differentiation in many systems, has also been of interest in elucidating the molecular events that occur in these leukemic cells, since it inhibits DMSO-induced differentiation. As has been found by others, the incorporation of BUdR into DNA appears essential for the inhibitory effects. The BUdR appears to act by interfering with transcription, since the synthesis of globin mRNA is decreased. It is of interest that BUdR alone induced a slight increase in the globin mRNA content of FLC. This raises the possibility that BUdR can work as a two-way switch, i.e., it can inhibit stimulated differentiation and yet may also be able to act itself to stimulate differentiation, although to a lesser extent. This latter property was evident in the studies on the induction of differentiation of neuroblastoma *in vitro* (Schubert and Jacob, 1970) where it was found that BUdR-induced differentiation of neuroblastoma cells was not dependent on the synthesis of DNA. It is interesting to speculate on whether or not the induction of the small amount of globin mRNA detected in the BUdR-treated FLC is similarly independent of DNA synthesis. The use of thymidine-kinaseless mutant FLC lines that have been isolated by J. Paul (personal communication) and Ostertag (1973) will be most helpful in answering some of these questions.

In the light of the finding that FLC cultured in the presence of DMSO or DMF alone or in combination with BUdR have increased numbers of budding viruses on their cell membranes, the role of the virus may have to be reevaluated. It would appear that cells synthesizing murine leukemia Type C virus particles are not necessarily malignant, for the agents (DMSO, DMF) that stimulate differentiation with a concomitant decrease in malignant potential of FLC also increase the number of budding virus particles. On the other hand, BUdR inhibits differentiation, yet also increases the number of budding viruses. In fact, when BUdR is added in combination with DMSO or DMF, the effect on the virus is additive in that the number of budding viruses is greater than the number observed with each of the drugs alone. Bromodeoxyuridine and the combination of BUdR with DMSO have been reported to induce the production of viruses in mouse embryo (Aaronson et al., 1971) cells and in human tumors (Stewart et al., 1972a, b), in which viruses had not been observed before treatment. The viruses induced in the murine cultures can be detected by the X-C cell assay but have not as yet been shown to be leukemogenic in animals. Thus it may be possible to study virus production and malignancy as separate phenomena. Under certain, as yet unclear, conditions, virus synthesis may be compatible with normal cell growth and differentiation. The C-type virus particles are ubiquitous in mice of many strains, yet for the most part apparently live symbiotically with the cells without causing any detectable derangement.

The mechanism of action of DMSO in stimulating differentiation of the erythroleukemic cells is yet to be understood. This compound, at the same concentration as used in our studies, also inhibits the blastogenic transformation of lymphocytes by phytohemagglutinin (PHA), a process associated with morphological changes suggesting increasing immaturity (Mangi and Mardiney, 1970).

Evidence that it affects the cell membrane comes from the studies of Weiner et al. (1972) who found the penetrative ability of DMSO might be due to some alteration of protein structure as a result of dehydration of the biomembrane. Phospholipids protected the protein from attack by DMSO. That DMSO exerts an effect on the regulatory role of lipids for RNA synthesis in mammalian cells has been suggested by Lezius and Müller-Lorensen (1972) who found that DMSO both stabilizes and stimulates the activity of RNA polymerase A, an enzyme stimulated by neutral phospholipids, by changing the template specificity from doublestranded in favor of single-stranded DNA. Other activities of DMSO as well as of DMF, which may be significant, are their abilities to stimulate microsomal Ca^{2+} uptake and to inhibit Na^+, K^+-dependent adenosine triphosphatase (Burgess et al., 1969). They vary in their effect on adenyl cyclase in that DMSO stimulates the enzyme, whereas DMF inhibits it. In an extension of these studies, Spilker (1970) concluded that the inotropic actions of these solvents were nonspecific. It remains to be determined whether many of the other biological activities attributed to DMSO are also nonspecific. The fact that its effects on muscle (Spilker, 1972), on strain L-929 fibroblast (Berliner and Ruhmann, 1967), and on the erythroleukemic cell cultures (Friend et al., 1971) may be reversible would tend to support the lack of specificity in the action of DMSO.

Regardless of what the mode of action of DMSO might be in stimulating the differentiation of leukemic cells, it offers the possibility of a new approach in cancer therapy.

REFERENCES

Aaronson, S. A., Todaro, G. J., and Scolnick, E. M. (1971). *Science* **174**, 157–159.

Bader, J. P., and Brown, N. R. (1971). *Nature (London)* **234**, 11–12.

Berliner, D. L., and Ruhmann, A. G. (1967). *Ann. N.Y. Acad. Sci.* **141**, 159–164.

Bishop, J. M., Levinson, W. E., Quintrell, N., Fanshier, L. (1970). *Virology* **42**, 927–937.

Boyer, S. H., Wuu, K. D., Noyes, A. N., Young, R., Scher, W., Friend, C., Preisler, H. D., and Bank, A. (1972). *Blood* **40**, 823–835.

Braun, A. C. (1969). "The Cancer Problem: A Critical Analysis and Modern Synthesis," pp. 1–209. Columbia Univ. Press, New York.

Braun, A. C. (1972). *In* "Progress in Experimental Tumor Research" (A. C. Braun, ed.), Vol. 15, pp. 165–187. Karger, Basel.

Burgess, R. A., Blackburn, K. J., and Spilker, B. A. (1969). *Life Sci.* **8**, 1325–1335.

Clarkson, B., Strife, A., and deHarven, E. (1967). *Cancer* **20**, 926–947.

Farnes, P., and Trobaugh, F. E., Jr. (1961). *J. Lab. Clin. Med.* **57**, 568–573.

Fiala, S. (1968). *Neoplasma* **15**, 607–622.

Fibach, E., Hayashi, M., and Sachs, L. (1973). *Proc. Nat. Acad. Sci U.S.* **70**, 343–346.

Friend, C. (1957). *J. Exp. Med.* **105**, 307–318.

Friend, C. (1959). *J. Exp. Med.* **109**, 217–228.

Friend, C. (1973). *In* "Virus Tumorigenesis and Immunogenesis" (W. Ceglowski and H. Friedman, eds.), pp. 387–391. Academic Press, New York.

Friend, C., Patuleia, M. C., and deHarven, E. (1966). *Nat. Cancer Inst., Monogr.* **22**, 505–522.

Friend, C., and Haddad, J. R. (1960). *J. Nat. Cancer Inst.* **25**, 1279–1289.

Friend, C., and Rossi, G. B. (1968). *Int. J. Cancer* **3**, 523–529.

Friend, C., and Rossi, G. B. (1969). *In* "Canadian Cancer Conference" (J. F. Morgan, ed.), Vol. **8**, pp. 171–182. Pergamon, Oxford.

Friend, C., Scher, W., Holland, J. G., and Sato, T. (1971). *Proc. Nat. Acad. Sci. U.S.* **68**, 378–382.

Friend, C., Scher, W., Preisler, H. D., and Holland, J. G. (1973). *In* "Unifying Concepts of Leukemia," Proc. Int. Symp. Comp. Leuk. Res., Vth (R. M. Dutcher, ed.). Karger, Basel. In press.

Gallwitz, D., and Mueller, G. C. (1969). *J. Biol. Chem.* **244**, 5947–5952.

Gaskill, P., and Kabat, D. (1971). *Proc. Nat. Acad. Sci. U.S.* **68**, 72–75.

Golde, D. W., and Cline, M. J. (1973). *Blood* **41**, 45–57.

Goldstein, M. N., Burdman, J. A., and Journey, L. C. (1964). *J. Nat. Cancer Inst.* **32**, 165–199.

Ichikawa, Y. (1969). *J. Cell. Physiol.* **74**, 223–234.

Ikawa, Y., Furusawa, M., and Sugano, H. (1973). In "Unifying Concepts of Leukemia," Proc. Int. Symp. Comp. Leuk. Res., Vth (R. M. Dutcher, ed.). Karger, Basel. In press.

Jacob, S. W., Rosenbaum, E. E., and Woods, D. C., eds. (1971). "Dimethyl Sulfoxide," Vol. 1, pp. 1–479. Dekker, New York.

Jensen, F. C., Gwatkin, R. B. I., and Biggers, J. D. (1964). *Exp. Cell Res.* **34**, 440–447.

Kacian, D. L., Spiegelman, S., Bank, A., Terada, M., Metafora, L., Dow, L., and Marks, P. A. (1972). *Nature (London) New Biol.* **235**, 167–169.

Kawai, S., and Hanafusa, H. (1971). *Virology* **46**, 470–479.

Kedes, L. H., and Gross, P. R. (1969). *Nature (London)* **223**, 628–630.

Kleinsmith, L. J., and Pierce, G. B. (1964). *Cancer Res.* **24**, 1544–1552.

Klement, V., Rowe, W. P., and Hartley, J. W. (1969). *Proc. Nat. Acad. Sci. U.S.* **63**, 753–758.

Labrie, F. (1969). *Nature (London)* **221**, 1217–1222.

Leake, C. D., ed. (1967). "Biological Actions of Dimethyl Sulfoxide," Ann. N.Y. Acad. Sci., Vol. 141, pp. 1–671. N.Y. Acad. Sci., New York.

Lezius, A., and Müller-Lorensen, B. (1972). *Hoppe–Seyler's Z. Physiol. Chem.* **353**, 1872–1876.

McKinnell, R. G., and Ellis, V. L. (1972). "Oncogenesis and Herpesviruses," pp. 183–197. Int. Agency for Res. on Cancer, Lyon.

Mangi, R. J., and Mardiney, M. R., Jr. (1970). *J. Exp. Med.* **132**, 401–416.

Markert, C. L. (1968). *Cancer Res.* **28**, 1908–1914.

Metcalf, D., Moore, M. A. S., and Warner, N. (1969). *J. Nat. Cancer Ins.* **43**, 983–1001.

Miura, Y., and Wilt, F. H. (1971). *J. Cell Biol.* **48**, 523–531.

Nowell, P. C. (1960). *Exp. Cell Res.* **19**, 267–277.

Ostertag, W., Crozier, T., Kluge, N., Melderis, H., and Dube, S. (1973). *Nature (London), New Biol.* **243**, 203–205.

Ostertag, W., Melderis, H., Steinheider, G., Kluge, N., and Dube, S. (1972). *Nature (London) New Biol.* **239**, 231–234.

Paran, M., Sachs, L., Barak, Y., and Resnitzky, P. (1970). *Proc. Nat. Acad. Sci. U.S.* **67**, 1542–1549.

Patuleia, M. C., and Friend, C. (1967). *Cancer Res.* **27**, 726–730.

Pierce, G. B. (1970). *Fed. Proc., Fed. Amer. Soc. Exp. Biol.* **29**, 1248–1254.

Pierce, G. B., and Johnson, L. D. (1971). *In Vitro* **7**, 140–145.

Pogo, B., and Friend, C. (1973). In preparation.

Prasad, K. N. (1972). *Cytobios* **6**, 163–166.

Preisler, H. D., Scher, W., and Friend, C. (1973a). *Differentiation* **1**, 27–37.

Preisler, H. D., Housman, D., Scher, W., and Friend, C. (1973b). *Proc. Nat. Acad. Sci. U.S.* **70**, 2956–2959.

Preisler, H. D., Housman, D., Scher, W., and Friend, C. (1973c). In preparation.

Ross, J., Aviv, H., Scolnick, E. M., and Leder, P. (1972a). *Proc. Nat. Acad. Sci. U.S.* **69**, 264–268.

Ross, J., Ikawa, Y., and Leder, P. (1972b). *Proc. Nat. Acad. Sci. U.S.* **69**, 3620–3623.

Rossi, G. B., and Friend, C. (1967). *Proc. Nat. Acad. Sci. U.S.* **58**, 1373–1380.

Sato, T., Friend, C., and deHarven, E. (1971). *Cancer Res.* **31**, 1402–1417.

Sato, T., deHarven, E., Friend, C., Scher. W., and Preisler, H. D. (1972). *30th Annu. Proc. Electron. Microsc. Soc. Amer.* (C. J. Arceneaux, ed.) pp. 70–71.

Scher, W., Holland, J. G., and Friend, C. (1971). *Blood* **4**, 428–437.

Scher, W., Preisler, H. D., and Friend, C. (1973). *J. Cell. Physiol.* **81**, 63–70.

Schochetman, G., and Perry, R. P. (1972). *J. Mol. Biol.* **63**, 577–590.

Schubert, D., and Jacob, F. (1970). *Proc. Nat. Acad. Sci. U.S.* **67**, 247–254.

Schubert, D., Humphreys, S., Baroni, C., and Cohn, M. (1969). *Proc. Nat. Acad. Sci. U.S.* **64**, 316–323.

Scolnick, E. M., Stephenson, J. R., and Aaronson, S. A. (1972). *J. Virol.* **10**, 653–657.

Spilker, B. (1970). *J. Pharmacol. Exp. Ther.* **175**, 361–367.

Spilker, B. (1972). *Arch. Int. Pharmacodyn. Ther.* **200**, 153–167.

Stephenson, J. R., Reynolds, R. K., and Aaronson, S. A. (1973). *J. Virol.* **11**, 218–222.

Stewart, S. E., Kasnic, G., Jr., Draycott, C., Feller, W., Golden, A., Mitchell, E., and Ben, T. (1972a). *J. Nat. Cancer Inst.* **48**, 273–275.

Stewart, S. E., Kasnic, G., Jr., and Draycott, C. (1972b). *Science* **175**, 198–199.

Tavassoli, M., and Crosby, W. H. (1973). *Science* **179**, 912–913.

Temin, H., and Mizutani, S. (1970). *Nature (London)* **226**, 1212–1213.

Toyoshima, K., and Vogt, P. K. (1969). *Virology* **39**, 930–931.

Tumilowicz, J. J., Nichols, W. W., Cholon, J. J., and Greene, A. E. (1970). *Cancer Res.* **30**, 2110–2118.

Verma, I. M., Temple, G. E., Fan, H., and Baltimore, D. (1972). *Nature (London), New Biol.* **235**, 163–166.

Weiner, N. D., Lu, M. Y., and Rosoff, M. (1972). *J. Pharm. Sci.* **61**, 1098–1101.

Williamson, R., Lanyon, G., and Paul, J. (1969). *Nature (London)* **223**, 628–630.

CHAPTER 4

CONCEPTS AND MECHANISMS OF CARTILAGE DIFFERENTIATION

Daniel Levitt and Albert Dorfman

DEPARTMENT OF PEDIATRICS, BIOCHEMISTRY, AND BIOLOGY
JOSEPH P. KENNEDY, JR., MENTAL RETARDATION RESEARCH CENTER
LA RABIDA INSTITUTE, PRITZKER SCHOOL OF MEDICINE, UNIVERSITY OF CHICAGO
CHICAGO, ILLINOIS

I. Introduction

In a previous volume of this series the differentiation of connective tissues was reviewed (Thorp and Dorfman, 1967). Since that time the accumulation of new information concerning the biochemical characteristics of cartilage and the observation that 5-bromo-2′-deoxyuridine (5-BUdR), a thymidine analog, inhibits the expression of certain characteristics of differentiated cells permit a new view of this problem. This chapter will attempt to review some of these newer results in view of the rapidly evolving concepts of differentiation.

The use of the term *differentiation* to describe factors that modulate phenotypic expression of eukaryotic cells as well as to describe new patterns of gene expression has resulted in considerable confusion in developmental and cell biology. A complete understanding of the process of differentiation must include an explanation of those processes that govern changes from fertilization to development of the complete organism. However, a simpler definition of differentiation is necessary for operational purposes. For the study of cartilage it is useful to restrict the discussion to biological processes that result in the conversion of a precursor cell (mesenchyme) to a cell that shows the characteristic morphology and biochemical phenotype of the chondrocyte. Whether this process is reversible in the same manner as modulation of phenotypic expression remains unclear.

The more general problem of reversion of a differentiated eukaryote cell to a precursor cell which may, in turn, be converted to another type of differentiated cell has received considerable attention. The behavior of certain plant tissues as well as the results of studies of nuclear transplantation and possibly regeneration indicate that true dedifferentiation of a cell or its nucleus to a more primitive state of development may occur (Gurdon, 1964; Hay, 1968; Braun, 1968). However, the use of the term *dedifferentiation* for the failure of cells to express differentiated functions in cell culture seems inappropriate. Apparent loss of phenotypic expression may result from restrictive culture conditions (e.g., medium, O_2 tension, and pH), overgrowth by contaminating cells, or aging of cultures. It, therefore, seems useful to attempt to distinguish between conditions that promote differentiation of a precursor cell to a differentiated cell and conditions that are necessary for expression of phenotype in cells already differentiated. Such a distinction is not always experimentally possible but is nevertheless important. Studies of chondrogenesis appear to afford such an opportunity

II. Definition of Cartilage

Most early studies were based on the morphological recognition of cartilage. Improved knowledge of the biochemistry of cartilage has permitted other criteria, such as the appearance of large quantities of chondroitin sulfate, incorporation of high levels of $^{35}SO_4$ into macromolecular products, or presence of metachromatic matrix to become the hallmarks of cartilage formation. The elucidation of the pathway of biosynthesis of chondroitin sulfate proteoglycan and the discovery of a unique cartilage collagen have made possible a more sophisticated approach to the biochemical definition of cartilage. At present, it seems reasonable that a chondrocyte may be defined as a cell that synthesizes large amounts of chondroitin sulfate proteoglycan and collagen of the composition $[\alpha 1(II)]_3$.[*] As will be indicated subsequently, preliminary evidence suggests that the protein core of cartilage chondroitin sulfate proteoglycan may be unique.

---

[*] See footnote in discussion on collagen (Section V) for an explanation of the notation.

III. Glycosaminoglycans of Cartilage

The principal glycosaminoglycans of cartilage are chondroitin 4-sulfate, chondroitin 6-sulfate, and keratan sulfate. Although there are available extensive data concerning the relative quantities of these glyco-saminoglycans in cartilage of different species, ages, and locations, information regarding the presence of other glycosaminoglycans is limited. Analyses of limb bud cultures have been carried out and will be detailed in another context in Section VIII.

Characteristic of cartilage is the proteoglycan illustrated in Fig. 1.

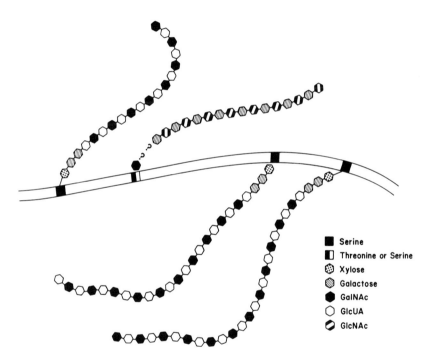

■ Serine
▯ Threonine or Serine
⊕ Xylose
▨ Galactose
● GalNAc
○ GlcUA
◑ GlcNAc

FIG. 1. Structure of cartilage proteoglycan. GalNAc, N-acetylgalactosamine; GlcUA, glucuronic acid; GlcNAc, N-acetylglucosamine.

The exact structure of the fundamental protein unit is not yet known. Chondroitin sulfate chains are attached to a protein core by way of a galactosyl–galactosyl–xylosyl linkage to the hydroxyl group of serine in the protein (Rodén, 1970). The length of polysaccharide chains, the extent and position of sulfation varies with age, species, and location of cartilage (Mathews, 1967). It is possible that the failure to identify the fundamental protein chain may be due to the existence of more than

one species of protein core (see Section VIII) or the inability to separate this protein from glycoproteins and other contaminants. Certain
details regarding the structure of this protein are, however, emerging.
Mathews (1971) has proposed that the core protein is a single peptide
of 2000 amino acids that contains repeating regions of 45 amino acid
residues with 10 amino acids in the doublets carrying two polysaccharide
chains and 35 amino acids separating the doublets. Whether the 45 amino
acid sequence can be regarded as a true repeating unit is not clear since
detailed, amino acid, sequence data are not available. There may be a
variation in the extent to which all positions for attachments of polysaccharide are occupied. There is also evidence that in some tissues both
keratan sulfate and chondroitin sulfate chains may be present on the
same peptide core (Rodén, 1970). Bovine nasal septum contains large
aggregates which may be dissociated to units of approximately 2.5 to
3.5×10^6 daltons. Hascall and Sajdera (1969, 1970) have dissociated
preparations to proteoglycan subunits of average molecular weight of
2.5×10^6 daltons and an additional protein subunit which they have
considered a "link protein." The latter fraction, however, does not appear
to be a single substance. Nevo *et al.* (1972) found that the proteoglycan
isolated from culture media of chick chondrocytes grown in suspension
culture contained only 8.2% protein and exhibited an amino acid analysis
similar to that of proteoglycan isolated from epiphyses and bovine nasal
septum. The proteoglycan appeared to be more readily separable from
contaminating glycoprotein than in preparations from bovine nasal septum.

IV. Biosynthesis of Chondroitin Sulfate

The pathway of biosynthesis of chondroitin sulfate proteoglycan has
now been elucidated and is summarized in Fig. 2. The glycosyl residues
all derive ultimately from glucose by way of a series of uridine nucleotide
sugars. The pathway of formation of nucleotide sugars has been reviewed elsewhere (Stoolmiller and Dorfman, 1969; Rodén, 1970).

Chondroitin sulfate chains are formed by the coordinated action of
six distinct glycosyl transferases and appropriate sulfotransferases. The
structure of the chondroitin sulfate chains appears to be determined by
the specificity of the glycosyl transferases for both donor and acceptor.
The position of sulfation is probably determined by the specificity of the
individual sulfotransferase enzymes. As indicated in Fig. 2, biosynthesis
appears to be initiated by the formation of a protein core presumably
on the rough endoplasmic reticulum. Initiation of polysaccharide chain
formation results from the transfer of xylose from UDP–xylose followed

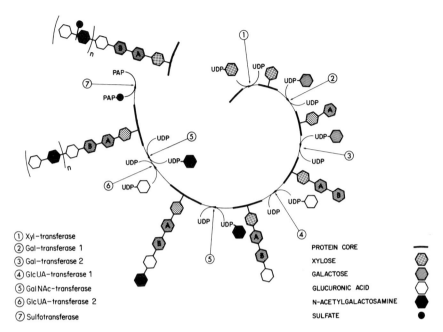

① Xyl-transferase
② Gal-transferase 1
③ Gal-transferase 2
④ GlcUA-transferase 1
⑤ GalNAc-transferase
⑥ GlcUA-transferase 2
⑦ Sulfotransferase

PROTEIN CORE
XYLOSE
GALACTOSE
GLUCURONIC ACID
N-ACETYLGALACTOSAMINE
SULFATE

FIG. 2. Biosynthesis of chondroitin sulfate. UDP, uridine-5'-diphosphate; GlcUA, glucuronic acid, GalNAc, N-acetylgalactosamine, PAP, 5'-adenosine-3'-phosphate.

by the addition of two galactose residues by distinct galactosyl transferases (enzymes 2 and 3). Enzyme 4 catalyzes the addition of glucuronic acid (GLcUA) by transfer of a glucuronyl residue from UDP–GlcUA. This reaction initiates the growth of chondroitin sulfate chains which then proceeds with the alternate transfer of N-acetylgalactosamine (GalNAc) and GlcUA residues by enzymes 5 and 6. Sulfation results from transfer of sulfate from 5'-phosphoadenosine 3'-phosphosulfate to the appropriate hydroxyl groups. Sulfation appears to occur after glycoside bond formation is terminated. However, studies of Silbert and De Luca (1969) suggest that sulfation may be initiated as polysaccharide chain growth proceeds.

Like other glycosyl transferases, the enzymes involved in chondroitin sulfate synthesis are primarily membrane-associated. Studies on the purification of these transferases indicate that xylosyl transferase is most soluble. This enzyme has now been isolated from embryonic chick epiphyses as a single protein of molecular weight approximately 95,000 daltons (Schwartz and Rodén, 1973) and from a rat chondrosarcoma (Stoolmiller, Schwartz, and Dorfman, unpublished results). Evidence that the xylosyl transferase interacts with the first galactosyl transferase (enzyme 2) has been obtained (Schwartz, Rodén, and Dorfman, unpublished results). These results support the suggestion (Horwitz and Dorfman, 1968) that the various glycosyl transferases are associated in a multienzyme complex which is inserted into the endoplasmic reticulum. Such an arrangement seems plausible on the basis of kinetic considerations.

The cellular site of proteoglycan synthesis is not yet clearly determined, but available evidence suggests that formation is started by the synthesis of the core protein on polyribosomes of the rough endoplasmic reticulum. The initiation of carbohydrate chain growth occurs by addition of xylose to appropriate serine residues probably in the rough and smooth endoplasmic reticulum. Whether xylose transfer occurs before peptide chains are completed has not yet been ascertained. Chondroitin sulfate chain growth proceeds as the proteoglycan traverses the endoplasmic reticulum, probably being completed in the Golgi apparatus. Migration to extracellular matrix is probably by way of excretion vacuoles.

The biosynthetic events have been described only briefly. A number of important parameters of chondroitin sulfate proteoglycan chemistry and biosynthesis are not yet sufficiently understood to be adequately considered in interpreting studies on differentiation of cartilage. Among these are (1) the detailed structure of the core protein of chondroitin sulfate proteoglycan; (2) control of synthesis of the enzymes involved in chondroitin sulfate biosynthesis; (3) factors that influence the activity of the complex of enzymes within the cell; (4) the mechanism of chain termination; and (5) the relationship of cellular architecture to control of synthesis of proteoglycans.

Little is known regarding mechanism of control of synthesis of extracellular substances. At the level of nucleotide precursors, two points of control have been demonstrated. The pool of UDP-N-acetylhexosamine appears to be regulated by a feedback mechanism since UDP-N-acetylglucosamine (GlcNAc) inhibits the conversion of fructose-6-phosphate to Glc-NAc-6-phosphate (Kornfeld et al., 1964). A more specific mechanism for the regulation of glycosaminoglycan synthesis may derive from the inhibition of UDP-Glc dehydrogenase by UDP-xylose (Neufeld and Hall, 1965). In the absence of core protein, this inhibition would shut off the formation of UDP-GlcUA.

Whereas such controls may serve as mechanisms for regulating nucleotide pools, they give no insight into the manner by which concentrations of extracellular substances affect their own synthesis or that of other related compounds. Several recent observations suggest such regulation. Hardingham et al. (1972) have shown that treatment of tibial explants of chick embryos with testicular hyaluronidase results in removal of extracellular matrix followed by a compensatory increase in chondroitin proteoglycan synthesis. Toole *et al.* (1972) have reported that hyaluronate in low concentrations prevents the segregation and aggregation of cells liberated from stage 17 and 26 somites and stage 26 limb buds. They suggest that hyaluronate inhibits chondrogenesis under these conditions. Certain hormones, such as thyroxine, calcitonin, and growth hormone can overcome the hyaluronate-induced suppression of cartilage formation (Toole, 1973). In contrast, Pessac and Defendi (1972) have presented evidence that suggests hyaluronate serves as an aggregation factor for a variety of cell lines in culture. Nevo and Dorfman (1972) have observed stimulation of chondroitin sulfate proteoglycan synthesis by suspensions of chondrocytes when exposed to chondroitin sulfate proteoglycan or other polyanionic substances. Whereas these observations have not yet furnished a mechanism for control of proteoglycan synthesis, they do indicate that matrix macromolecules influence their own formation. Conditioned medium obtained from high-density chondrocyte cultures also appears to enhance glycosaminoglycan synthesis by cultured chondrocytes. The stimulatory factor is a nondialyzable, heat- and trypsin-sensitive molecule; stimulation was not obtained by adding chondroitin sulfate, chondromucoprotein, or cartilage collagen to growing chondrocytes (Solursh and Meier, 1973).

V. Collagen

The fundamental structural unit of collagen, tropocollagen, consists of three polypeptide chains, each containing 1000 amino acid residues. The complete molecule has a molecular weight of slightly less than 300,000 daltons and a length of 3000 Å (Gallop *et al.*, 1972). In fibers, these molecules are aligned in a quarter stagger parallel fashion which gives rise to the characteristic axial repeating period of 650 to 700 Å. Approximately 33% of the amino acid residues are glycine, and approximately 20% of the residues are composed of the imino acids, proline, and hydroxyproline.

The three polypeptide chains are helically coiled and associated in a triple helix. Cross-linking occurs between chains and between molecules primarily by way of lysine and hydroxylysine residues. Cross-links are formed by oxidation of lysine and hydroxylysine to corresponding aldehydes, which, in turn, undergo aldol and other types of condensations.

A number of different individual chains exist in different species and tissues. Rapid strides are being made in determining the amino acid sequence of specific chains. Calf skin collagen, which has been studied most thoroughly, contains tropocollagen molecules with the structure $[\alpha 1(I)]_2 \alpha 2.$ *

Carbohydrate side chains are present in varying amounts on collagen chains and consist of glucosylgalactosyl disaccharide units glycosidically linked to the hydroxyl group of hydroxylysine. The extent of glycosylation varies in different collagens.

For purposes of this discussion it is important to emphasize that there appears to be multiple genes for synthesis of collagen chains. The discovery by Miller and Matukas (1969) of $\alpha 1(II)$ chains in chick cartilage furnished a new biochemical marker for the differentiation of cartilage cells.

Recent reports indicate that collagen peptides are synthesized as a precursor molecule now referred to as procollagen. The precursor peptide contains a nonhelical region at the amino terminal end which constitutes approximately 15–30% of the molecule (Bornstein et al., 1972; Layman et al., 1971). The amino terminal region appears to be removed by a specific procollagen protease. Recently, Goldberg and co-workers (Goldberg et al., 1972; Goldberg and Sherr, 1973) reported the existence of procollagen in human diploid fibroblasts of molecular weight 360,000 daltons which they believe to be [pro $\alpha 1(I)]_2$ pro $\alpha 2$ held together by disulfide bonds between cysteine residues in the amino terminal telopeptides. Limited digestion with pepsin excised the nonhelical telopeptides to yield a triple helical tropocollagen. They suggest that procollagen, formed intracellularly, is converted to tropocollagen by protease activity.

There is now abundant evidence to indicate that formation of hydroxyamino acids occurs by hydroxylation of lysine and proline following peptide bond formation. The extent of hydroxylation of lysine varies greatly in different collagen molecules. Glycosylation occurs by transfer of galactose and glucose from their respective uridine sugar nucleotides.

VI. In Vitro Studies

The following discussion attempts to distinguish studies on maintenance of cartilage phenotype in culture from studies of the differentiation of cartilage.

---

* Nomenclature: the term *tropocollagen* is used to denote the triple helical structure consisting of three chains. Individual chains are referred to as α, two chains cross-linked as β, and three chains cross-linked as γ. Chains are designated as $\alpha 1$ and $\alpha 2$. Because a variety of different $\alpha 1$ chains are now known, these are designated as $\alpha 1(I)$, $\alpha 1(II)$, $\alpha 1(III)$. Thus the tropocollagen molecule of calf skin is designated as $[\alpha 1(I)]_2 \alpha 2$, whereas that of chick cartilage is $[\alpha 1(II)]_3$. The term *procollagen* is now used to designate the precursor peptide or peptides of higher molecular weight requiring cleavage of the telopeptide section. *Protocollagen* refers to precursor molecules that have not been hydroxylated.

A. CULTURE OF CARTILAGE

Moscona (1952) showed that $3\frac{1}{2}$ to 4-day-old limb bud cells dissociated by trypsin reaggregated and formed cartilage nodules. Subsequently a large number of studies have been concerned with culture of chondrocytes, primarily from avian embryonic tissue. Only limited success has been achieved in the culture of mammalian chondrocytes (Ham and Sattler, 1968; Ham et al., 1970). Holtzer et al. (1960) observed the loss of the cartilage phenotype when chondrocytes were maintained in cell culture. When cells were pelleted before culture, cartilage nodules were formed. Following monodisperse culture the capacity to form nodules on subsequent pelleting was lost. These observations gave rise to the concept of dedifferentiation which was thought to be a consequence of the incompatability between cell division of chondrocytes in culture and expression of cell specialization (Holtzer, 1964). This concept was challenged by Coon (1966) who was able to clone cells from embryonic chick cartilage that grew and retained the chondrocyte phenotype. Cartilage formation was either inhibited or promoted by the addition of specific fractions of embryo extract. Cahn and Lasher (1967), using radioautographic methods, showed that clones of chondrocytes incorporate both $^{35}SO_4$ into chondroitin sulfate, and thymidine-^3H into DNA. Bryan (1968a,b) suggested that dedifferentiation of cartilage in cell culture was due to partial overgrowth by noncartilage cells present in the original population followed by suppression of the chondrocyte phenotype by noncartilage cells. True cartilage clones were observed to undergo an alteration of morphology after long periods in culture. "Variant cells" appeared more frequently at low growth rates. Recent studies by Holtzer and Abbott (1968) utilizing cloned cartilage cells, emphasize that a spectrum of morphologically different cells may be derived from a given clone; some of these cells resemble cells previously identified as having dedifferentiated during culture.

Horwitz and Dorfman (1970) found that epiphyseal chondrocytes of 13-day-old chick embryos could be cultured in soft agar or in liquid culture over agar. Under these conditions, fibroblast-like cells do not multiply. At very low density, dissociated epiphyseal cells grown on plastic plates give rise to two morphologically distinct types of clones. The fibroblast-like clones could not be subcultured in soft agar, whereas chondrocyte clones gave rise to cartilage nodules within the agar.

A number of studies have been directed toward the examination of factors that influence chondrocyte growth and metabolism in culture. Levenson (1969) stressed that the presence of ascorbic acid affects nodule morphology. Pawelek (1969) showed that low oxygen tension and added thyroxine promotes chondrocyte-like morphology and high levels of $^{35}SO_4$ uptake in embryonic chick cartilage cultures. The stimulation of $^{35}SO_4$ uptake by low oxygen tension was only apparent in the presence of added thyroxine. Lavietes (1970) found that the extent of formation of organized cartilage nodules in cultures of dissociated chick chondrocytes was a function of density of inoculum and medium composition. More characteristic nodules were found under clonal conditions and at high densities (10^6 cells/60-mm dish) than at intermediate densities.

Glick and Stockdale (1964) demonstrated in cultured chondrocytes the synthesis of a glycosaminoglycan which migrated electrophoretically as does chondroitin sulfate. Additionally, an unidentified glucosamine-containing sulfated polysaccharide was produced which was not further characterized. Nameroff and Holtzer (1967) observed the synthesis by cultured chondrocytes of chondroitin sulfate as well as of a glucosamine-containing polysaccharide with the electrophoretic mobility of hyaluronic acid but which is not completely digested by testicular hyaluronidase. The chondroitin sulfate proteoglycan produced by chondrocyte culture from 10-day-old chick vertebrae was found to contain predominantly chondroitin 4-sulfate by Shulman and Meyer (1970). Small amounts of keratan sulfate were tentatively identified. Nevo et al. (1972) isolated chondroitin sulfate proteoglycan from suspension cultures of epiphyseal cartilage. Amino acid composition of material prepared by the procedure of Hascall and Sajdera (1970) was similar to that from chick embryo epiphyseal cartilage and bovine nasal septum. The presence of four of the six glycosyl transferases and sulfotransferase involved in chondroitin sulfate synthesis was demonstrated. Ascorbic acid and low oxygen tension stimulated the synthesis of chondroitin sulfate proteoglycan. Nevo and Dorfman (1972) also found that the synthesis of chondroitin sulfate by suspension-cultured chondrocytes was stimulated by chondroitin sulfate proteoglycan and other polyanions.

Layman et al. (1972) reported that rabbit articular chondrocytes produced a collagen with a composition of $[\alpha 1]_2 \alpha 2$ similar to that of cultured fibrocytes. The cells were, however, poorly characterized as cartilage cells.

The reported results clearly indicate that differentiated avian chondrocytes multiply in culture and continue to produce chondroitin sulfate proteoglycan in quantities commensurate with the maintenance of the cartilage phenotype. The striking effect of BUdR on such cultures will be detailed in a subsequent section.

B. FORMATION OF CARTILAGE BY SOMITES

The demonstration that extirpation of portions of the spinal cord and notochord result in interference with formation of vertebrae stimulated extensive investigation of the induction chondrogenesis in embryonic chick somites. These studies have been extensively reviewed elsewhere (Thorp and Dorfman, 1967). Extirpation, transplantation, and *in vitro* culture studies all pointed to the fact that the ventral spinal cord and notochord are responsible for "induction" of cartilage in somites. A specific inducer secreted by notochord and ventral spinal cord was thought to promote differentiation of somite mesenchyme to cartilage. In most cases, cartilage formation was identified by cell morphology, appearance of metachromatic matrix, and incorporation of $^{35}SO_4$ into macromolecular substances with properties of chondroitin sulfate.

Lash *et al.* (1961) claimed somitic chondrogenesis resulted from exposure to a nucleotide component that could be obtained from cold perchloric acid extracts of embryonic spinal cord and notochord. Strudel (1963) reported that saline extracts of spinal cord and notochord promote chondrogenesis in somites. The concept that a specific component produced by one tissue (spinal cord or notochord) induced the appearance of specific biochemical reactions in another cell type (somite mesenchyme) seemed at first attractive; however, a number of observations raised important questions regarding this interpretation. The finding by Franco-Browder *et al.* (1963) that chondroitin sulfate is present in preinduced somites, spinal cord, and notochord and other early embryonic tissues indicated that the enzymatic pathway for synthesis of this polysaccharide is present before cartilage induction. Strudel (1962) showed that the requirement for an inducer to promote chondrogenesis in cultured somites was dependent on culture conditions. In the absence of spinal cord or notochord, no differentiation *in vitro* occurred when somites younger than stage 27–30 were cultured on a medium containing dilute embryo extract. However, if the somites were wrapped in vitelline membrane and cultured in a medium containing undiluted embryo extract, chondrogenesis was observed in somitic mesenchyme of stage 17 chick embryos. If somites were both wrapped in vitelline membrane and cultured in a medium containing undiluted embryo extract, chondrogenesis was observed in mesenchyme taken from embryos of 8-somite stage.

A number of studies have now confirmed that chondrogenesis in culture is dependent on culture conditions as well as on the presence of specific inducers (Lash, 1968a,b; Ellison and Lash, 1971; Ellison *et al.*, 1969; Kvist and Finnegan, 1970a,b). These findings raise questions regarding the specificity of an inducer required for the differentiation of somite mesenchyme of cartilage. Several recent studies point to the possibility that matrix materials secreted by spinal cord and notochord may themselves be requisite for differentiation of somite mesenchyme to cartilage. Ruggeri (1972) conducted a careful ultrastructural, histo-

chemical, and radioautographic study of the development of the notochord of chick embryos in the period between stage 9 and 26. Starting
at stage 10 the notochord becomes hypertrophic and acquires the characteristics of secretory elements with the production of chondroitin sulfate
and possibly collagen microfibrils. The perichordal sheath thus formed
may serve as a source for the diffusion of materials among the sclerotome
cells. Ruggeri points out that the putative sclerotome differentiates only
after the halo derived from the notochord has enlarged and diffused.

These results are consistent with the observations of Strudel (1971,
1972) who noted that the appearance of metachromatic material surrounding the notochord precedes differentiation of the sclerotome. When
somites of $2\frac{1}{2}$-day-old embryos were excised and cultured in the presence
of hyaluronidase or collagenase, differentiation did not occur. Under
similar conditions of cultivation somites from 4-day-old embryos formed
cartilage. Likewise, O'Hare (1972a,b) has concluded that limb bud
ectoderm promotes somite differentiation as determined by synthesis
of sulfated glycosaminoglycans and collagen. Cohen and Hay (1971)
demonstrated the synthesis of collagen by ventral neural tube of 2-day-
old embryos and suggested that the collagen secreted may play a role
in spinal cord–somite interaction.

These observations suggest that the enzymatic system needed for
the synthesis of chondroitin sulfate is present not only in precartilage
mesenchyme but in notochord and spinal cord. The recent studies of
Trelstad et al. (1973) indicate that early neural epithelium may produce
a collagen of $[\alpha 1]_3$ type. The fact that even early somites differentiate in
absence of spinal cord or notochord indicates that it is difficult to impli-
cate a specific inducer, and it seems possible that matrix materials may
themselves act as promotors or stabilizers of chondrogenesis.

C. Limb Chondrogenesis

The sequence of events involved in limb chondrogenesis has been
examined on both morphological and biochemical levels. Light microscope descriptions of chick limb bud development (Fell and Canti, 1934)
indicated that mesodermal condensations occurred in the proximal leg
bud at approximately stage 22 (3 days). This process proceeded centro-
distally, where branching of the condensed region ultimately gave a
Y-shaped appearance to the core area. Metachromasia, associated with
cartilage formation, was first evident during stage 25 (5 days).

Limb bud cells undergo distinct changes in their fine structure
between stages 22 and 25 (Searls et al., 1972; Gould et al., 1972; Goel,
1970). Stage 19 limb cells maintain extensive intercellular connections
but produce scant amounts of extracellular material. By stage 21 (Gould

et al., 1972) or late stage 22 (Searls *et al.*, 1972), the area of contact between the central precartilage cells has greatly diminished. Extracellular matrix and banded collagen fibers are first recognized at stage 22, and the concentration of both increase by stage 25. The typical scalloped-shaped cartilage cell becomes prevalent after stage 27.

Several biochemical changes occur in the developing limb. The rate of $^{35}SO_4$ uptake increases in the central, prechondrogenic area during stage 22 (Searls, 1965a) as demonstrated by radioautography, whereas the peripheral, myogenic region decreases its incorporation of $^{35}SO_4$. The sulfated material in stage 22–23 limbs was shown to be predominantly chondroitin 4- and 6-sulfate (Franco-Browder *et al.*, 1963; Searls, 1965b). Chondroitin sulfate is also synthesized by stage 19 limb bud cells and is probably produced by the prelimb region of stage 15 chick embryos (Medoff, 1967). Enzymes involved in glycosaminoglycan formation, such as UDP–glucose dehydrogenase, UDP–N-acetylhexosamine-4-epimerase, sulfate-activating enzymes, and UDP–glucuronic acid transferase are detectable in limb buds as early as stages 19–20 and increase in activity through the tenth day of development *in ovo* (Medoff, 1967). These studies indicate that prior to the morphological appearance of cartilage, limb tissue possesses several enzymes necessary for the synthesis of chondroitin sulfate and actually does synthesize small amounts of sulfated glycosaminoglycans. The observation that cells prior to overt cytodifferentiation display enzymes involved in the production of specialized macromolecules and synthesize molecules similar to differentiated products has important implications for determining control mechanisms of biochemical differentiation. This relationship will be considered in detail below.

If tissue is removed from the central region of limbs at stage 24 and placed in both chondrogenic and myogenic regions of host limbs, only that part of the implant in register with the cartilage-forming area of the host will form cartilage matrix (Searls, 1967; Searls and Janners, 1969). However, when tissue from the central region of stage 25 limbs is grafted into the soft tissue-forming area of host limbs, ectopic cartilage is produced (Searls and Janners, 1969). Therefore, despite earlier morphological and metabolic changes in the central region of the limb, the chondrogenic phenotype is not stabilized until stage 25, the time when the first metachromatic extracellular material can be detected.

Migration of determined chondroblasts into the chondrogenic region from other limb regions plays no role in establishing the central area as precartilaginous (Searls, 1967). It is believed that cells in the limb periphery halt chondroitin sulfate synthesis by stage 25, whereas cells lying in the interior begin to produce increased amounts of sulfated glycosaminoglycans (Searls, 1965a, 1967). The observation that limb bud cells, even at stage 25–26 when cartilage becomes apparent, do not segregate from limb mesenchyme cells of stage 20–21 chick embryos supports this hypothesis. The early limb cells will, however, sort out from mature cartilage or muscle cells for which they serve as a precursor population (Searls, 1971, 1972). These data argue against a model of limb chondrogenesis caused by inward migration of cells to an active chondrogenic center similar to the process of aggregation in the cellular slime mold (Ede and Agerbak, 1968).

The increase in $^{35}SO_4$ uptake in the central and proximal regions of stage 22 limbs is associated with a diminution in the number of dividing cells in this region when compared with the number of dividing cells in peripheral areas (Janners and Searls, 1970). The correlation between cessation of cell division and increased production of special macromolecules associated with cell differentiation has been noted (Lasher, 1971). It is important to remember, however, that limb cells that have stopped dividing at stages 22–24 are not irreversibly programmed to become chondrocytes. Thus, termination of division by early limb cells does not determine the eventual differentiation of these cells into chondrocytes.

The description of events surrounding cartilage formation in the limb served as a basis for separation of limb development into morphogenetic and cytodifferentiation phases by Zwilling (1968). Through stage 25, all cells in the limb are merely *limb cells,* and not stably determined as chondroblasts or myoblasts. Cytodifferentiation results from the position of a cell in the limb and not from inherent qualities possessed prior to differentiation. This assumption forms the foundation for the *in vitro* analysis of embryonic limb chondrogenesis.

Other factors, such as synthesis and removal of hyaluronic acid, may play a role in limb chondrogenesis *in vivo* (Toole, 1972). Exposure of stage 26 limb chondrocytes to small amounts of hyaluronate severely depresses their production of sulfated glycosaminoglycans (Toole *et al.,* 1972).

Tissue from all areas of the developing limb through stage 24 (4 to $4\frac{1}{2}$ days) produce cartilage in tissue culture (Zwilling, 1966). The chondrogenic propensity of early limb tissue *in vitro* has been the basis of studies of the factors influencing cartilage development. Aggregates of limb bud tissue demonstrate high levels of some of the enzymes required for synthesis of glycosaminoglycans (Medoff, 1967). However, hydroxyproline and collagen could not be detected in cultures after 7 days of growth (Mottet, 1967).

Growth of dissociated limb bud cells in tissue culture dishes established a means of probing individual determinants of cartilage differentiation. High cell densities (up to 30×10^6 cells/60-mm dish) or cell aggregation appear necessary for differentiation of early limb mesenchyme into cartilage (Umansky, 1966; Caplan, 1970). Cessation of cell division is concomitant with the increase in sulfated glycosaminoglycan synthesis, paralleling the sequence of events *in ovo* (Caplan, 1972b; Searls, 1965a; Janners and Searls, 1970).

The effects of a variety of substances, such as the teratogens, 3-acetylpyridine (3AP) and 6-amino nicotinamide (6AN), or conditioned media, have stimulated interesting theories of limb chondrogenesis. 3-Acetylpyridine and 6AN seem to induce increased "chondrogenic expression" in cultured limb mesoderm (Caplan *et al.*, 1968; Caplan, 1970, 1972a). Chondrogenic expression was defined as an increase in the number of cells exhibiting metachromasia. The significance of this increase is difficult to interpret in view of the finding that 3AP appears to inhibit incorporation of $^{35}SO_4$ into glycosaminoglycan. Cultures treated with 3AP showed abnormal morphology of cartilage nodules, decreased total metachromasia, and reduced protein and RNA synthesis. Although synthesis of glycosaminoglycans was decreased, increased activities were demonstrated with three enzymes involved in chondroitin sulfate formation: UDP–glucose pyrophosphorylase, xylosyl transferase, and *N*-acetylgalactosamine transferase (Caplan, 1972b; Stoolmiller and Caplan, 1973). It is difficult to interpret these somewhat inconsistent results. It was shown that 3AP also reduces the size of nicotinamide di- and trinucleotide phosphate pools, suggesting that the chondrogenic phenotype is favored by a less "reductive environment," i.e., one with limited quantities of nicotinamide–pyridine nucleotides.

Conditioned media from limb bud cultures at different stages of chondrogenesis and from muscle and neural retina cultures suppressed chondrogenic expression of limb bud cells by 50 to 80% (Schacter, 1970a). Changes in nodule morphology and staining patterns differ with the use of various types of conditioned media. The effects of certain media do not seem to be the result of depletion of nutrients but stem from specific products of the various cell types. The studies were, however, qualitative and the effects of pure substances, such as specific glycosaminoglycans, were not tested. Large reductions in deoxyribonucleic acid (DNA), protein, collagen, and sulfated glycosaminoglycan synthesis, as well as total DNA, protein content, and cell numbers were typical of cultures fed conditioned media; specific patterns of reduction were correlated with each type of media. The author did not eliminate the possibility of toxic components present in conditioned media (Schacter, 1970b). It was concluded that cells at each stage of development influence surrounding tissue by secreting specific substances that inhibit either chondrogenesis or myogenesis. Once cartilage formation is extensive in the core of the limb, the chondrocytes synthesize a product that inhibits further chondrogenesis in this region. Chondrogenesis might be prevented in the limb periphery by a substance secreted by myoblasts that stimulates myogenesis but inhibits chondrogenesis.

Limb bud cells can be separated according to their buoyant density (Flower, 1972). Only after stage 25 can a sizeable population of cells be obtained at a specific buoyant density that contains a high percentage of cartilage-making clones. This work supports the concept that stabilization of the cartilage phenotype in the limb occurs at stage 25.

D. Postembryonic Cartilage Differentiation

Any explanation of the differentiation of cartilage must consider the formation of cartilage in the postembryonic period. Hall (1970) has reviewed the evidence for the concept that fibroblasts, osteoblasts, osteocytes, chondroblasts, and chondrocytes are interrelated and interconvertible cells. A striking example of the production of cartilage in the postembryonic period is described in the interesting studies of Urist and co-workers (Urist and Strates, 1971; Urist and Nogami, 1970) and Huggins and co-workers (Huggins and Urist, 1970; Reddi and Huggins, 1972) who have shown that powder prepared from acid-extracted bone or dentin injected into muscle results in the formation of cartilage and subsequently bone. Urist and Nogami (1970) have reported that cartilage formation may occur *in vitro* when minced muscle is incubated with decalcified bone. Reddi and Huggins (1972) suggest that this phenomenon represents the transformation of fibroblasts to chondroblasts which they regard as an unstable transformation. The transformation of fibroblasts to osteoblasts, on the other hand, is considered stable.

VII. Effects of 5-Bromo-2′-deoxyuridine

The nucleoside, BUdR, an analog of thymidine, selectively interferes with processes involving cell specialization in a variety of systems. A review of some of the effects of BUdR on differentiating and differentiated tissues will precede a description of the authors' studies utilizing this compound to examine chondrogenesis *in vitro*.

Early studies demonstrated the incorporation of BUdR into the genome of bacteria and bacteriophages with resultant transitions from adenine–thymine to guanine–cytidine base pairing, demonstrating a mutagenic potential in prokaryote DNA (Freese, 1959). The addition of BUdR to cultures of certain eukaryote cell lines results in decreased DNA, ribonucleic acid (RNA), and protein synthesis, cell growth, and survival as well as diminished cloning efficiencies (Hakala, 1959, 1962; Littlefield and Gould, 1960; Kajiwara and Mueller, 1964; Kim *et al.*, 1967). The BUdR is incorporated into DNA; and the deleterious effects of the analog can be prevented by the simultaneous addition of excess molar concentrations of thymidine. Substitution for only 20% of the thymidine residues by BUdR results in an 80–95% decrease in cell viability.

Diminution of cloning efficiency appears to be dosage-dependent. Inhibition of DNA synthesis prevents the influences of BUdR on cloning efficiency. In synchronized HeLa cells, the effects of BUdR are most apparent when it is introduced into DNA synthesized during the first 2 hours of the S period (Kajiwara and Mueller, 1964). 5-Bromo-2′-deoxyuridine also induces severe chromosomal abnormalities including breaks and fragmentation (Somers and Hsu, 1962; Mazia and Gontcharoff, 1964). Since growth rates and cloning efficiency are often restored to normal within one generation after removal of the drug, it is unlikely that induced mutations or chromosomal anomalies are the causes of altered cell growth and survival.

5-Bromo-2′-deoxyuridine prolongs the cell cycle in HeLa cells by increasing the duration of S phase (Toliver and Simon, 1967). This prolonged period of DNA synthesis corresponds with a decrease in the activity of DNA polymerase (Kim *et al.*, 1967). Thus BUdR is toxic to certain cell lines, possibly interfering with production of molecules mandatory for cell growth and survival.

However, BUdR treatment is not deleterious to growth of all cell lines. In fact, a subline of mouse melanoma cells requires the presence of the drug to divide (Davidson and Bick, 1973). In contrast to results to be presented for differentiated cells cultured in the presence of BUdR, the BUdR-dependent cells flatten and enlarge in the *absence* of the drug. The capacity of certain cell lines to grow in the presence of high concentrations of BUdR has been previously correlated with lack of thymidine kinase or an altered thymidine uptake system (Kit *et al.*, 1963; Breslow and Goldsby, 1969). Since BUdR-dependent cells lack neither of these properties, mutation of the DNA synthetic machinery in dependent cells might involve alteration of the specificity of DNA polymerase so that it recognizes a bromine atom instead of a methyl group.

A complicating factor is the sensitivity of cells containing BUdR to fluorescent light and ionizing radiation (Puck and Kao, 1967; Elkind and Whitmore, 1967). Absorbance at 313 mμ by bromine results in an increased incidence of both single- and double-stranded breaks in DNA; these are lesions that can be rapidly repaired (Ben-Hur and Elkind, 1972; Smets and Cornelis, 1971; Buhl *et al.*, 1972). Since in many systems, cells that incorporate BUdR are not irradiated (or are only briefly exposed to fluorescent light) yet display altered growth characteristics and phenotypic expression, BU-substituted DNA may be susceptible to increased damage without exposure to ultraviolet or ionizing radiation. Whether chromosomal damage occurs frequently in differentiating systems exposed to the drug in the absence of radiation or light is unknown.

As will be detailed in the following, BUdR selectively interferes with either differentiation or the expression of the differentiated state in several systems. The drug is relatively nontoxic to differentiated cells at doses that inhibit the expression of cell specialization.

The anamnestic antibody response of spleen and lymph node cells is exquisitely sensitive to BUdR treatment following exposure to a specific antigen (Dutton et al., 1960). The depression of antibody synthesis is greatest at high rates of DNA synthesis; no inhibition of antibody formation is detected if BUdR is added prior to antigenic stimulation (O'Brien and Coons, 1963; Herscowitz et al., 1971). Inhibition of antibody produced against one type of antigen does not preclude subsequent synthesis of other antibodies by the same group of cells when challenged with a different antigen. It is proposed that BUdR affects the division of antibody-producing cells but does not inhibit the synthesis of specific antibodies. This conclusion is at variance with the results obtained with other cell types.

The inhibitory effects of BUdR on gene expression of developing chick myoblasts are not due to induced mutation. 5-Bromo-2'-deoxyuridine is incorporated into nuclear DNA and prevents fusion of presumptive myoblasts and subsequent myofibrillogenesis (Stockdale et al., 1964). Normal myogenesis, including myotube formation and the synthesis of actin and myosin occurs after removal of the drug and growth for several days in its absence. These results were confirmed with cloned myoblasts (Coleman et al., 1969). In contrast to cell lines, BUdR does not decrease the cloning efficiency of myoblasts but dramatically reduces the number of clones that contain myotubes. All clones recover from the suppressive influences of BUdR a few days after its removal. Unifilar incorporation of BUdR into DNA is sufficient to prevent myoblast fusion and contractile protein synthesis (Bischoff and Holtzer, 1970). Simultaneous addition of cytochalasin B prevents the inhibition of myogenesis by BUdR with the formation of large numbers of binucleate myotubes with normal-appearing cross-striated myofibrils. This phenomenon has been termed *nuclear complementation* (Sanger and Holtzer, 1970).

Differentiated characteristics of chondrocytes and amnion cells cultured from chick embryos are reversibly suppressed by treatment with BUdR. Cloned chondrocytes demonstrate profound changes in cell morphology including flattening and spreading to diameters of several hundred micrometers (Abbott and Holtzer, 1968; Holtzer and Abbott, 1968). Large reductions in the amount of rough endoplasmic reticulum and Golgi apparatus are coupled with an increase in numbers of free ribosomes in treated cells (Anderson et al., 1970). As will be detailed later, alterations of cell structure at both the light and electron-microscopic levels apparently depend on culture conditions and may not be specific for incorporation of the analog into DNA.

Production of cartilage matrix by cultured chondrocytes is reduced after exposure to BUdR; the duration of treatment necessary for inhibition of cartilage formation varies from 3 hours to 3 days (Lasher and Cahn, 1969; Coleman et al., 1970). When BUdR-treated chondrocytes are mixed with cloned vertebral cartilage cells, chondroitin sulfate production by the latter is severely inhibited. The BUdR-treated cells seem to behave as heterotypic or "foreign" cells under mixed-culture conditions (Chacko et al., 1969).

The mechanisms by which BUdR inhibits glycosaminoglycan biosynthesis in cartilage are unknown. Several investigators claim this inhibition is due to depression of activities of enzymes involved in the production of nucleotide sugars and sulfate activation (Schulte-Holthausen et al., 1969; Marzullo, 1972). The results from the authors' laboratory to be discussed in detail in following sections are not consistent with this interpretation.

Cultured chick amniotic cells synthesize large amounts of hyaluronic acid and smaller amounts of chondroitin 4-sulfate. 5-Bromo-2'-deoxyuridine treatment reversibly suppresses the synthesis of these molecules but does not greatly affect several parameters of cell growth and metabolism (Bischoff, 1971; Mayne et al., 1971). Cell spreading and increased adhesion to the culture dish also occurs in amnion cell cultures exposed to BUdR.

It has been postulated that the presence of BUdR alters the cell membrane, perhaps by direct or indirect modification of the glycoproteins and glycolipids of the cell surface. In fact, it has been claimed that BUdR induces an increase in neurite extension of cultured mouse neuroblastoma. This effect is believed to be due to an increased affinity between cells and the surface of the tissue culture dish. 5-Bromo-2'-deoxyuridine stimulates neuroblastoma "differentiation" in the presence of the drug 1-β-D-arabinofuranosylcytosine (ara-C), an inhibitor of DNA synthesis, implying a mechanism of action for BUdR that does not involve incorporation into DNA (Schubert and Jacob, 1970).

It is possible that BUdR alters specific macromolecules located at the cell surface. To approach this problem, glycosphingolipids believed to be associated with cell membranes were examined in progeny of BUdR-treated and control limb bud cells. The authors were unable to find qualitative differences and only minor quantitative differences between the two types of cells. Further studies are necessary to determine if significant changes in cell surface "recognition factors" occur after exposure to BUdR, altering the capacity of BUdR-treated and control cells to sort out from each other.

Such differentiated characteristics are usually suppressed after BUdR-exposure, the observation that BUdR stimulates neuroblastoma neurite extension is unusual. In a mouse–hamster hybrid cell line, BUdR inhibits production of hyaluronic acid but enhances seven- to eightfold the activity of alkaline phosphatase (Koyama and Ono, 1971, 1972a,b). Acid phosphatase activity was only slightly elevated; other enzymes were not measured.

Induction of cyclic adenosine monophosphate (cAMP) formation by norepinephrine is prevented in a clonal strain of rat glial cells, C-6, by exposure to BUdR. Depression is not due to decreased activity of adenylate cyclase but is correlated with a marked stimulation of cAMP phosphodiesterase (Schwartz et al., 1973). These systems present the only available evidence of activation of specific cellular properties after exposure to BUdR; these changes are reversible upon removal of the drug.

The activity of tyrosine aminotransferase (TAT) in cultured rat hepatoma cells is greatly reduced after exposure to BUdR (Stellwagen and Tomkins, 1971a). This enzyme activity is markedly increased after treatment with glucocorticoids; both induced and uninduced levels are diminished in BUdR-treated cells. Diminution is prevented by the presence of a molar excess of thymidine. When cells are exposed to BUdR for two generations, the analog is incorporated into DNA and does not greatly inhibit cell division, metabolism, or several other enzyme activities. The extent of depression of TAT activity is independent of the time during S phase when BUdR is present; exposure to the drug during M or G_1 has no effect on TAT activity. 5-Bromo-2′-deoxyuridine treatment does not result in synthesis of aberrant enzyme, as judged by K_m values, thermal stability, and antigenicity, nor does it cause an increased rate of degradation of TAT. Growth in BUdR does not lower the rate of synthesis of a specific class of RNA. The activities of enzymes not induced by glucocorticoids are depressed in hepatoma cells following treatment with BUdR for several days but to a lesser extent and at a slower rate than is TAT activity. It is postulated that BUdR slows the transcription rate of certain groups of messenger RNA. The period when a decrease in enzyme activity is apparent correlates with the stability of the enzyme and its messenger RNA. Stable enzymes with stable messages would respond more slowly to BUdR treatment than enzymes and messages that are rapidly turning over. Differences in turnover account for differences in activities of enzymes following exposure to the drug (Stellwagen and Tomkins, 1971b).

5-Bromo-2'-deoxyuridine has been recently employed as an antitumorigenic agent. When cultures of pigmented mouse melanoma cells are exposed to $3-10 \times 10^{-6}$ M BUdR, they lose their pigment, display contact inhibition, and demonstrate markedly diminished capacity to produce tumors when reinjected into mice (Silagi and Bruce, 1970). Pigmentation and tumorigenicity return upon subculture of cells in the absence of the drug. More interesting is the observation that mice injected continuosly with BUdR-treated melanoma cells become immune to a subsequent challenge with malignant cells (Silagi, 1971). Melanotic melanoma cells that do not revert to a normal morphology and pigment production in the absence of BUdR and BUdR-tolerant cells both form amelanotic tumors after injection into mice (Pasztor and Hu, 1971). Decreased tumor formation of BUdR-treated melanoma cells correlates with the number of virus particles released by these cells. An increase in the number of virus particles observed in the electron microscope parallels a decrease in cell tumorigenicity and an increase in immunogenicity by mice that are subsequently challenged with malignant melanoma cells (Silagi et al., 1972). Production of SV40 T antigen is also suppressed in transformed hamster cells after long exposure to BUdR. Measurements of tumor formation by these cells were not attempted (Kreider et al., 1972).

5-Bromo-2'-deoxyuridine induces virus formation in certain virus-negative cell lines that do release murine leukemia virus in vivo (Lowy et al., 1971; Rowe et al., 1972). Cloned mouse cell lines that have never previously produced virus release high titers of virus when exposed to BUdR (Aaronson, et al., 1971). 5-Bromo-2'-deoxyuridine also induces virus formation in human cell lines previously believed to be free of virus particles (Gerber, 1972; Hampar et al., 1972). Since BUdR and iododeoxyuridine (IUdR) release viruses from apparently "virus-free" cells, and release of virus has been correlated with the loss of at least one differentiated characteristic (pigment production), it is possible that virus formation following an exposure to BUdR is correlated with specialized macromolecule synthesis in differentiated cells. An examination of virus release by differentiated cells treated with BUdR should be undertaken in light of the foregoing evidence. These studies might be difficult in material derived from chick embryos since apparently many types of chick cells normally contain C-type virions (Hanafusa et al., 1970; Vogt and Friis, 1971).

The ability of BUdR to suppress expression of differentiated function in certain systems depends upon the period of development when exposure occurs. When pancreatic rudiments are organ-cultured, treatment with BUdR decreases zymogen production only early in culture. When added after the cessation of thymidine incorporation and decrease in mitotic rates, synthesis of zymogen is no longer inhibited (Wessells, 1964; Rutter et al., 1968). In a similar fashion, cessation of pinocytosis by epithelial cells in the small intestine of suckling rats (a differentiated characteristic induced by glucocorticoid administration) can be prevented by addition of BUdR. Cells distal on the intestinal villi that had ceased dividing were unaffected by drug treatment (Clark, 1971).

Cultured chondrocytes are more sensitive to BUdR under conditions that foster high mitotic indices and rapid cell division (Lasher and Cahn, 1969; Coleman et al., 1970; Mayne et al., 1973). When such cells are exposed to BUdR after 7 days in culture, inhibition of cartilage production is minimal. Cartilage cells that are either organ-cultured or incubated in the presence of inhibitors of DNA synthesis are also relatively insensitive to BUdR.

Mammary epithelial cells synthesize normal levels of casein and lactalbumin when treated with BUdR prior to exposure to insulin. However, when exposed to BUdR after cell division is stimulated by insulin, casein and lactalbumin synthesis is diminished (Turkington et al., 1971).

The effect of BUdR on differentiation in a number of systems is dependent on the specific time of exposure to the analog. Specific teratogenic lesions in both *Drosophila* larvae and mouse embryos are associated with administration of the drug during defined time intervals (Rizki and Rizki, 1969; Rizki et al., 1972; Skalko et al., 1971). Brain development, including brain growth (Zamenhof et al., 1971) and myelin formation by cerebellar oligodendrocytes (Younkin and Silberberg, 1973) are hindered by exposure to BUdR at certain periods *in vivo* or *in vitro*. Sea urchin embryos incubated with BUdR prior to the 8-cell stage undergo abnormal blastulation, fail to gastrulate, and do not synthesize echinochrome pigments (Gontcharoff and Mazia, 1967). Abnormal echinoderm development depends on the specific stage when BUdR is first administered to the embryo. Stage-specific sentivity to BUdR is also observed during chick erythoid cell development. Insensitivity to inhibition of hemoglobin formation appears both *in vitro* (Miura and Wilt, 1971; Hagopian et al., 1972) and *in vivo* (Weintraub et al., 1972), although erythroblasts unaffected by BUdR treatment actively incorporate the molecule into DNA. No significant differences in incorporation of BUdR into DNA between BUdR-resistant and -sensitive erythoblasts can be detected. In contrast to previous quoted examples in which insensitivity is due to cessation of DNA synthesis, these systems are characterized by BUdR insensitivity at later periods of differentiation even when the analog is incorporated into the DNA.

Finally, recent observations indicate that when early embryonic cells are exposed to BUdR prior to a crucial determinative event, they may be irreversibly prevented from differentiating into mature cells that exhibit specialized functions (Levitt and Dorfman, 1972; Abbott *et al.*, 1972). In the cartilage system, the response to BUdR by precursor cells differs from their mature cell types and will be examined in greater detail in the next section.

Possible mechanisms of the multiple effects of BUdR on developing systems will be explored in the last section. A brief summary of the influences of BUdR can be detailed as follows:

1. At moderate doses, it inhibits growth and viability of several cell lines but not differentiated or differentiating tissues.

2. It reversibly suppresses the phenotypic expression of differentiated cells, inhibiting the formation of special macromolecules associated with the differentiated state while minimally interfering with general DNA, RNA, and protein synthesis.

3. It induces the release of virus in several types of cells that do not otherwise exhibit virus formation.

4. In at least one system, BUdR treatment of cultured cells results in diminished malignancy on reinjection to animals.

5. It interferes with specific developmental programs when incorporated during critical periods of differentiation, often but not always correlated with stages of active cell division.

6. The inhibitory effect of BUdR on early, precursor cell populations, prior to a crucial stage in development, appears to be irreversible and contrasts with its action on differentiated cells.

VIII. Differentiation of Limb Bud Cells *in Vitro*

Earlier studies on the effects of BUdR on expression of differentiated function utilized cells stably determined as to phenotype. In order to distinguish between influences on the expression of differentiated function and influences affecting the process of differentiation, the authors have investigated the behavior of cells prior to irreversible commitment.

As mentioned in Section VI, C, stage 24 limb bud cells are labile with respect to differentiation into any of the major limb cell types, i.e., myoblast, fibroblast, or chondrocyte. Future specialization depends on the environment at this particular period of development. Cell culture of stage 24 limb bud mesenchyme under appropriate conditions permits chondrogenesis. At high density, large amounts of cartilage are formed; at lower densities only cells with a fibroblastic morphology are recognizable. Horwitz and Dorfman (1970) demonstrated that cartilage cells divide in soft agar more readily than do fibrobasts and that prior growth over agar enriches a culture of chondrocytes by diminishing overgrowth by fibroblasts (Bryan, 1968a,b). In order to take advantage of this selective property, limb bud cells were cultured over agar at densities that do not permit chondrogenesis on plastic dishes. After 2 days, the suspension was plated on plastic dishes, again at low density, and formation of cartilage was monitored by morphology, metachromasia, and incorporation of $^{35}SO_4^=$ into glycosaminoglycans. The results presented in Table I indicate that initial culture over agar permits differentiation of limb bud cells to cartilage at low densities. This chondrogenic enhancement by agar does not depend on increased aggregation of limb bud cells. Growth of limb bud mesenchyme in gyratory shaking flasks

TABLE I

EFFECT OF GROWTH ON AGAR ON DIFFERENTIATION OF LIMB BUD MESENCHYME[a]

Experiment No.	A[b] (cpm/10^6 cells)	B[c] (cpm/10^6 cells)	C[d] (cpm/10^6 cells)
1	16,500	348	—
2	6,200	590	—
3	4,630	595	428
4	53,800	5,760	7,050
5	245,000	4,950	—
6	26,300	—	1,610

[a] To each culture 6 hours before harvest was added 3.3 µCi $H_2^{35}SO_4$ per milliliter of medium. On the ninth day of culture, chondroitin sulfate was isolated (Dorfman and Ho, 1970).

[b] Dissociated cells plated at 10^7 cells in 10 ml media for 48 hr in 100-mm dishes containing 0.5% agar bases, then redissociated and placed on 60-mm plates at a density of 0.5×10^6 cells per dish for 7 days.

[c] Dissociated cells plated for 48 hours at a density of 10^7 cells in 10 ml of medium on 100-mm dishes without agar, then redissociated and placed on 60-mm dishes at a density of 0.5×10^6 cells per dish for 7 days.

[d] Dissociated cells plated at a density of 3.6×10^6 cells in 3 ml of medium on 60-mm tissue culture dishes and grown for 9 days. All three cell densities are below confluency (Levitt and Dorfman, 1972).

for 2 days followed by subculture on plastic dishes does not allow cartilage to form.

The mechanism whereby growth over agar or growth at high density promotes subsequent chondrogenesis is not clear. Nevo and Dorfman (1972) have shown that a number of highly charged polyanionic substances stimulate synthesis of chondroitin sulfate proteoglycan by chondrocytes previously grown in suspension culture. Since agar is a sulfated polysaccharide, it is possible that the augmented differentiation of limb bud cells may result from this property. Some support for this idea was obtained by the observation that agarose and pectin were less effective in promoting chondrogenesis. However, addition of chondroitin 4-sulfate, keratan sulfate, or heparan sulfate did not permit chondrogenesis of limb bud cells grown at low density on plastic dishes. In view of the accumulating evidence that proteoglycan and/or collagen may play a role in differentiation in other systems (see the foregoing), it is possible that some critical interaction of highly charged polyanions and collagen may be necessary to create local conditions that stimulate chondrogenesis.

If during the brief period of culture over agar, limb bud cells are exposed to BUdR, subsequent subculture at low density on plastic dishes (in the absence of BUdR) is accompanied by marked inhibition of cartilage formation. No cartilage is evident 40 days after subculture in the absence of BUdR and under culture conditions that normally permit chondrogenesis. The BUdR effect is dose-dependent and can be prevented by simultaneous but not subsequent addition of thymidine. Parameters of cell metabolism, such as cell division, protein content, and total DNA, RNA, and protein synthesis were unaffected by previous drug treatment.

When limb bud cells are treated with BUdR while growing over agar and are then subcultured onto plastic dishes, the cells flatten and spread in a manner similar to other BUdR-treated cells (Holtzer and Abbott, 1968; Silagi and Bruce, 1970). 5-Bromo-2'-deoxyuridine-treated cells subcultured from agar to plastic appear similar to control cells initially cultured on plastic at low density. Scant amounts of extracellular matrix are present, and the Golgi apparatus is poorly developed. Large bundles of microfilaments are arranged longitudinally beneath the cell membrane (Fig. 3). The rough endoplasmic reticulum is fairly extensive and often distended. Control cells initially cultured over agar resemble normal chondrocytes in their morphology and ultrastructure (Fig. 4). At high densities (2.5×10^7 cells per 60-mm dish), BUdR-treated limb bud cells are morphologically similar to control cells and exhibit no spreading or flattening. The fine structure of these cells is hardly distinguishable

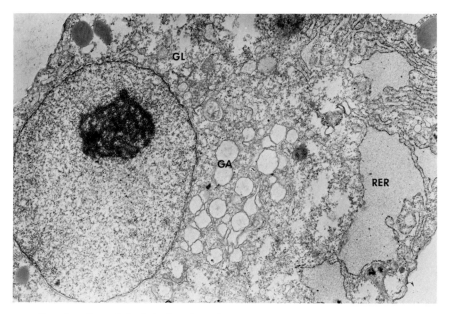

Fig. 3. Control limb bud cell 7 days after subculture from agar to plastic tissue culture dish. Rough endoplasmic reticulum (RER) and Golgi area (GA) are extensive and distended. Numerous glycogen lakes (GL) can be recognized. ×12,000.

from control cultures. Both contain a highly developed rough endoplasmic reticulum and Golgi apparatus, and extensive extracellular fibers can be detected. It is likely, therefore, that culture conditions play a crucial role in determining gross morphological and ultrastructural differences between BUdR-treated and control cultures.

A detailed study was undertaken of the nature and quantity of glycosaminoglycans produced by cultured limb bud cells. Glycosaminoglycans labeled with acetate-^{3}H and $^{35}SO_4^=$ were purified from control and BUdR cells following papain digestion, two precipitations with cetylpyridinium chloride, and reprecipitation with ethanol and ether. Total polysaccharide from cells plus media was estimated on the basis of uronic acid and hexosamine content. The nature and quantity of individual glycosaminoglycans were determined by susceptibility to streptococcal and testicular hyaluronidase, chondroitinase ABC, and nitrous acid as evidenced by change in chromatographic behavior on Sephadex G-25. The results displayed in Table II indicate that cells previously exposed to BUdR synthesize less total glycosaminoglycans than do control cells. The BUdR-treated cells contain only one-tenth as much chon-

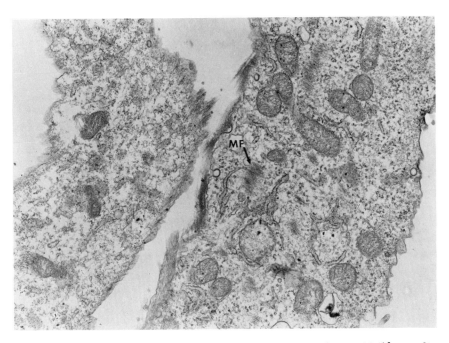

FIG. 4. Limb bud cell grown for 2 days over agar with 32 μM 5-bromo-2'-deoxyuridine (BUdR), then 7 days on plastic in the absence of BUdR. Cells appear elongate, with bundles of microfilaments (MF) present beneath the cell membrane and throughout the cytoplasm. Microtubules often traverse the cell parallel to the cell membrane. Note scant amounts of rough endoplasmic reticulum and Golgi apparatus. ×13,500.

droitin 4- and 6-sulfate as do control cells. Separation of chondroitinase digests by paper chromatography indicates that chondroitin 6-sulfate constitutes about 70 to 75% of the chondroitin sulfate fraction in both BUdR-treated and control cultures. To a lesser extent than chondroitin sulfate, hyaluronic acid content is also decreased in limb bud cells that had been initially exposed to BUdR. Only small amounts of heparan sulfate and dermatan sulfate were present in both types of cells.

The most striking effect of previous exposure to BUdR was diminution in the quantity of chondroitin sulfate, presumably present as proteoglycan. Such a decrease might result from a decrease in the rate of synthesis or an increase in the rate of degradation.

In order to determine the role of degradation, the rates of turnover of sulfated glycosaminoglycans were compared in control cells and cells previously treated with BUdR. The data summarized in Fig. 5 indicate a slightly increased turnover rate in the progeny of BUdR-treated cells;

TABLE II

Effect of 5-Bromo-2'-deoxyuridine on Glycosaminoglycan Synthesis[a]

	Total glyco-samino-glycans (μM UA/ 10^9 cells)	Hyal-uronic acid (μM UA/ 10^9 cells)	Chon-droitin 4- and 6-sulfates (μM UA/ 10^9 cells)	Dermatan sulfate (μM UA/ 10^9 cells)	Heparan sulfate (μM UA/ 10^9 cells)	Keratan sulfate (μM UA/ 10^9 cells)
Control	9.82	1.20	8.92	0.16	0.14	0.01
BUdR	1.31	0.36	0.94	0.08	0.16	0.01

Glycosaminoglycans were isolated from cells and media and fractionated as indicated in the text. UA, uronic acid; BUdR, 5-bromo-2'-deoxyuridine.

the magnitude of this change was not sufficient to account for the large differences in polysaccharide content in the two types of cultures.

Since the effects of BUdR could not be attributed to changes in degradation, a further analysis of glycosaminoglycan synthesis was undertaken. On the basis of the known pathways of biosynthesis summarized

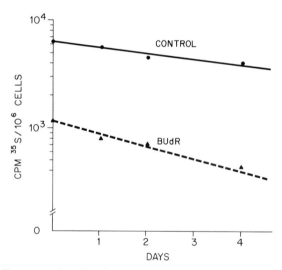

FIG. 5. Turnover of sulfated glycosaminoglycans in limb bud cell cultures. Cultures were labeled with 5 μCi/ml $H_2{}^{35}SO_4$ for 6 hours on the ninth day of culture. Each dish was washed twice with media, then cells plus fresh media were assayed for sulfate-labeled glycosaminoglycans on the ninth, tenth, eleventh, and thirteenth days of growth (0, 1, 2 and 4 days of chase). BUdR, 5-bromo-2'-deoxyuridine (Levitt and Dorfman, submitted for publication).

in Section IV, a diminished synthesis of chondroitin sulfate proteo-glycan may result from (a) diminished pools of nucleotide precursors, (b) diminished levels of activity of the enzymes involved in polysac-charide chain synthesis, or (c) diminished synthesis of core protein as observed following exposure to puromycin (de la Haba and Holtzer, 1965; Telser et al., 1965).

In order to determine the effect of BUdR treatment on nucleotide sugar synthesis in progeny of cells treated with BUdR, the activities of two critical enzymes involved in synthesis of nucleotide sugar precursors were measured. The results shown in Table III indicate only minor

TABLE III

ACTIVITY OF NUCLEOTIDE SUGAR SYNTHETIC ENZYMES

Assay	Control	5-Bromo-2'-deoxyuridine
UDP–N-acetylhexosamine-4-epimerase[a]	27,650	15,600
UDP–glucose dehydrogenase[b]	56.5	51.0
Glucose-6-phosphate dehydrogenase[c]	5.4	5.0

[a] Expressed as cpm N-acetylglucosamine-^{14}C/mg protein/hour. Determination of uridine 5'-diphosphate (UDP)-N-acetylhexosamine epimerase activity involved measurement of the conversion of UDP-N-acetylgalactosamine-[^{14}C] to UDP-N-acetylglucosamine-[^{14}C] by the 20,000 g supernatant. The UDP sugars were then hydrolyzed in 0.2 N HCl at 100°C for 30 minutes, neutralized with 0.4 N NaOH, and N-acetylgalactosamine was separated from N-acetylglucosamine by descending paper chromatography (Davidson, 1966). Dehydrogenase activities were deter-mined by the reduction of either nicotinamide adenine dinucleotide (NAD) or NAD phosphate (NADP), measured spectrophotometrically as increased absorbance at 340 nm (Levitt and Dorfman, submitted for publication).

[b] Expressed as μmoles reduced NAD/mg protein/minute.

[c] Expressed as μmoles reduced NADP/mg protein/minute.

depression of levels of activity of UDP–glucose dehydrogenase (EC 1.1.1.22) and UDP–N-acetylhexosamine-4-epimerase. Additionally the activity of glucose-6-phosphate dehydrogenase (EC 1.1.1.49), an enzyme not involved in this pathway, was not decreased in limb bud cells exposed to BUdR during the first 2 days of culture. As a further check, pool sizes of UDP–GlcUA, UDP–GalNAc, and UDP-GlcNAc were determined. No significant differences between control cells and progeny of BUdR-treated cells were observed (Table IV).

The levels of activity of two of the glycosyl transferases involved in chondroitin sulfate chain synthesis were measured. Xylosyl transferase

TABLE IV

Estimates of Uridine-5'-diphosphate–Sugar Pools in Limb Bud Cell Cultures

UDP–sugar	Control (cpm ^{14}C/10^8 cells)	BUdR (cpm ^{14}C/10^8 cells)
UDP–glucuronic acid	2525	2375
UDP-N-acetylglucosamine	2240	2930
UDP-N-acetylgalactosamine	2110	2025

^{a} Uridine-5'-diphosphate (UDP)–sugar pools were estimated on 9-day high-density cultures. Cells were labeled for 1 hour with either galactose-^{14}C or sodium acetate-^{14}C, then sonicated for 10 seconds in cold 5% Cl$_3$CCOOH. After 1 hour, the trichloroacetic acid supernatant was neutralized and applied to either Dowex 1 × 8 (Cl$^-$ form, 200–400 mesh) for separation of UDP–glucuronic acid (GlcUA) or Dowex 1 × 2 (Cl$^-$ form, 200–400 mesh) for UDP–N-acetylglucosamine (GlcNAc) and UDP-N-acetylgalactosamine (GalNAc). The UDP–GlcNAc and UDP–GalNAc were hydrolyzed for 30 minutes in 0.5M HCl at 100°C and then separated on Whatman No. 1 paper according to Davidson (1966).

(enzyme 1, Fig. 2) catalyzes the addition of D-xylose from UDP-xylose to a core protein acceptor, initiating the formation of chondroitin sulfate chains. N-Acetylgalactosamine transferase (enzyme 5, Fig. 2) adds GalNAc from UDP–GalNAc to oligosaccharides containing a terminal glucuronic acid residue.

The results shown in Table V indicate that the levels of xylosyl and GalNAc transferases are reduced only 35–40%, whereas glycosaminoglycan synthesis is reduced 85–90% in progeny of BUdR-treated cells.

Because these data suggest that BUdR-treated cells demonstrate at least part of the enzymatic machinery necessary for chondroitin sulfate chain synthesis, the possibility that the marked diminution in proteogylcan synthesis was due to deficient core protein formation was examined. In view of the fact that no method is yet available for direct measurement of core protein, an indirect procedure was adopted. Brett and Robinson (1971) had previously shown that high concentrations of xylose partially overcome the inhibition by puromycin of chondroitin sulfate synthesis in minced cartilage. A series of experiments were conducted to measure the ability of xylose to increase chondroitin sulfate synthesis in progeny of BUdR-treated limb bud cells.

As seen in Table VI, addition of xylose stimulates glycosaminoglycan synthesis in control cells by only 40% but cells previously treated with BUdR are stimulated 240–300%. Xylose appears to act as a chondroitin sulfate chain initiator, eliminating the need for core protein. In the presence of puromycin, addition of xylose partially overcomes the severe

TABLE V

CHONDROITIN SULFATE SYNTHESIS AND TRANSFERASE ACTIVITIES[a]

	cpm/10^6 cells	
Chondroitin sulfate synthesis	Control	5-Bromo-2'-deoxyuridine
$^{35}SO_4$ incorporation	13,600	1,680
Acetate-^{14}C incorporation	7,840	1,160

	cpm/mg protein/hour	
Transferase activities	Control	5-Bromo-2'-deoxyuridine
Xylosyltransferase	2,060	1,390
N-Acetylgalactosamine transferase	24,200	13,800

[a] Chondroitin sulfate synthesis was determined as previously described. Xylosyltransferase activity was assayed by measuring the transfer of xylose from uridine-5'-diphosphate (UDP)–xylose-^{14}C to Smith-degraded proteoglycan according to Stoolmiller et al. (1972). N-Acetylhexosamine transferase activity was determined by measuring the addition of N-acetylgalactosamine from UDP-N-acetylgalactosamine-^{14}C to a hexasaccharide acceptor possessing a terminal β-glucuronic acid residue (Horwitz and Dorfman, 1968; Levitt and Dorfman, submitted for publication).

suppression of chondroitin sulfate formation (Table VI); this result confirms the findings of Brett and Robinson (1971). Xylose is incorporated directly into polysaccharide chains that lack core protein (Levitt and Dorfman, unpublished results). These chains are approximately the same size as chondroitin sulfate chains synthesized by control cultures.

The synthesis of chondroitin sulfate in 1-day cultures of chick limb bud mesenchyme (prior to differentiation to cartilage) was not stimulated by addition of xylose. Such cells were found to exhibit approximately 30 and 60% of the specific activities of xylosyl transferase and GalNAc transferase, respectively, as do cells in culture for 9 days (which had differentiated), but they synthesize only 10% as much glycosaminoglycans. Since assays have not been performed for all of the glycosyl transferases, any interpretation is necessarily tentative. It is possible that the limited ability of these predifferentiated cells to synthesize chondroitin sulfate is not due to lack of enzymes but rather a failure of organization on the endoplasmic reticulum of the appropriate multienzyme complex. Such a lack of organization may result in an inability to utilize xylose as a chain initiator. This possibility is supported by the observation that

TABLE VI

EFFECT OF XYLOSE ON GLYCOSAMINOGLYCAN SYNTHESIS IN CONTROL AND
5-BROMO-2′-DEOXYURIDINE-TREATED LIMB BUD CELLS[a]

D-Xylose (mM)	Puromycin	$^{35}SO_4^=$ cpm/10^6 cells		[^{3}H] cpm/10^6 cells	
		Control	BUdR	Control	BUdR
0	−	10,000	2,220	5,050	970
10.6	−	14,400	5,060	7,820	2,250
42.4	−	13,700	6,000	7,180	2,210
0	+	840	340	260	160
10.6	+	3,100	2,720	920	700
42.4	+	4,380	2,780	1,320	890

[a] High-density cultures of limb bud cells were labeled with 5 μCi/ml $H_2^{35}SO_4$ and 10 μCi/ml acetate-^{3}H plus the indicated concentration of ^{4}D-xylose with or without 10 μg/ml puromycin for 6 hours on the ninth day of culture. Glycosaminoglycans were isolated from pooled cells plus media, according to Dorfman and Ho (1970). BUdR, 5-bromo-2′-deoxyuridine (Levitt and Dorfman, submitted for publication).

1-day cultures of limb bud cells lack the extensive endoplasmic reticulum displayed by high-density cultures of both control and BUdR-treated mesenchyme.

Because previous studies had shown that BUdR treatment also depresses chondroitin sulfate synthesis in differentiated chondrocytes, it was necessary to determine whether xylose reverses BUdR effects in such cells. When cultured chondrocytes from 15-day embryonic chick sternae were treated with BUdR, chondroitin sulfate synthesis was diminished to 10 to 20% of control levels. Addition of xylose resulted in no increase in glycosaminoglycan production by control cells; however, a seven-fold increase in chondroitin sulfate synthesis by BUdR-treated cultures occurred (Table VII).

An unusual reproducible observation in these experiments was that chondrocytes treated with both BUdR and puromycin were stimulated by xylose to produce larger amounts of glycosaminoglycans than were chondrocytes treated with only puromycin. The interpretation of this observation is not entirely obvious.

These effects of xylose on differentiated cartilage conflict with interpretations of experiments measuring enzymes involved in synthesis of nucleotide sugars (Schulte-Holthausen et al., 1969; Marzullo, 1972). A diminution of 75 to 90% of UDP–N-acetylhexosamine-4-epimerase and UDP–glucose dehydrogenase activities was found. It was concluded that

TABLE VII

EFFECT OF D-XYLOSE ON GLYCOSAMINOGLYCAN SYNTHESIS IN
CULTURED CHONDROCYTES[a]

D-Xylose (mM)	Puromycin	$^{35}SO_4$ cpm/10^6 cells		[^{3}H] cpm/10^6 cells	
		Control	BUdR	Control	BUdR
0	−	89,400	13,400	63,200	10,200
10.6	−	85,900	87,400	67,800	47,000
42.4	−	81,700	95,300	54,400	57,600
0	+	4,860	2,420	2,540	1,380
10.6	+	29,620	60,750	17,600	35,800
42.4	+	34,000	71,000	25,800	43,600

[a] On the tenth day of culture, chondrocytes growing in the presence or absence of 32 μM 5-bromo-2'-deoxyuridine (BUdR) were labeled with 5 μCi/ml $H_2^{35}SO_4$ and 10 μCi/ml acetate-^{3}H plus the indicated concentration of D-xylose and with or without 10 μg/ml puromycin for 6 hours. Glycosaminoglycans were isolated from pooled cells plus media as in Table VI (Levitt and Dorfman, submitted for publication).

these reduced enzyme activities were responsible for decreased levels of glycosaminoglycan synthesis in BUdR-treated cells.

We have examined the activities of xylosyl transferase and GalNAc transferase and find only a 40–50% decrease in activity in chondrocytes exposed to BUdR. Therefore, despite some inhibition of enzyme activity in BUdR-treated chondrocytes, these transferases are able to synthesize high levels of glycosaminoglycans when a chain initiator is present.

The results obtained with the use of xylose in both the progeny of BUdR-treated mesenchymal cells and BUdR-treated chondrocytes indicate a high level of competence for the synthesis of chondroitin sulfate chains. It seems probable that BUdR treatment affects the synthesis of core protein. In the case of mesenchymal cells, the irreversible nature of the effect suggests that a short exposure to BUdR inhibits the acquisition of the ability to synthesize this protein, whereas in the case of BUdR treatment of differentiated chondrocytes, inhibition of synthesis of the core protein is transient if the analog is ultimately removed. In experiments with both limb bud mesenchyme and with differentiated chondrocytes, inhibition of chondroitin sulfate synthesis is never complete. It, therefore, became of great interest to investigate the nature of the proteoglycan produced by BUdR-treated cells as compared to that produced by control cells.

Limb bud mesenchyme cultures were established and the proteoglycan was labeled with $^{35}SO_4$. Proteoglycan patterns were obtained from
the three types of cultures: (a) stage 24 limb bud cells grown at high
density for 1 day; (b) high-density cultures grown for 9 days by which
time cartilage differentiation had occurred; and (c) high-density cultures
treated with BUdR for 2 days and maintained in culture for 7 additional
days.

Chondroitin sulfate proteoglycan was extracted from each culture
with 4.0 M guanidinium chloride and chromatographed on Bio-Gel A 50
M columns.

Elution patterns are displayed in Fig. 6A and B. These results indicate the presence of three peaks—one located near the void volume, one
significantly retarded, and one in the salt fraction. When this same

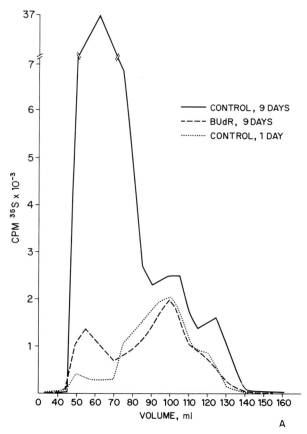

FIG. 6A.

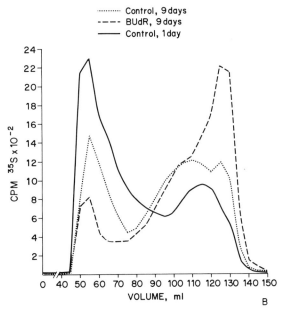

FIG. 6. Separation of proteoglycans from cultured limb bud cells. (A) cells; (B) media. Limb bud cells cultured for 1, 9, and 2 days with 32 μM 5-bromo-2'-deoxyuridine (BUdR) and then 7 days in the absence of BUdR, were labeled with 5 $\mu Ci/ml$ $H_2{}^{35}SO_4$ for 6 hours. Cells and media were separated. Cells were extracted overnight at room temperature with 4.0 M guanidine HCl. Soluble material was dialyzed against distilled water, then redissolved in 4.0 M guanidine HCl. Media was dialyzed against distilled water, lyophilized, then dissolved in 4.0 M guanidine HCl. Material was separated on a 1.3 $\times$ 100-cm column Bio-Gel A 50 M and eluted with 0.5 M NaCl at room temperature.

material was chromatographed on Bio-Gel A 15 or A 0.5 M, only two peaks could be detected, one in the void volume and another in the salt fraction. Thus, two of the three peaks appear to be large molecular weight species, whereas the smallest entity could be a product of abortive synthesis or degradation. Both of the large molecular fractions are digested more than 85% with chondroitinase ABC. When papain digested or 0.5 N KOH-treated proteoglycan was chromatographed over Sephadex G-200 or Ecteola-cellulose, chain length distribution patterns were similar in 9-day control, 1-day control, and BUdR-treated limb bud cell cultures. The major difference between these three cultures is the amount of chondromucoprotein in the void volume peak on Bio-Gel A 50 M. This type of chondroitin sulfate proteoglycan appears to be specific for cartilage cells, whereas the second peak is present in similar quantities in all three cultures. The smaller size of the retarded molecule might be due to either fewer polysaccharide chains per core protein molecule or two types of core proteins, one that is cartilage-specific and another that is nonspecific with fewer serine residues available for xylosylation. Similar results have been obtained for cultured chondrocytes treated with BUdR and sternal cartilage from nanomelic chick embryos (Palmoski and Goetinck, 1972).

Since treatment of limb bud cells with BUdR before determination prevents their subsequent differentiation to cartilage, it became of interest to examine collagen synthesis. The first experiments measured the capacity of progeny of BUdR-treated cells to incorporate proline-^{3}H into hydroxyproline of protein. The results are summarized in Table VIII. No inhibition of collagen synthesis was observed; in fact a slight

TABLE VIII

BIOSYNTHESIS OF COLLAGEN BY CULTURED LIMB BUD CELLS[a]

| | Hydroxyproline/proline/10^6 cells | | | |
| | Control | | BUdR | |
Ascorbate	Cells	Media	Cells	Media
−	0.8×10^{-2}	2.1×10^{-2}	1.2×10^{-2}	4.0×10^{-2}
+	3.4×10^{-2}	10.5×10^{-2}	4.5×10^{-2}	17.2×10^{-2}

[a] Cells were grown over agar for 48 hours with or without 32 μM 5-bromo-2′-deoxyuridine (BUdR). Cells were subcultured onto plastic dishes, grown for 7 more days, then incubated for 16 hours with 2 μCi/ml proline-^{14}C in the presence or absence of 50 μg/ml ascorbic acid. Incorporation of label into hydroxyproline was determined according to Lukens (1965).

but reproducible stimulation was evident. As indicated in the foregoing, it is now known that cartilage collagen differs from that produced by skin fibroblasts. In collaboration with Barbara D. Smith and George R. Martin, experiments were undertaken to determine the nature of the collagen produced. When limb bud cells were cultured at high density for 1 day (before cartilage differentiation had taken place), the ratio of α1 to α2 chains was 2:1, characteristic of skin collagen. However, after 9 days in culture, when differentiation had occurred, the ratio of α1 to α2 was 10:1, a value more characteristic of cartilage collagen. In contrast, cells that were exposed to BUdR (which subsequently did not differentiate to cartilage) produced collagen with a α1 to α2 ratio of 2:1. These results indicate that BUdR treatment of predifferentiated cells prevents the subsequent expression of the cartilage phenotype with respect to collagen synthesis.

5-Bromo-2′-deoxyuridine appears to exert its irreversible inhibition of chondrogenesis in limb bud cells by substituting for thymidine in cellular DNA. The effects of this drug can be prevented by simultaneous addition of thymidine and no other nucleoside. Radioautographs with BUdR-^{3}H localize this label in the nucleus, and it is not extracted after treatment with cold 5% Cl_3CCOOH. Label is incorporated into cold Cl_3CCOOH-precipitable material that is sensitive to deoxyribonuclease but insensitive to ribonuclease and treatment with alkali. Finally, DNA isolated from cultured limb bud cells growing in the presence of BUdR reveals a shift in density upon CsCl equilibrium gradient centrifugation (Fig. 7). Caluculations indicate that less than 10% substitution of BUdR for thymidine in DNA is required for an irreversible inhibition of differentiation to occur.

We have observed an abnormally rapid loss of BUdR from the DNA of cultured limb bud cells after removal of the drug and continued cul-

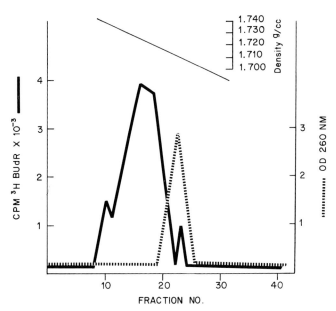

FIG. 7. Buoyant density of bromouridine–deoxyribonucleic acid (DNA) from limb bud cell cultures. Limb bud cells were grown over agar for 2 days with 32 μM 5-bromo-2′-deoxyuridine (BUdR) and 2 μCi/ml BUdR-^{3}H. The DNA was isolated from these cultures using unlabeled carrier DNA from 4-day-chick embryos (Levitt and Dorfman, unpublished). The CsCl equilibrium density centrifugation was performed in a Spinco L2-65 centrifuge using a 65-fixed-angle rotor at 45,000 rpm for 42 hours, 21°C. Density was determined for every fifth fraction by measuring the refractive index.

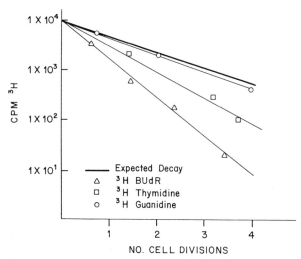

FIG. 8.   Turnover of deoxyribonucleic acid in 5-bromo-2′-deoxyuridine (BUdR)-treated limb bud cell cultures. Freshly dissociated bud cells were cultured over agar for 48 hours in the presence of 32 μM BUdR and 1 μCi/ml of either BUdR-^{3}H, thymidine-^{3}H, or guanidine-^{3}H. Cells were trypsinized with 0.25% trypsin, washed 3 times with media, and subcultured in the absence of label on 60-mm plastic culture dishes. Radioactivity in cold 5% Cl$_3$CCOOH-material was measured after digestion with Tl and pancreatic ribonuclease at 0, 2, 4, 6, and 8 days of chase. Cell number was determined in a Coulter Counter Model B. Plating efficiency on subculture was greater than 95%.

ture in its absence for 6 to 8 days. As demonstrated in Fig. 8, BUdR is diluted from limb bud DNA more rapidly than can be accounted for by a simple exponential loss due to cell division. Thymidine is also removed at a more rapid rate than that which is expected by cell doubling alone. Adenine and guanine inserted into DNA during the first 2 days of growth in BUdR are diluted at a rate corresponding to the number of cell divisions. The excised pieces of DNA-containing BU appear to be low molecular weight, since they are dialyzable and are not precipitated with cold Cl$_3$CCOOH. This abnormal removal of BUdR in limb bud cells was quite unexpected; mature chondrocytes do not appear to demonstrate this abnormal metabolism of BU (Fig. 9). These results may be of great interest in explaining why BUdR effects are irreversible in early embryonic cells yet reversible in differentiated cells.

IX.   Discussion

The wide interest in elucidation of the mechanisms involved in differentiation has recently led to the use of *in vitro* systems in a large

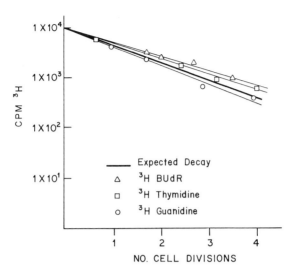

FIG. 9. Turnover of deoxyribonucleic acid (DNA) in 5-bromo-2′-deoxyuridine (BUdR)-treated chondrocytes. Sternal chondrocytes were treated with 32 μM BUdR and 1 μCi/ml of either BUdR-³H, thymidine-³H, or guanidine-³H 4 days after cultures were initiated. Nonradioactive BUdR and labeled nucleotides were present for 2 days, after which cells were washed 3 times with media. Label in DNA and cell counts were determined as in Fig. 8 after 0, 2, 4, 6, and 8 days of chase.

number of studies. In some of these model systems it is extremely difficult to distinguish those factors that facilitate expression of a differentiated characteristic from those that actually promote the process of differentiation. As is obvious from this review such a distinction is not always possible or even warranted. The situation is further complicated by the widespread use of the term *dedifferentiation* which carries the implication of a change from a differentiated state to a more primitive state. Clearly the loss of expression of a specific characteristic in cultured cells, even when derived from a clone, does not indicate a return to the predifferentiated state. In the case of culture of cartilage, the factors that may influence expression of the cartilage phenotype are numerous and have been reviewed. It would seem that for operational purposes the demonstration of true dedifferentiation would require that the following conditions be met: (a) the isolation of a clone of cells that displays the specific cartilage phenotype, (b) the reversion of the progeny of such a clone to a cell type that demonstrates characteristics of the precursor cells of cartilage, and (c) the differentiation of such cells to some defined phenotype other than cartilage. Clearly, these criteria have not yet been met; for our purposes we consider the process of differentiation to be normally irreversible. There is no theoretical reason why reversibility is impossible; indeed, nuclear transplantation studies would seem to establish that reversal does occur.

In the case of study of connective tissue cells, this problem has become particularly complicated by the loose use of the term *fibroblast*. The assumption that cells in culture that morphologically resemble fibroblasts in tissues represent a uniform cell type is unjustified. The previous chemical definition of fibroblasts on the basis of secretion of glycosaminoglycans and collagen is no longer valid since it is now clear that both of these products are synthesized by various other types of cells.

In the case of cartilage there now seems to be two identifying biochemical markers—a specific type of collagen $[\alpha 1(II)]_3$ and high levels of synthesis of chondroitin 4- and/or 6-sulfate. It is possible that the core protein of the chondroitin sulfate proteoglycan differs from that produced by other types of connective tissue cells. This attractive idea requires further study. It seems likely that these two chemical parameters are well correlated with the morphological and staining characteristics usually utilized to identify cartilage. With these characteristics in mind, one might attempt to examine the cell types that have been presented in previous studies of cartilage. Clearly there exist in limb bud as well as in somites, mesenchymal cells having properties that differ from those of chondrocytes. Obviously they cannot be considered completely undifferentiated with respect to all properties. In the case of limb bud mesenchyme, certain characteristics that distinguish these cells from chondrocytes have been observed. These may be enumerated as follows: (1) electron microscope studies show a poorly developed rough endoplasmic reticulum, Golgi apparatus, and scant amounts of extracellular material, (2) collagen synthesized by such cells is of the $[\alpha 1]_2 \alpha 2$ type, (3) the level of chondroitin sulfate synthesis is low, and (4) the addition of xylose results in negligible stimulation of chondroitin sulfate synthesis.

The exact nature of the collagen synthesized by the mesenchymal cells remains to be determined. Although it appears to be of the $[\alpha 1]_2 \alpha 2$ type, it is not certain that the $\alpha 1$ chains are identical with those of skin and bone collagen. Likewise the nature of the core protein of the chondroitin sulfate proteoglycan secreted by such cells remains to be elucidated. The progeny of BUdR-treated cells (which do not differentiate to cartilage) share certain properties with limb bud mesenchyme yet differ with respect to others. Like limb bud mesenchyme, these cells synthesize $[\alpha 1]_2 \alpha 2$ collagen and produce low levels of chondroitin sulfate proteoglycan, but, unlike the mesenchyme cells, they contain a well-developed rough endoplasmic reticulum and are markedly stimulated by xylose. These findings suggest that the BUdR progeny have possibly undergone some differentiation, namely, the development of the machinery for synthesis of the complex macromolecule, chondroitin sulfate proteoglycan, consisting of rough endoplasmic reticulum and the multienzyme system for synthesis of chondroitin sulfate chains. These cells may be incapable of achieving a high rate of synthesis of chondromucoprotein because of lack of formation of the appropriate core protein (or formation of an abnormal protein which is poorly xylosylated).

The sequence of events that results in transition of a mesenchymal cell to a chondrocyte is not understood. Holtzer *et al.* (1973) have emphasized the need for cell divisions that permit critical changes to occur during differentiation. Clearly the development of all differentiated tissues follows a series of cell divisions. However, the necessity for cells to divide prior to a specific differentiative event has recently been questioned (Cooke, 1973). It is untenable to conclude that differentiation occurs following a given number of cell divisions because of the unmasking of an innate genomic program. It this were the case, all progeny of the fertilized ovum would be phenotypically identical. One must examine the nature of influences external to the cell that are responsible for the selective phenotypic expression in different cell types. The long history of search for specific inducers has been concerned with this problem. In view of the special relationship of spinal cord and notochord to the formation of vertebral cartilage, considerable effort has been made to identify specific products of these tissues as inducers of cartilage. So far these studies have been inconclusive. No evidence that similar induction is required for cartilage formation in the case of limb bud has been forthcoming. As already reviewed, recent studies have emphasized the possible role of matrix materials, chondroitin sulfate proteoglycan and/ or collagen, themselves influencing the conversion of mesenchymal cells to chondrocytes. A number of facts point to the importance of such interactions, although no clear-cut cause and effect relationship has yet been established.

It has become apparent that BUdR treatment has striking effects on eukaryotic cells. These have already been summarized in an earlier section. No simple clear-cut explanation for these effects is yet apparent. In the case of the limb bud system, exposure of limb bud cells to BUdR in low concentrations at a critical period of determination irreversibly prevents differentiation to cartilage. Although there is some decrease in activity of certain enzymes involved in synthesis of chondroitin sulfate chains, the major lesion appears to be the failure to acquire the capacity to synthesize a cartilage-type collagen and the core protein of chondroitin sulfate proteoglycan. Although not conclusive, there is a suggestion that in the latter case the failure may be in the formation of a specific core protein (or the formation of an abnormal core protein) characteristic of cartilage. Since BUdR treatment exerts similar effects on acquisition of capacity to form certain other phenotypically specific proteins but does not result in a general decrease of protein synthesis, it is difficult to attribute the effect to random substitution for thymidine in structural genes. It would seem instead that some particular portion of the genome which governs the control of production of specialized molecules is particularly sensitive to BUdR incorporation. The fact that the progeny of BUdR-treated cells continue to secrete collagen of the $[\alpha 1(I)]_2 \alpha 2$ type but do not form $[\alpha 1(II)]_3$ type collagen suggests that synthesis of the two types of collagen may be under different controls. A similar conclusion may be valid for chondroitin sulfate proteoglycan if, indeed, it is firmly established that there is a cartilage-specific core protein. This conclusion has interesting evolutionary implications. It might be postulated that certain highly specialized molecules [*luxury molecules* in the terminology of Holtzer and Abbott (1968)] arise as a result of duplication of genes coding for more ubiquitous molecules. The examples of collagen and chondroitin sulfate core protein might be likened to the relationship of the actin and myosin-like molecules present in cells as diverse as slime molds and fibroblasts to muscle actin and myosin. One may postulate that in the course of evolution, gene duplication has resulted in the production of new structural genes that have not only mutated independently but have also come under new control mechanisms. In view of the effect of BUdR on both reversible suppression of differentiated phenotypic expression and acquisition of capacity for differentiated phenotypic expression, it might be suggested that some portion of the genome exists, involved in both of these functions, that is either high in thymidine or has thymidine situated in certain strategic locations. Britten and Davidson (1969, 1971) have suggested that a large portion of the DNA of eukaryotic cells is concerned with such functions. They have proposed mechanisms by which a series of structural genes not geometrically contiguous may be derepressed. Substitution of BUdR for thymidine may allow certain "repressor" molecules to bind to regulatory regions with an increased affinity (Lin and Riggs, 1972). Alternatively BUdR may prevent the synthesis of certain classes of nuclear DNA, or enhance the degradation of certain species of DNA molecules [see the foregoing; and Kotzin and Baker (1972)]. It is obvious that this discussion does not propose a detailed mechanism for differentiation. It is hoped that the striking effects of BUdR perhaps will furnish a probe for further study of this complex problem at the molecular level.

ACKNOWLEDGMENTS

Original research in this article was supported by U.S. Public Health Service Grants AM-05996, HD-04583, and HD-00001.
We deeply appreciate the assistance of Ms. Pei-Lee Ho in several aspects of this work and especially for preparing the electron micrographs. We thank Ms. Cherie Mulcahy for typing this manuscript.

REFERENCES

Aaronson, S. A., Todaro, G. J., and Scolnick, E. M. (1971). *Science* **174,** 157.
Abbott, J., and Holtzer, H. (1968). *Proc. Nat. Acad. Sci. U.S.* **59,** 1144.
Abbott, J., Mayne, R., and Holtzer, H. (1972). *Develop. Biol.* **28,** 432.
Anderson, H. C., Chacko, S., Abbott, J., and Holtzer, H. (1970). *Amer. J. Pathol.* **60,** 289.
Ben-Hur E., and Elkind, M. M. (1972). *Biophys. J.* **12,** 636.
Bischoff, R. (1971). *Exp. Cell Res.* **66,** 224.
Bischoff, R., and Holtzer, (1970). *J. Cell Biol.* **44,** 134.
Bornstein, P., Von Der Mark, L., Wyke, A. W., Ahrlich, H. P., and Monson, J. M. (1972). *J. Biol. Chem.* **247,** 2808.
Braun, A. C. (1968). *In* "The Stability of the Differentiated State" (H. Ursprung, ed.), p. 128. Springer-Verlag, Berlin and New York.
Breslow, R., and Goldsby, R. (1969). *Exp. Cell Res.* **55,** 339.
Brett, M. J., and Robinson, H. C. (1971). *Proc. Aust. Biochem. Soc.* **4,** 92 (abstr.).
Britten, R. J., and Davidson, E. H. (1969). *Science* **165,** 349.
Britten, R. J., and Davidson, E. H. (1971). *Quart. Rev. Biol.* **46,** 111.
Bryan, J. (1968a). *Exp. Cell Res.* **52,** 319.
Bryan, J. (1968b). *Exp. Cell Res.* **52,** 327.
Buhl, S. N., Setlow, R. B., and Regan, J. D. (1972). *Int. J. Radiat. Biol.* **22,** 417.
Cahn, R. D., and Lasher, R. (1967). *Proc. Nat. Acad. Sci. U.S.* **58,** 1131.
Caplan, A. I. (1970). *Exp. Cell Res.* **62,** 341.
Caplan, A. I. (1972a). *Exp. Cell Res.* **70,** 185.
Caplan, A. I. (1972b). *J. Exp. Zool.* **180,** 351.
Caplan, A. I., Zwilling, E., and Kaplan, N. O. (1968). *Science* **160,** 1009.
Chacko, S., Holtzer, S., and Holtzer, H. (1969). *Biochem. Biophys. Res. Commun.* **34,** 183.
Clark, S. L., Jr. (1971). *Amer. J. Anat.* **132,** 319.
Cohen, A. M., and Hay, E. D. (1971). *Develop. Biol.* **26,** 578.
Coleman, A. W., Coleman, J. R., Kankel, D, and Werner, I. (1970). *Exp. Cell Res.* **59,** 319.
Coleman, J. R., Coleman, A. W., and Hartline, E. J. H. (1969). *Develop. Biol.* **19,** 527.
Cooke, J. (1973). *Nature (London)* **242,** 55.
Coon, H. G. (1966). *Proc. Nat. Acad. Sci. U.S.* **55,** 66.
Davidson, E. A. (1966). *In* "Methods in Enzymology" (E. F. Neufeld and V. Ginsburg, eds.), Vol. 8, p. 277. Academic Press, New York.
Davidson, R. L., and Bick, M. D. (1973). *Proc. Nat. Acad. Sci. U.S.* **70,** 138.
de la Haba, G., and Holtzer, H. (1965). *Science* **149,** 1263.

Dorfman, A., and Ho, P.-L. (1970). *Proc. Nat. Acad. Sci. U.S.* **66**, 495.

Dutton, R. W., Dutton, A. H., and Vaughan, J. H. (1960). *Biochem. J.* **15**, 230.

Ede, D. A., and Agerbak, G. S. (1968). *J. Embryol. Exp. Morphol.* **20**, 81.

Elkind, M. M., and Whitmore, G. F. (1967). "The Radiobiology of Cultured Mammalian Cells." Gordon & Breach, New York.

Ellison, M. L., and Lash, J. W. (1971). *Develop. Biol.* **26**, 486.

Ellison, M. L., Ambrose, E. J., and Easty, G. C. (1969). *J. Embryol. Exp. Morphol.* **21**, 331.

Fell, H. B., and Canti, R. G. (1934). *Proc. Roy. Soc. Ser. B* **116**, 316.

Flower, M. J. (1972). *Develop. Biol.* **28**, 583.

Franco-Browder, S., DeRydt, J., and Dorfman, A. (1963). *Proc. Nat. Acad. Sci. U.S.* **49**, 643.

Freese, E. (1959). *J. Mol. Biol.* **1**, 87.

Gallop, P. M., Blumenfeld, O. O., and Seifter, S. (1972). *Annu. Rev. Biochem.* **41**, 617.

Gerber, P. (1972). *Proc. Nat. Acad. Sci. U.S.* **69**, 83.

Glick, M., and Stockdale, F. E. (1964). *Develop. Biol.* **83**, 61.

Goel, S. C. (1970). *J. Embryol. Exp. Morphol.* **23**, 169.

Goldberg, B., and Sherr, C. J. (1973). *Proc. Nat. Acad. Sci. U.S.* **70**, 361.

Goldberg, B., Epstein, E. H., and Sherr, C. J. (1972). *Proc. Nat. Acad. Sci. U.S.* **69**, 3655.

Gontcharoff, M., and Mazia, D. (1967). *Exp. Cell Res.* **46**, 315.

Gould, R. P., Day, A., and Wolpert, L. (1972). *Exp. Cell Res.* **72**, 325.

Gurdon, J. B. (1964). *Advan. Morphog.* **4**, 1.

Hagopian, H. K., Lippke, J. A., and Ingram, V. M. (1972). *J. Cell Biol.* **43**, 98.

Hakala, M. T. (1959). *J. Biol. Chem.* **234**, 3072.

Hakala, M. T. (1962). *Biochim. Biophys. Acta* **61**, 815.

Hall, B. K. (1970). *Biol. Rev.* **45**, 455.

Ham, R. G., and Sattler, G. L. (1968). *J. Cell Physiol.* **72**, 109.

Ham, R. G., Murray, L. W., and Sattler, G. L. (1970). *J. Cell Physiol.* **75**, 353.

Hampar, B., Derge, J. G., Martos, G. M., and Walker, J. L. (1972). *Proc. Nat. Acad. Sci. U.S.* **69**, 78.

Hanafusa, T., Hanafusa, H., and Miyamoto, T. (1970). *Proc. Nat. Acad. Sci. U.S.* **67**, 1767.

Hardingham, T. E., Fitton-Jackson, S., and Muir, H. (1972). *Biochem. J.* **129**, 101.

Hascall, V. C., and Sajdera, S. W. (1969). *J. Biol. Chem.* **244**, 2384.

Hascall, V. C., and Sajdera, S. W. (1970). *J. Biol. Chem.* **245**, 4920.

Hay, E. D. (1968). *In* "Stability of the Differentiated State" (H. Ursprung, ed.), p. 85. Springer-Verlag, Berlin and New York.

Herscowitz, A. B., Stavitsky, A. B., and Tew, J. G. (1971). *Cell Immunol.* **2**, 259.

Holtzer, H. (1964). *Biophys. J.* **4**, 239.

Holtzer, H., and Abbott, J. (1968). *In* "The Stability of the Differentiated State" (H. Ursprung, ed.), p. 1. Springer-Verlag, Berlin and New York.

Holtzer, H., Abbott, J., Lash, J., and Holtzer, S. (1960). *Proc. Nat. Acad. Sci. U.S.* **46**, 1533.

Holtzer, H., Weintraub, H., Mayne, R., and Mochan, B. (1973). *Curr. Top. Develop. Biol.* **8**, 229.

Horwitz, A. L., and Dorfman, A. (1968). *J. Cell Biol.* **38**, 358.

Horwitz, A. L., and Dorfman, A. (1970). *J. Cell Biol.* **45**, 434.

Huggins, C., and Urist, M. R. (1970). *Science* **167**, 896.

Janners, M. Y., and Searls, R. L. (1970). *Develop. Biol.* **23**, 136.
Kajiwara, K., and Mueller, G. C. (1964). *Biochim. Biophys. Acta* **91**, 486.
Kim, J. H., Gelbard, A. S., Perez, A. G., and Eidinoff, M. L. (1967). *Biochim. Biophys. Acta* **134**, 388.
Kit, S., Dubbs, D., Pickarski, L., and Hsu, T. (1963). *Exp. Cell Res.* **31**, 297.
Kornfeld, S., Kornfeld, R., Neufeld, E. F., and O'Brien, P. J. (1964). *Proc. Nat. Acad. Sci. U.S.* **52**, 371.
Kotzin, B. L., and Baker, R. F. (1972). *J. Cell Biol.* **55**, 74.
Koyama, H., and Ono, T. (1971). *J. Cell Physiol.* **78**, 265.
Koyama, H., and Ono, T. (1972a). *Biochim. Biophys. Acta* **264**, 497.
Koyama, H., and Ono, T. (1972b). *Exp. Cell. Res.* **69**, 468.
Kreider, J. W., Del Villano, B., Shoff, W. H., and Davidson, E. A. (1972). *Cancer Res.* **32**, 2148.
Kvist, T. N., and Finnegan, C. V. (1970a). *J. Exp. Zool.* **175**, 241.
Kvist, T. N., and Finnegan, C. V. (1970b). *J. Exp. Zool.* **175**, 221.
Lash, J. W. (1968a). *J. Cell Physiol.* **72**, 35.
Lash, J. W. (1968b). *In* "Epithelial Mesenchymal Interactions" (R. Fleischmeyer and R. E. Billingham, eds.), p. 165. Williams & Wilkins, Baltimore, Maryland.
Lash, J. W., Hommes, F. A., and Zilliken, F. (1961). *Biochim. Biophys. Acta* **56**, 313.
Lasher, R. (1971). *In* "Developmental Aspects of the Cell Cycle" (I. L. Cameron, G. M. Padilla, and A. M. Zimmerman, eds.), p. 223. Academic Press, New York.
Lasher, R., and Cahn, R. D. (1969). *Develop. Biol.* **19**, 415.
Lavietes, B. B. (1970). *Develop. Biol.* **21**, 584.
Layman, D. L., McGoodwin, E., and Martin, G. R. (1971). *Proc. Nat. Acad. Sci. U.S.* **68**, 454.
Layman, D. L., Sokoloff, L., and Miller, E. J. (1972). *Exp. Cell Res.* **73**, 107.
Levenson, G. E. (1969). *Exp. Cell Res.* **55**, 225.
Levitt, D., and Dorfman, A. (1972). *Proc. Nat. Acad. Sci. U.S.* **69**, 1253.
Lin, S.-Y., and Riggs, A. D. (1972). *Proc. Nat. Acad. Sci. U.S.* **69**, 2574.
Littlefield, J. W., and Gould, E. A. (1960). *J. Biol. Chem.* **235**, 1129.
Lowy, D. R., Rowe, W. P., Teich, N., and Hartley, J. W. (1971). *Science* **174**, 155.
Lukens, L. N. (1965). *J. Biol. Chem.* **240**, 1661.
Marzullo, G. (1972). *Develop. Biol.* **27**, 20.
Mathews, M. B. (1967). *Biol. Rev. Cambridge Phil. Soc.* **42**, 499.
Mathews, M. B. (1971). *Biochem. J.* **125**, 37.
Mayne, R., Sanger, J. W., and Holtzer, H. (1971). *Develop. Biol.* **25**, 547.
Mayne, R., Abbott, J., and Holtzer, H. (1973). *Exp. Cell Res.* **77**, 255.
Mazia, D., and Gontcharoff, M. (1964). *Exp. Cell Res.* **35**, 14.
Medoff, J. (1967). *Develop. Biol.* **16**, 118.
Miller, E. J., and Matukas, V. J. (1969). *Proc. Nat. Acad. Sci. U.S.* **64**, 1264.
Miura, Y., and Wilt, F. H. (1971). *J. Cell Biol.* **48**, 523.
Moscona, A. A., (1952). *J. Anat.* **86**, 287.
Mottet, N. K. (1967). *J. Exp. Zool.* **165**, 279.
Nameroff, M., and Holtzer, H. (1967). *Develop. Biol.* **16**, 250.
Neufeld, E. F., and Hall, C. W. (1965). *Biochem. Biophys. Res. Commun.* **19**, 456.
Nevo, Z., and Dorfman, A. (1972). *Proc. Nat. Acad. Sci. U.S.* **69**, 2069.
Nevo, Z., Horwitz, A. L., and Dorfman, A. (1972). *Develop. Biol.* **28**, 219.
O'Brien, T. F., and Coons, A. H. (1963). *J. Exp. Med.* **117**, 1063.

O'Hare, M. J. (1972a). *J. Embryol. Exp. Morphol.* **27**, 229.

O'Hare, M. J. (1972b). *J. Embryol. Exp. Morphol.* **27**, 235.

Palmoski, M. J., and Goetinck, P. F. (1972). *Proc. Nat. Acad. Sci. U.S.* **69**, 3385.

Pasztor, L. M., and Hu, F. (1971). *Cytobios* **4**, 145.

Pawelek, J. (1969). *Develop. Biol.* **19**, 52.

Pessac, B., and Defendi, V. (1972). *Science* **175**, 898.

Puck, T. T., and Kao, F.-T. (1967). *Proc. Nat. Acad. Sci. U.S.* **58**, 1227.

Reddi, A. H., and Huggins, C. (1972). *Proc. Nat. Acad. Sci. U.S.* **69**, 1601.

Rizki, R. M., and Rizki, T. M. (1969). *Cancer Res.* **29**, 201.

Rizki, T. M., Rizki, R. M., and Douthit, H. A. (1972). *Biochem. Genet.* **6**, 83.

Rodén, L. (1970). *In* "Metabolic Conjugation and Metabolic Hydrolysis" (W. Fishman, ed.), Vol. 2, p. 345. Academic Press, New York.

Rowe, W. P., Lowy, D. R., Teich, N., and Hartley, J. W. (1972). *Proc. Nat. Acad. Sci. U.S.* **69**, 1033.

Ruggeri, A. (1972). *Z. Anat. Entwicklungsgesch.* **138**, 20.

Rutter, W. J., Kemp. J. D., Bradshaw, W. S., Clark, W. R., Ronzio, R. A., and Sanders, T. G. (1968). *J. Cell. Physiol.* **72**, 1.

Sanger, J. W., and Holtzer, H. (1970). *J. Cell Biol.* **47**, 178 (abstr.).

Schacter, L. P. (1970a). *Exp. Cell Res.* **63**, 19.

Schacter, L. P. (1970b). *Exp. Cell Res.* **63**, 33.

Schubert, D., and Jacob, F. (1970). *Proc. Nat. Acad. Sci. U.S.* **67**, 247.

Schulte-Holthausen, H., Chacko, S., Davidson, E. A., and Holtzer, H. (1969). *Proc. Nat. Acad. Sci. U.S.* **63**, 864.

Schwartz, J. P., Morris, N. R., and Breckenridge, B. M. (1973). *J. Biol. Chem.* **248**, 2699.

Schwartz, N. B., and Rodén, L. (1973). *Fed. Proc., Fed. Amer. Soc. Exp. Biol.* **32**, 560 (abstr.).

Searls, R. L. (1965a). *Develop. Biol.* **11**, 155.

Searls, R. L. (1965b). *Proc. Soc. Exp. Biol. Med.* **118**, 1172.

Searls, R. L. (1967). *J. Exp. Zool.* **166**, 39.

Searls, R. L. (1971). *Exp. Cell Res.* **64**, 163.

Searls, R. L. (1972). *Exp. Cell Res.* **73**, 57.

Searls, R. L., and Janners, M. Y. (1969). *J. Exp. Zool.* **170**, 365.

Searls, R. L., Hilfer, S. R., and Mirow, S. M. (1972). *Develop. Biol.* **28**, 123.

Shulman, H. J., and Meyer, K. (1970). *Biochem. J.* **120**, 689.

Silagi, S. (1971). *In Vitro* **7**, 105.

Silagi, S., and Bruce, S. A. (1970). *Proc. Nat. Acad. Sci. U.S.* **66**, 72.

Silagi, S., Beju, D., Wrathall, J., and Deharven, E. (1972). *Proc. Nat. Acad. Sci. U.S.* **69**, 3443.

Silbert, J. E., and De Luca, S. (1969). *J. Biol. Chem.* **244**, 876.

Skalko, R. G., Packard, Jr., D. S., Schwendimann, R. N., and Raggio, J. F. (1971). *Teratology* **4**, 87.

Smets, L. A., and Cornelis, J. J. (1971). *Int. J. Radiat. Biol.* **19**, 445.

Solursh, M., and Meier, S. (1973). *Develop. Biol.* **30**, 279.

Somers, C. E., and Hsu, T. C. (1962). *Proc. Nat. Acad. Sci. U.S.* **48**, 937.

Stellwagen, R. H., and Tomkins, G. M. (1971a). *J. Mol. Biol.* **56**, 167.

Stellwagen, R. H., and Tomkins, G. M. (1971b). *Proc. Nat. Acad. Sci. U.S.* **68**, 1147.

Stockdale, F., Okazaki, K., Nameroff, M., and Holtzer, H. (1964). *Science* **146**, 533.

Stoolmiller, A. C., and Caplan, A. I. (1973). *Fed. Proc., Fed. Amer. Soc. Exp. Biol.* **32**, 573 (abstr.).

Stoolmiller, A. C., and Dorfman, A. (1969). *In* "Comprehensive Biochemistry" (M. Florkin and E. H. Stotz, eds.), Vol. 17, p. 243. Elsevier, Amsterdam.

Stoolmiller, A. C., Horwitz, A. L., and Dorfman, A. (1972). *J. Biol. Chem.* **247**, 3525.

Strudel, G. (1962). *Develop. Biol.* **4**, 67.

Strudel, G. (1963). *J. Embryol. Exp. Morphol.* **11**, 399.

Strudel, G. (1971). *C. R. Acad. Sci., Ser. D* **272**, 473.

Strudel, G. (1972). *C. R. Acad. Sci., Ser. D* **274**, 112.

Telser, A., Robinson, H. C., and Dorfman, A. (1965). *Proc. Nat. Acad. Sci. U.S.* **54**, 912.

Thorp, F. K., and Dorfman, A. (1967). *Curr. Topics Develop. Biol.* **2**, 151.

Toliver, A., and Simon, E. H. (1967). *Exp. Cell Res.* **45**, 603.

Toole, B. P. (1972). *Develop. Biol.* **29**, 321.

Toole, B. P. (1973). *Science* **180**, 302.

Toole, B. P., Jackson, G., and Gross, J. (1972). *Proc. Nat. Acad. Sci. U.S.* **69**, 1384.

Trelstad, R. L., Kang, A. H., Cohen, A. M., and Hay, E. D. (1973). *Science* **173**, 295.

Turkington, R. W., Majumder, G. C., and Riddle, M. (1971). *J. Biol. Chem.* **246**, 1814.

Umansky, R. (1966). *Develop. Biol.* **13**, 31.

Urist, M. R., and Nogami, H. (1970). *Nature (London)* **225**, 1051.

Urist, M. R., and Strates, B. S. (1971). *J. Dent. Res.* **50**, 1392.

Vogt, P. K., and Friis, R. R. (1971). *Virology* **43**, 223.

Weintraub, H., Campbell, G. L., and Holtzer, H. (1972). *J. Mol. Biol.* **70**, 337.

Wessells, N. K. (1964). *J. Cell Biol.* **20**, 415.

Younkin, L., and Silberberg, D. (1973). *Exp. Cell Res.* **76**, 455.

Zamenhof, S., Grauel, L., and Van Marthens, E. (1971). *Res. Commun. Chem. Pathol. Pharmacol.* **2**, 261.

Zwilling, E. (1966). *Ann. Med. Exp. Biol. Fenn.* **44**, 134.

Zwilling, E. (1968). *Develop. Biol. Suppl.* **2**, 184.

CHAPTER 5

CELL DETERMINATION AND BIOCHEMICAL DIFFERENTIATION OF THE EARLY MAMMALIAN EMBRYO

M. C. Herbert and C. F. Graham

ZOOLOGY DEPARTMENT
OXFORD, UNITED KINGDOM

In the Placental Mammals, the first act of differentiation is the separation of the inner mass from the outer layer, and, as we are now to see, the inner mass contains within itself the material for the embryo, its amnion, yolk-sac and allantois. . . . It cannot be too often insisted that all Placental Mammals pass through this stage in which the material for the embryo with its membranes is shut up within the sac of the trophoblast.

J. W. Jenkinson, "Vertebrate Embryology,"
Oxford University Press, London, 1913.

I. Introduction

Our intention is to contrast the approach of an embryologist and of a biochemist to the problem of cell differentiation within the mammalian embryo. On the one hand, we will discuss experiments that identify the time at which the developmental fate of cells becomes fixed (the time of determination). The experiments attempt to analyze the determination to form trophoblast or not to form trophoblast in the preimplantation embryo. On the other hand, we will describe the appearance of biochemical differences between the cells of the embryo during the first 10 days of development. In this section we will concentrate on the development of tissue-specific biochemical markers.

The discussion will be limited to experiments concerned with the early development of the mouse unless a phenomenon is particularly clearly illustrated by another mammalian embryo. Early stages of mouse development are illustrated diagrammatically in Fig. 1. The mouse embryo develops inside the mother for approximately 19 days; for the first 4 days the embryo is free in the reproductive tract and it is separated from the maternal cells by a jelly coat, the zona pellucida. On the morning of the fifth day, the blastocyst (64–128 cells) emerges from the zona pellucida and becomes directly attached to the cells of the uterine lining (implantation).

II. Emancipation from the Female Reproductive Tract

Both implantation and the further development of the embryo is from now on controlled by the physiology of the mother. There are, however, several reasons (as described in the following) for thinking that the extrinsic effects of the maternal environment on the embryo are limited to the control of embryonic growth and that they have no effect on the range of different cell types generated within the embryo.

A. The Embryo Can Develop *in Vitro* in Simple Media

The 1-cell egg may be fertilized *in vitro* (Mukherjee and Cohen, 1970). The fertilized 1-cell egg will develop into a viable blastocyst in a medium which consists of no more than four cations (Na^+, K^+, Ca^{2+}, Mg^{2+}), three anions (Cl^-, PO_4^{3-}, HCO_3^-), and pyruvate (reviewed by Whitten, 1971). Blastocysts will remain viable in this medium for several days (Sherman and Barlow, 1972) but they will not develop further until five amino acids are added to the culture medium (arginine, cysteine, histidine, leucine, and threonine) (Gwatkin, 1966a,b). Development from the blastocyst to an egg cylinderlike stage (seventh day of pregnancy) has only been obtained in two situations: the blastocysts

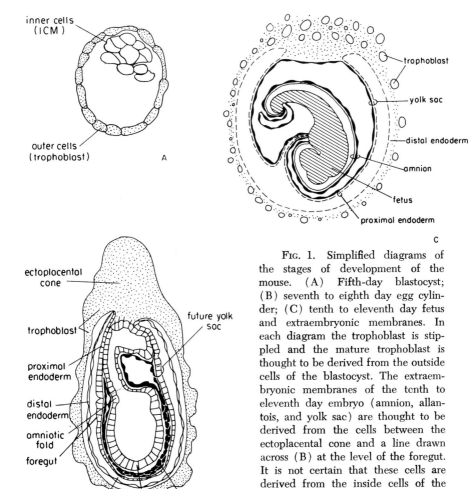

FIG. 1. Simplified diagrams of the stages of development of the mouse. (A) Fifth-day blastocyst; (B) seventh to eighth day egg cylinder; (C) tenth to eleventh day fetus and extraembryonic membranes. In each diagram the trophoblast is stippled and the mature trophoblast is thought to be derived from the outside cells of the blastocyst. The extraembryonic membranes of the tenth to eleventh day embryo (amnion, allantois, and yolk sac) are thought to be derived from the cells between the ectoplacental cone and a line drawn across (B) at the level of the foregut. It is not certain that these cells are derived from the inside cells of the blastocyst but this is thought to be the case. The fetus is thought to be derived from the rest of the egg cylinder.

have either been cultured in bovine eye lens jelly (Jenkinson and Wilson, 1970) or they have been cultured in Eagle's minimal essential medium on a collagen substrate (Hsu, 1972).

Egg cylinders and later somite stages can develop normally for about 2 days in well-gassed circulating serum if they are placed in culture at any time during the first three-quarters of pregnancy (reviewed by New, 1971). The culture experiments, therefore, show that for prolonged periods the maternal environment can be replaced by particular culture conditions at most stages of pregnancy.

B. THE EMBRYO CAN DEVELOP IN EXTRAUTERINE SITES

In the mouse, consistent postimplantation development has been obtained by transferring blastocysts to the kidney, spleen, brain, liver, and testis of male animals (reviewed by Kirby, 1965). The ability of embryos to develop away from the influence of the female reproductive tract has been most clearly shown in the following experiment. Two-cell embryos were grown to the blastocyst stage *in vitro* and subsequently transferred beneath the testis or kidney capsule of a male. Approximately a quarter of the transferred blastocysts formed morphologically normal ninth-day fetuses with characteristic neural tube tissue. Since a similar number of blastocysts, which had been transferred directly from the uterus to an extrauterine site, also formed normal fetuses, it was concluded that there was no evidence that the female reproductive tract was required to promote cell differentiation early in pregnancy (Table

TABLE I

CAPACITY OF OVIDUCAL STAGES AND OF BLASTOCYSTS EXPOSED TO VARYING CONDITIONS TO GIVE RISE TO DIFFERENTIATED EMBRYOS IN ECTOPIC SITES[a]

Stage at transfer	Cultured from[b]	Medium	Transfer site	No. transferred	Fetuses (%)
2 Cell, 8 Cell	—	—	Kidney	34	3
Blastocyst	2 Cell	Brinster's	Kidney	19	21
Blastocyst	8 Cell	Brinster's[c]	Kidney	24	21
Blastocyst	—	—	Kidney	10	20

[a] Data from Billington *et al.*, 1968.

[b] Blastocysts that had either developed from the 2-cell and 8-cell stages in culture or developed *in vivo* were transferred beneath the kidney capsule of a male. Approximately 20% of both types of blastocysts were found to have developed fetuses 5–9 days after transfer. It appears that the maternal environment is not required for the development of the embryo up to the eighth day of pregnancy.

[c] With 3 mg/ml albumin.

I; Billington *et al.*, 1968). It is also the case that 1-cell embryos can undergo limited postimplantation development in the anterior chamber of the eye (Runner, 1947), and 1-cell eggs can give rise to teratomas containing at least 12 differentiated cell types when they are transferred directly to the testis (Stevens, 1970; Dunn and Stevens, 1970).

These studies on development in extrauterine sites in male animals, therefore, demonstrate that the maternal environment is not required for cell differentiation during the first third of pregnancy. Although it has so far proved impossible to culture 1-cell mouse eggs to the stage that they would normally reach at birth, it is, nevertheless, possible to support development outside the mother for prolonged periods. Thus, there is no reason to believe that the mother is any more than a cheap heart, lung, and kidney machine that is required to support, but not to control, cell differentiation in the developing embryo. If this conclusion is correct, then it is necessary to look inside the embryo for the causes of cell determination.

III. Determination inside the Preimplantation Embryo

A. THEORIES OF DETERMINATION

The mammalian egg develops into an embryo consisting of the trophoblast, the extraembryonic membranes, and the fetus (Fig. 1). The decision to form trophoblast or not to form trophoblast appears to be the earliest determinative event inside the embryo, and this section will be largely concerned with trophoblast determination.

Three hypotheses have been put forward to explain how determination occurs within the mammalian embryo.

In the first hypothesis, it is supposed that determination occurs by the unequal segregation of morphogenetic factors that are present in the cytoplasm of the fertilized egg (reviewed by Dalcq, 1957; Mulnard, 1971).

The second hypothesis suggests that there are fixed reference points in the 1-cell egg and that determination occurs because blastomeres differ in their relationship to these points. Theories of this general kind have been described for other embryos, e.g., gradients (Child, 1941; Wolpert, 1969), and Seidel (1960) has proposed that the mammalian egg has a localized activation center.

According to the third hypothesis, determination depends solely on the position of the cells within the embryo (Tarkowski and Wroblewska, 1967). It is proposed that cells on the outside of the morula are determined to form trophoblast and that cells on the inside are determined not to do so. In this case, determination is believed to occur without either morphogenetic factors or reference points in egg cytoplasm.

In order to decide which of these hypotheses is correct, it is necessary to describe the most recent work on early mouse development.

B. THE PATTERN OF CLEAVAGE

During the first 4 days of mouse development, the cytoplasm of the egg is cleaved into approximately 64 cells. Because the egg cytoplasm is divided by the cleavage furrows, therefore some cells are formed with membranes excluded from the surface of the embryo (inside cells) and the proportion of these cells increases as development proceeds (Table II). At the 64-cell stage, about a quarter of the embryo's cells are "inside."

TABLE II

INCREASE IN NUMBER OF INSIDE CELLS DURING EMBRYONIC DEVELOPMENT[a]

	No. of inside cells at different stages			
Range of cell stages	No. of embryos	Range of no. of inside cells	Mean no. of inside cells	Ratio inside/outside cells between particular cell stages[b]
8	4	0–2	0.50	—
9–16	58	0–3	0.98	0.1070
17–32	20	2–10	5.50	0.2534
33–64	7	9–13	10.86	0.2768
65–128	27	12–37	24.04	0.3390
129–256	3	44–59	51.00	0.4330

[a] Data of Barlow et al., 1972.
[b] The numbers of inside and outside cells were counted in reconstructions from serial sections of each embryo.

The blastocoel is formed by the fourth day of pregnancy, and blastocysts are found with cell numbers ranging from 21 to 41 cells at this time (McLaren, 1968). Small cracks are found between the blastomeres at the 16–32 cell stages, and these spaces gradually coalesce to form the definitive blastocoel.

During these early divisions, the cytoplasm is cleaved in a regular manner. This regularity has been recently demonstrated by Wilson and his colleagues (1972). Oil droplets were injected beneath the cell membrane of 2- and 4-cell embryos. The injected embryos developed into blastocysts in culture, and the location of the oil droplets was recorded (Table III). If the oil droplets were placed beneath the cell membrane at the periphery of the embryo, then they were always found in the outside layer of the blastocysts that developed. This observation suggests that the outside cytoplasm of 2- and 4-cell stage blastomeres is usually incorporated into the outside cells of the blastocyst. In contrast, if oil droplets were placed beneath the cell membrane near the center of the embryo, then about a quarter of the droplets were subsequently found in the inside cells of the blastocysts. This observation suggests that the central cytoplasm of 2- and 4-cell stage blastomeres is usually

TABLE III

DISTRIBUTION OF OIL DROPLETS IN THE BLASTOCYSTS THAT DEVELOP
FROM INJECTED 2- AND 4-CELL EMBRYOS[a]

Stage of injection	Position at time of injection	No. of injected embryos studied	Position of drops in blastocysts[b]
2-cell stage	Drop, peripheral	2	100% in outside layer
4-cell stage	Drop, peripheral	13	100% in outside layer
2-cell stage	Drop, internal	10	77% in outside layer
4-cell stage	Drop, internal	20	83% in outside layer

[a] Data from Wilson et al., 1972.

[b] Notice that drops placed in a peripheral position are always subsequently found in the outside cells of the blastocyst, whereas drops placed internally are found both in the inside and the outside cells of the blastocyst.

incorporated into both inside and outside cells, and its developmental fate is, therefore, different from that of the peripheral cytoplasm.

It is therefore possible to conclude that within an intact embryo contained inside the zona pellucida, there is some degree of regularity in the cleavage of the cytoplasm.

C. CHARACTERISTICS OF THE INSIDE AND THE OUTSIDE CELLS OF THE BLASTOCYST

Two distinct cell populations have developed inside the embryo by the blastocyst stage. These two cell populations are identified by their location (inside and outside cells) and they possess distinct properties. We will now describe the stages of development at which differences between them can be first detected.

The inside and outside cells can first be distinguished by their rate of cell multiplication. Inside cells are first found at the 8–16 cell stages (Table II). At the time of their first appearance and up to the blastocyst stage, a higher percentage of the inside cells incorporate tritiated thymidine into deoxyribonucleic acid (DNA) compared to the outside cells. The higher labeling index of the inside cells is particularly obvious at short times after the exposure of the embryos to tritiated thymidine (Table IV; Barlow et al., 1972). This observation must be interpreted with caution because there is no direct relationship between a high labeling index and a high rate of cell multiplication. For instance, if cells were synthesizing DNA and not dividing or if some cells were not proceeding around the cell cycle at all, then the labeling index would be a distorted measure of rates of cell multiplication. It is unlikely that

TABLE IV

LABELING DIFFERENCE OF INSIDE AND OUTSIDE CELLS[a]

Cell stages	Time label (hours)	No. of embryos	Total no. of inside cells	Total no. of outside cells	Inside cells labeled[b] (%)	Outside cells labeled[b] (%)	Significantly different (5% level)
9–16	0.25	3	6	42	100.00	61.40	—
	0.45	15	23	183	92.00	72.67	c
	1.00	8	5	115	100.00	98.26	—
	1.15	8	13	87	84.62	75.86	—
	1.90	5	5	67	100.00	94.03	—
	3.00	7	9	99	88.88	91.91	—
	4.15	4	1	59	100.00	100.00	—
	5.00	8	5	109	100.00	95.41	—
	6.00	7	7	108	100.00	100.00	—
	7.00	10	10	129	90.00	98.44	—
17–32	0.25	14	88	337	84.09	66.46	c
	0.45	5	16	83	87.50	67.49	—
	1.00	1	4	17	75.00	47.06	—
	1.15	6	40	141	95.00	85.81	—
	6.00	3	9	44	100.00	100.00	—
33–128	0.75	6	183	503	77.59	50.09	c
	2.00	6	179	432	70.39	49.76	c
	3.00	7	149	498	74.49	52.61	c
	4.00	5	165	365	81.21	60.54	c
	5.00	9	163	578	88.34	66.26	c

[a] Data from Barlow et al., 1972.

[b] Notice that the inside cells have a higher labeling index than the outside cells after short times of exposure to tritiated thymidine. The inside cells also show 100% labeling earlier than the outside cells under continuous labeling conditions.

[c] Significance tested for difference in two observed proportions (Bailey, 1959, Eq. 18).

either of these effects occur in the early mouse embryo; there is no accumulation of nuclei with greater than 4 C amounts of DNA until the late blastocyst stage (Fig. 2), and it therefore seems likely that all the cells are proceeding around the cell cycle. It is also known that, under continuous labeling conditions, all the nuclei of the embryo eventually become labeled demonstrating that all the cells are engaged in DNA synthesis. The high labeling index of the inside cells probably does, therefore, indicate a high rate of cell multiplication. This view is supported by the observation that the inside cells become 100% labeled before the outside cells (Table IV), and by the observation that the inside cells increase in number faster than the outside cells (Table II).

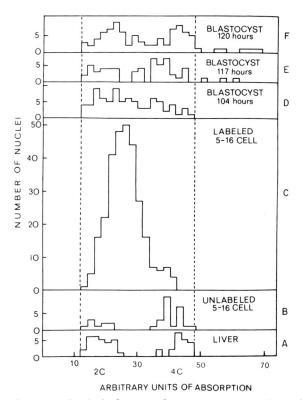

FIG. 2. The onset of polyploidy. Microdensitometry on morulae and blastocysts of the mouse. (A) Forty-nine liver nuclei used as absorbance standards of the 2 C and 4 C DNA amounts. (B) Unlabeled nuclei in a sample of 324 nuclei from 5–16 cell embryos fixed at 69–72 hours post-HCG after 15 minutes in tritiated thymidine. The distribution of these nuclei is bimodal and their deoxyribonucleic acid (DNA) contents fall in the same range as the 2 C and 4 C amounts of the liver nuclei standard. This is evidence for the G_1 and the G_2 phases of the cell cycle being present at the 8-cell stage onward. (C) Labeled nuclei from the same sample as B. The histogram has one mode and most of the nuclei have a DNA content inter-mediate between the 2 C and the 4 C amount. (D) Eighty-one nuclei from two blastocysts at 104 hours post-HCG. Note the absence of nuclei with greater than the 4 C amount of DNA. (E) Fifty-five nuclei from four blastocysts at 117 hours post-HCG. Note that some nuclei contain more DNA than the 4 C amount. These nuclei all incorporated tritiated thymidine in a 30-minute labeling period before fixation. This shows that they are actively engaged in DNA synthesis. (F) Eighty-nine nuclei from four blastocysts at 120 hours post-HCG. Again note DNA contents in excess of the 4 C amount. (From Barlow *et al.*, 1972.)

Rate of cell multiplication is, therefore, the first apparent difference between the inside and the outside cells.

The second difference to develop is that of cell contact structures. The cell membranes of the outside cells closely interdigitate with each other in the early morula, and focal tight junctions have developed between them by the late morula stage (32 cells). In contrast, such junctions are rarely found either between inside cells or between inside and outside cells. In fact, the inside cells are separated from the outside cells of the blastocyst by material that appears amorphous under the electron microscope (Enders and Schlafke, 1965; Kirby *et al.*, 1967; Calarco and Brown, 1969).

The third distinction between these cell groups involves their behavior in culture (Gardner, 1971, 1972). A sheet of outside cells was cut from the roof of the blastocoel, and it was found that these cells could seal together and form liquid-filled vesicles, presumably by a pumping mechanism (Fig. 3). Different groups of outside cells were

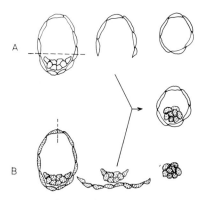

FIG. 3. Blastocyst manipulation. (A) An isolated group of ouside cells can seal and form a liquid-filled vesicle. This will induce a decidual reaction but can only develop into trophoblast cells. (B) An isolated group of inside cells dissected free. These cells cannot pump and therefore cannot form a vesicle. They remain as a solid lump and are unable to induce a decidual response or develop further in the uterus. If the group of inside cells is placed inside the outside cell vesicle, then the combination may develop into a mouse. Experiments of Gardner (1971).

unable to seal together to form a common structure. The behavior of the inside cells in culture was different: groups of inside cells were able to form a common structure, but these cells in either large or small masses were unable to form vesicles and the cell group remained as a solid lump. At the blastocyst stage, these two cell groups, therefore, differ in both their capacity to stick and to integrate with other cells of their own type and in their ability to form vesicles. The formation of a liquid-filled vesicle almost certainly depends on an active pumping process; studies on the rabbit blastocyst suggest that an energy coupled mechanism is involved (Tuft and Boving, 1970).

It is also known that these cell groups differ in their capacity to induce an implantation response in a pseudopregnant uterus (decidual reaction). Groups of outside cells are able to induce a decidual reaction, whereas groups of inside cells lack this capacity (Gardner, 1972). Although the nature of the stimulus that produces a uterine response is uncertain, this observation does suggest that the cell types differ in yet another property.

A fifth distinction claimed is that cytochemical tests demonstrate that the inside and outside cells of the blastocyst contain different activities of the enzymes, acid and alkaline phosphatase, and different amounts of mucopolysaccharide and ribonucleic acid (RNA) (reviewed Dalcq, 1957; Mulnard, 1965, 1971). These studies have mainly been conducted on whole mounts and showed that the greatest enzyme activity and amounts of RNA were found in the inside cells. This distribution of RNA has been confirmed in another laboratory (Cerisola and Izquierdo, 1969). However, some workers have found an even distribution of acid and alkaline phosphatase in the rat blastocyst and they have argued that these apparent concentrations of activities and substances in the inside cells are the consequence of cell overlap in the center of whole mounts and other staining artifacts (Rodé et al., 1968). This may be a fair criticism of some of the observed differences between the inside and outside cells; nevertheless, high alkaline phosphatase activity has also been observed in the inside cells of blastocysts studied in serial sections (Mulnard, 1965). In fact, it is likely that the inside and the outside cells of the blastocyst do contain different amounts of many enzyme activities. Most of these differences still require an unequivocal biochemical demonstration at these early stages of development.

This discussion makes it clear that by the blastocyst stage the inside and outside cell groups differ in many properties. It is next necessary to enquire if these two groups of cells also differ in their developmental potential.

D. Cell Determination

The distinction between cell determination and cell differentiation has been made by many embryologists. Cell determination is the process by which the developmental potential of a cell becomes limited during embryogenesis. Usually the cell will divide many times before its progeny acquire properties which distinguish them from other cells (cell differentiation). It is, therefore, expected that overt differences between populations of cells will develop at a considerable time after cell determination. In fact the opposite appears to be the case in early mouse development—we will argue that differences between populations of cells are apparent some time before the populations of cells are determined to develop in different ways.

E. Cell Isolation Experiments

One of the simplest ways of discovering the stage of development at which some totipotential blastomeres are still present in the embryo is to single out blastomeres and to study their developmental potential either in isolation or in combination with other embryos. Many studies of this kind have been performed on the early mammalian embryo (Table V).

It has been clearly shown that one cell of a 2-cell stage can form a whole mouse. And it is also known that each cell of a 4-cell embryo can form a minute blastocyst and each blastomere can also form part of the trophoblast of a tenth-day embryo. However, it remains to be formally proved that each blastomere of either a 4- or an 8-cell stage is able to form all tissues of the developing embryo. In the case of the rabbit it is known that at least one blastomere of an 8-cell stage is capable of forming a whole rabbit; however, the success rate of development of these single blastomeres is so low (11%) that it is impossible to say if more than one blastomere at the 8-cell stage has this potential.

Multipotential stem cells remain inside the embryo for some time. A single cell from the inside cells of the blastocyst can form part of most of the tissues an adult mouse when it has previously been injected into a carrier blastocyst. And multipotential teratomas with the ability to form twelve different cell types can be derived from some cells of the embryo up to the tenth day of pregnancy (Stevens, 1970).

Taken together, cell isolation experiments suggest that each blastomere is able to form trophoblast, extraembryonic membranes, and the fetus up to the 8-cell stage. After this time, at least some of the inside cells of the blastocyst are able to form parts of most of the internal organs of the fetus.

F. Cell Combination Experiments

Cell combination experiments can also be used to gauge developmental lability—again these experiments support the view that cell determination does not occur until some time after cell differences are apparent in the embryo. It has been known for some time that chimeric mice can be formed by combining embryos from different strains (Tar-

TABLE V

SUMMARY OF CELL ISOLATION EXPERIMENTS WITH MAMMALIAN EMBRYOS

Species	Isolated cell	Culture conditions	Developmental fate	Reference
Mouse	One cell of a 2-cell embryo	Alone	Whole live mouse	Tarkowski (1959)
	Each cell of a 4-cell embryo	Alone	Each form minute blastocyst	Tarkowski and Wroblewska (1967)
	Each cell of an 8-cell embryo	Alone	Each forms liquid-filled vesicles and 15% of these contain inside cells	Tarkowski and Wroblewska (1967)
	Each cell of a 4-cell embryo	Combined with another embryo	Each cell can form part of the fetus on the tenth day of pregnancy	Kelly and Graham (1974)
	One cell from the inside of a 64-cell blastocyst	Injected into the blastocoel of another embryo	Can form half the coat color of the mouse	Gardner (1971)
Rabbit	One cell of a 2-cell embryo	Alone	30% Develop into live rabbits	Moore et al. (1968)
	One cell of a 4-cell embryo	Alone	19% Develop into live rabbits	Moore et al. (1968)
	One cell of an 8-cell embryo	Alone	11% Develop into live rabbits	Moore et al. (1968)

kowski, 1961; Mintz, 1962). The observation that two embryos can come together to form a common structure could be explained in two ways: either the different cell types of the two embryos could sort out or it might be that all the cells are developmentally labile at the time of cell combination. If these experiments are to be used as a measure of cell determination, it is necessary to show that presumptive inside cells and presumptive outside cells of the two genotypes do not migrate to their normal positions during the formation of the chimera. In practice it is difficult to prove that no cell sorting occurs because the position of particular cells cannot be followed throughout embryonic development. It has only been possible to show that cell sorting does not occur during the formation of the integrated blastocyst, and the assumption is made that, if cell sorting has not occurred by this stage of development, then it is unlikely to occur later (Mintz, 1965; Wilson *et al.*, 1972; Stern and Wilson, 1972).

Mintz (1965) has provided evidence that cell sorting does not occur during the formation of an integrated blastocyst. Neither complete intermingling nor orderly deployment of the blastomeres was observed when two 8-cell embryos (with distinct cytoplasms) formed a composite blastocyst. And cell sorting could hardly have occurred when sixteen 8-cell embryos were combined to form a single blastocyst. Mintz also showed that it was possible to form a whole blastocyst from pairs of 32-cell embryos, and there would be little time for all sorting to occur before blastocyst formation in this combination. Most impressively, it has recently been shown that cell sorting does not occur when two 32-cell embryos are combined. Some of the outside cells of one of the embryos were marked with oil droplets, and, after combination and development to the blastocyst stage, half of these marked cells were found in the inside cells of the composite (Stern and Wilson, 1972). Of course, it has not been formally shown that these cells, which were oustide at the 32-cell stage, are able to form part of the fetus, but, on its face value, this experiment suggests that the blastomeres are still totipotent in the late morula.

G. Determination of Trophoblast

So far the evidence suggests that at least some blastomeres remain labile up to the 32-cell stage. However, it now seems certain that, by the 64-cell stage, the cells are irreversibly determined to form trophoblast or not to form trophoblast (Gardner, 1971, 1972; Gardner *et al.*, 1973). This conclusion is based on fine microsurgery of the blastocyst. Blastocysts were divided by microsurgery into several parts. The inside cells were scraped clear of the surrounding outside cells to form a pure population, and a sample containing only outside cells was obtained by cutting across the blastocyst above the group of inside cells (Fig. 3). The developmental fate of the inside cells could not be studied because they were unable to induce a decidual response when transferred to a pseudopregnant uterus (see Section III). The group of outside cells healed together and formed a vesicle which was able to induce a decidual response, and the subsequent development of these cells was first studied in histological section at 3 or 4 days after transfer to a pseudopregnant uterus. In all cases except one, the development of these vesicles was surprisingly poor: 34 of these vesicles induced a decidual response, but each decidua contained less than 18 trophoblast giant cells. The exceptional decidua contained extensive trophoblast giant cells and some extraembryonic membrane. This experiment suggests that the outside cells of the blastocyst are only able to form trophoblast giant cells and that they are unable to proliferate. There would normally be at least 10 times this number of trophoblast giant cells derived from a normal blastocyst at this stage of pregnancy. The exceptional case probably developed from a vesicle contaminated with inside cells.

The failure of the outside cells to form an extensive trophoblast layer could be explained in several ways:

1. In the dissected vesicles there might have been insufficient cells to support extensive proliferation.
2. All the transferred outside cells might have been committed to become polyploid and, therefore, might have been unable to divide.
3. The outside cells, which are normally beside the inside cells in the blastocyst, might be required for trophoblast proliferation and this particular dissection precludes their inclusion in the transferred trophoblast vesicles.
4. The inside cells might contribute the main cellular bulk to the developing trophoblast.
5. The inside cells might be required to promote the development of trophoblast by the outside cells.

The following experiments support explanation 5. The group of inside cells from one blastocyst were recombined with the outside cell vesicle of another blastocyst (Fig. 3). These reconstituted blastocysts were transferred back to pseudopregnant recipients; nine implants were studied histologically later in pregnancy, and five of these contained normal fetuses (Gardner, 1971). It was next decided to study the contribution of the inside and the outside cells to the trophoblast and to the extraembryonic membrane and fetus. In this case the inside and outside cells in the reconstituted blastocysts contained different electrophoretic variants of the enzyme, glucose phosphate isomerase (Gpi–I). These blastocysts were transferred to pseudopregnant recipients and the glucose isomerase type in the ectoplacental cone (trophoblast) and egg cylinder was analyzed on about the eighth day of development (Fig. 1B). In all except one of the 18 embryos that were studied, the bulk of the trophoblast appeared to be derived from the outside cells. In the exceptional case, there was no evidence of the outside cell derivatives and presumably these had been damaged during the operation (Gardner *et al.*, 1973) or overgrown by an outside cell attached to the transferred cells.

Taken together, these experiments demonstrate that the proliferation of the outside cells depends in some way on the presence of inside cells. But during the formation of the trophoblast up to the eighth day of pregnancy, the inside cells of the blastocyst do not make a significant cellular contribution to the trophoblast layer. It seems reasonable to conclude that primary trophoblast determination is complete by the 64-cell stage. From now on the outside layer of the blastocyst will be referred to as the trophoblast layer and the inside cells will be referred to as the inner cell mass (ICM).

It is clear from this discussion that the determination of the outside layer of cells to form trophoblast probably occurs at the 32–64 cell stages. This is some time after the inside and outside cells of the embryo have developed distinct rates of division (8–16 cell stages) and cell contact structures (16–32 cell stages). It appears observable differences between cells do develop before cell determination in the early mouse embryo.

H. CELL POSITION

It is next necessary to decide which of the three theories of cell determination is likely to be correct. It seems likely that each blastomere is totipotent up to the 8-cell stage (cell isolation experiments) and at least some of the blastomeres of the 32-cell embryo are able to form both the ICM and trophoblast of the blastocyst (cell combination experiments). Under these circumstances, it is clear that any theory of determination that depends on the morphogenetic factors or reference points in the fertilized egg will be very difficult to prove. The extreme lability of the blastomeres will make it hard to discover if they have different developmental tendencies. And it is, perhaps, not surprising that faced with this difficulty, most mammalian embryologists support theories that suggest that the microenvironment (Mintz, 1965) and the position of cells in the embryo (Tarkowski and Wroblewska, 1967) are the most important determinants of cell fate.

It is only possible to prove the cell position theory by constructing composite embryos and showing that the genes that a particular cell and its daughters express are determined by the position of that cell in the morula. So far there has only been one attempt to provide such a proof (Hillman *et al.*, 1972).

In the first experiments, the nuclear DNA of the blastomeres of 4-cell embryos was labeled with tritiated thymidine, the embryos were dissociated into single cells, and the isolated labeled blastomeres were placed either outside or inside the unlabeled blastomeres of another embryo (Fig. 4). These composites developed into blastocysts in cul-

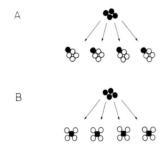

FIG. 4. Cell position experiments. Single, labeled, 4-cell stage embryos were disaggregated. In one set of experiments each of the four blastomeres was placed outside the unlabeled blastomeres of another embryo (A). In a second set of experiments, each blastomere was surrounded by the dissociated blastomeres of an unlabeled embryo (B).

ture and the position and the number of the labeled daughter cells was detected by radioautography (Table VI). If the daughter cells of the labeled blastomeres had been distributed at random, then one would expect three-quarters of them to be found in the trophoblast layer of the blastocyst (this is the normal distribution of cells in the 64 cell blastocyst (Table II)). In fact, when labeled blastomeres were placed in an outside position, then all their daughter cells were subsequently found in the trophoblast layer; and when the labeled blastomeres were placed in an inside position, then only 60% of their daughter cells were found in the trophoblast layer. These experiments also showed that every blastomere of a 4-cell embryo could be forced by an outside position to form only part of the trophoblast layer of the blastocyst (Table VI, donor embryos 1 and 2) and that every blastomere of a 4-cell embryo was capable of forming both the ICM and the trophoblast of the blastocyst (Table VI, donor embryo 3).

In the second set of experiments, an attempt was made to show that

TABLE VI

CONTRIBUTION OF LABELED BLASTOMERE TO THE INSIDE AND OUTSIDE
LAYERS OF THE BLASTOCYST[a,b]

Cell arrangement	Donor embryo	No. of labeled cells in inside/outside layers of the 4 blastocystes that developed	Labeled cells in inside layer (%)
Each labeled blas-tomere outside another embryo	1	0/12, 0/7, 0/7, 0/10	100
	2	0/9, 0/4, 0/10, 0/13	100
Each labeled blas-tomere outside another embryo	3	1/9, 5/7, 1/1, 4/1	62
	4	6/11, 4/1, 0/2, 3/2	55

[a] Data from Hillman et al., 1972.

[b] In these experiments, the fate of each blastomere of a labeled 4-cell embryo was studied in combination with an unlabeled 4-cell embryo.

cell position at the 8–16 cell stage could determine whether a blastomere would form either part of the trophoblast and yolk sac or part of the fetus on the tenth day of pregnancy (Fig. 1C). In these experiments, 8-cell embryos were disaggregated and pairs of blastomeres placed on the outside of 8 to 16 cell embryos. As in the previous experiment, studies with labeled pairs of 8-cell blastomeres showed that the main contribution of such cells in an outside position was to the trophoblast layer; in the forty blastocysts studied, 92% of the labeled daughter cells were in this layer. Next, the four pairs of blastomeres from a single 8-cell embryo were placed outside four other 8–16 cell embryos. These composites were cultured to the blastocyst stage and transferred to the uterus of pseudopregnant foster mothers. On the tenth day of pregnancy, the embryos were divided into trophoblast, yolk sac, and fetus (Fig. 1C), and the contribution of the originally external pair of blastomeres to these tissues was studied. The presence of daughter cells of the external blastomeres could be detected because they possessed a different electrophoretic variant of the enzyme, glucose phosphate isomerase, to that of the recipient embryo. Four donor embryos were used in these experiments and, therefore, sixteen composite blastocysts were transferred to foster mothers. Twelve of these embryos developed to the tenth day of pregnancy. In these, the outside pair of blastomeres had formed part of the trophoblast and/or part of the yolk sac in all cases; only in four cases had they also formed part of the fetus. In one set of transfers, it could be shown that each pair of blastomeres from one 8-cell embryo could form a significant part of the trophoblast on the tenth day of pregnancy. It seemed reasonable to conclude that an external position of blastomeres at the 8–16 cell stage decreased the chances of those blastomeres from contributing to the fetus on the tenth day of pregnancy.

In a third set of experiments, an attempt was made to show that cell position at the 8–16 cell stage could determine all the blastomeres of a 8 cell embryo not to express coat color genes. In these experiments, 8-cell embryos were disaggregated, and all the blastomeres of one embryo were placed around the outside of another 8–16 cell embryo; the two embryos differed both by the glucose phosphate isomerase type and by the coat color genes that they carried (Fig. 5). As in the previous experiment, a study was made of the contribution of the two embryos to trophoblast, yolk sac, and fetus on the tenth day of pregnancy. In this case chimerism was only found in 8 of 10 embryos studied, suggesting that some

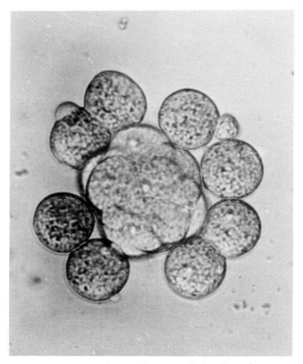

FIG. 5. The blastomeres of one dissociated 8-cell embryo surrounding the blastomeres of another embryo. The cells of the outside embryo tend only to contribute daughter cells to the trophoblast and yolk sac of the composite.

blastomeres were killed by the disaggregation procedure. In all cases in which both genotypes were present, the outside embryo formed part of the trophoblast and/or yolk sac, and in 5 of 8 cases the outside embryo also contributed to part of the fetus. After similar arrangements at the 8–16 cell stage, the composite embryos were allowed to develop until birth; the contribution of the daughter cells of the originally inside and outside whole embryos was studied by observing the coat color of the young. Ten mice developed into adults from such combinations; in 8 cases the embryo that was originally outside made no detectable contribution to the coat color of the adult, and in 2 cases small patches of the color of the outside embryo were detected. In approximately half of these whole embryo composites, the inside/outside position of the embryos of the different genotypes was reversed in order to avoid the possibility that the results were simply the consequence of inherent differences in growth rate between the two genotypes (Mintz, 1970; Mullen and Whitten, 1971).

It should be noted that in only 3 of the 22 composites studied on the tenth day of pregnancy was the contribution of one of the embryos completely undetected. This means that the blastomeres usually remain viable after the dissociation and reaggregation procedures to which they are exposed. The failure to see a contribution of the outside embryo to the coat color in 8 of 10 mice that were born in this last experiment is, therefore, unlikely to be the consequence of the death of the outside embryo. It is more likely that all the cells of the outside embryo have been prevented from expressing coat color genes in the adult as a consequence of their position in the morula. If this interpretation is correct, then this experiment shows that cell position at the 8–16 cell stages can determine the range of genes subsequently expressed by the cell.

Taken together, these experiments demonstrate that cell position can markedly alter cell fate. The cell position theory of determination put forward by Tarkowski and Wroblewska is, therefore, a sufficient explanation of trophoblast determination in the mouse embryo. And if there are gradients of morphogenetic substances and reference points within the fertilized egg, then these must have very slight effects on development.

IV. Trophoblast Differentiation

We have already noted that the inside and the outside cells of the embryo have quite distinct properties some time before trophoblast determination occurs in the blastocyst. At the same time, or soon after determination, the trophoblast cells acquire further distinct characteristics.

A. POLYPLOIDY

In the late blastocyst (64–128 cells), the trophoblast cells begin to contain nuclear DNA in excess of the normal diploid amounts. Nuclear DNA in excess of the 4 C amount has been demonstrated by microdensitometry in the implanting blastocyst (Barlow et al., 1972; Barlow and Sherman, 1972; Sherman and Barlow, 1972). During the fifth day of pregnancy, this excess DNA does not exceed the 8 C amount, but it rapidly increases so that some trophoblast nuclei contain 64 C amounts of DNA on the seventh day of pregnancy and by the eleventh day some nuclei contain over 512 C DNA amounts (Table VII).

TABLE VII

HIGHEST PLOIDY REACHED BY TROPHOBLAST OF DIFFERENT GESTATION AGE[a,b]

Day of pregnancy	C[c]
6	32–64
7	64–128
8	64–128
9	128–256
10	256–512
11	512–850

[a] Data from Barlow and Sherman, 1972.

[b] Nuclei from trophoblast from a number of embryos of the indicated ages were prepared for deoxyribonucleic acid (DNA) measurements and the largest nuclei were selected for microspectrophotometry.

[c] Values of DNA are expressed in terms of C, the haploid content for mouse.

There are various reasons for thinking that this excess nuclear DNA accumulates by polyploidization (reviewed by Graham, 1973). The assumption that this is the case at the start of the process is explained as follows. When excess nuclear DNA is first found, nuclei that contain between 4 C and 8 C amounts of DNA become labeled with tritiated thymidine in vitro after a brief exposure to the isotope. This observation shows that the nuclei are actively engaged in DNA synthesis and makes it highly unlikely that the excess nuclear DNA amounts are produced either by engulfment of maternal cell nuclei or by fusion of the trophoblast cells.

Polyploidy is, of course, not an exclusive feature of trophoblast cells; some cells of the extraembryonic membrane and the liver also become polyploid later in development. However, during the first half of pregnancy in the mouse, polyploidy appears to be a trophoblast-specific character, and neither the extraembryonic membranes nor the cells of the fetus ever contain such enormous DNA amounts.

The polyploid cells of the trophoblast have never been observed in mitosis in the mouse, implying that the trophoblast grows by the division of diploid stem cells and the subsequent polyploidization of one of their daughter cells. In fact, diploid cells comprise 80% of the cells in trophoblast samples dissected from the embryo at any time during the first half of pregnancy (Barlow and Sherman, 1972). Polyploidy is, therefore, characteristic of only a small proportion of the cells of the trophoblast.

It is possible that part of the mechanism of trophoblast determination depends on polyploidization. Once a cell has become polyploid in the trophoblast layer it appears to be unable to divide; this by itself would prevent such a cell from contributing daughter cells to any other part of the fetus.

B. ALKALINE PHOSPHATASE

Sherman (1972a) measured the phosphatase activity of homogenates of postimplantation embryo, yolk sac, trophoblast, and decidua. The variation of this activity with pH was also determined. Phosphatase activity was manifest (1) at a low pH (acid phosphatase, pH 3–5) and (2) at a high pH (alkaline phosphatase, pH 9–11).

The tissues examined had similar acid phosphatase activities. However, the alkaline phosphatase activity was found to vary with (1) the type of tissue and (2) the day of gestation at which the material was examined. The trophoblast showed a rise in alkaline phosphatase activity starting from about the eighth day of gestation. By day 12, the activity was at least 5 times that of embryo homogenates, and much higher than that of most adult tissues. The activity of the decidua, high on the eighth day, had declined to the embryonic level by the twelfth day. There was little change in the activities of homogenates of embryo or yolk sac. The results of mixing experiments demonstrated that these differences in activity were not due to the presence of activators or inhibitors in the homogenates.

Embryonic tissue homogenates were electrophoresed on polyacrylamide gels (1) in the presence of a nonionic detergent, Tween 80, and (2) after pretreatment with butanol. There were differences in the enzyme profile from embryo and trophoblast. Of 10 adult tissues examined, only uterine and lung alkaline phosphatase migrated similarly to the trophoblast enzyme.

The characteristic pattern of alkaline phosphatase activity found in the trophoblast was still observed when embryos, removed from the reproductive tract on the fourth day of development, were grown under the testis capsule of a male. Embryos grown from the 2-cell stage *in vitro* also produced an alkaline phosphatase electrophoretically similar to that of the trophoblast enzyme. This strongly implies that a specific uterine inducer or inductive event is not responsible for the appearance of the enzyme in trophoblast tissue.

It is necessary to be extremely cautious in describing the biochemical differentiation of the trophoblast cells. It now appears that enzymes of maternal origin may be bound to or incorporated into the cells of the trophoblast of embryos developing *in vivo*. During the eighth to tenth days of pregnancy, polyacrylamide gel electrophoresis has shown that the trophoblast possesses several bands of esterase activity which are not found in the fetus (Sherman, 1972b). One of these bands [probably Es-1 (Popp and Popp, 1962; Ruddle *et al.*, 1969)] was shown to be of maternal origin by transferring blastocysts with one electrophoretic form of the enzyme into mothers with a different electrophoretic form of the enzyme (Sherman and Chew, 1972). Formally it is necessary to perform similar experiments to prove that other enzymes found in trophoblast cells are the product of those cells' genetic activity.

V. Determination of Derivatives of the Inner Cell Mass

A. MANIPULATION STUDIES ON BLASTOCYSTS

Very little is known about determination in the cells of the ICM. At the blastocyst stage, it is possible to suck out between 5000 and 15,000 μm^3 of cellular material from the ICM and still obtain normal development (Lin, 1969). It, therefore, seems likely that the ICM can regulate and that, apart from the decision not to form trophoblast, no other determination has occurred.

B. BIOCHEMICAL DIFFERENTIATION OF YOLK SAC AND FETUS: HEMOGLOBIN, ESTERASE, AND LYSOSOMAL ENZYMES

It has not been proved that the yolk sac is derived from the ICM, but in this account we will assume that this is the case. On the eighth and the ninth day of pregnancy, extensive blood islets develop in the yolk sac (Moore and Metcalf, 1970) and this synthesis of hemoglobin precedes by 3 days its synthesis in the fetal liver. There are several reasons for thinking that different types of hemoglobin are synthesized in these early hematopoietic tissues.

The maturation of the erythropoietic cells of the yolk sac has been studied morphologically (Djaldetti *et al.*, 1972). In addition, the hemoglobin produced by the cells has been characterized by polyacrylamide gel electrophoresis and column chromatography (Fantoni *et al.*, 1969). Its behavior in these systems differs from that of the hemoglobin found

in the adult. Embryonic hemoglobin can be resolved into three components, Hb-E$_I$, Hb-E$_{II}$, and Hb-E$_{III}$, which differ with respect to the
globin chains they contain (Gilman and Smithies, 1968). The relative
rates of synthesis of the three types of embryonic hemoglobin change
as the erythroid cells differentiate.

Adult-type hemoglobin cannot be observed in the blood until day
11. By this time the yolk sac has ceased to be the primary erythropoietic
organ, this function being performed by the liver. (The spleen and bone
marrow later become the sole sites of erythropoiesis.) Barker (1968) has
argued that the liver produces the adult type of hemoglobin only,
whereas yolk sac can only synthesize embryonic types. She observed that
disappearance of embryonic hemoglobin in mouse embryos seemed to
be correlated with a decrease in the relative number of large nucleated
blood cells produced exclusively by the yolk sac. Furthermore, 10-day
yolk sac cultured *in vitro* for 3 days produced only embryonic hemoglobin. Support for this suggestion comes from similar work by Patton
et al. (1969).

It is not known whether the yolk sac stem cell is the precursor of all
the others or whether there is independent evolution of yolk sac, liver,
and spleen hematopoietic cells. This is clearly of fundamental importance
in understanding the processes of determination involved when the
hemoglobin changes from fetal to adult type. Moore and Metcalf (1970)
have presented evidence that yolk sac hematopoietic cells colonize
embryonic liver. (Hematopoietic stem cells were arbitrarily defined as
those cells that could produce hematopoietic colonies when injected into
the spleens of lethally irradiated mice.) Two lethally irradiated mice
that had survived for 30 days after injections of chromosomally marked
yolk sac cells showed 89–100% donor-type mitoses in bone marrow,
spleen, liver, thymus, and mesenteric lymph nodes.

There are also other biochemical differences between the fetus and
yolk sac during the first half of pregnancy. The electrophoretic profiles
of esterase activity in the two tissues are different (Sherman, 1972b),
and at mid-gestation yolk sac contains levels of N-acetyl-β-hexosaminidase
activity and a ratio of N-acetyl-β-hexosaminidase to β-glucuronidase activity much higher than in the fetus (Bell and Sherman, 1973). Both the
esterase and lysosomal enzyme characteristics developed in blastocyst
culture and they were therefore the consequence of genetic activity in
the embryo.

Histochemistry has shown that after mesoderm formation, and acid
phosphatase activity is restricted to the extra-embryonic endoderm of the
egg cylinder (Fig. 1b) while alkaline phosphatase is found throughout
the ectoderm (Solter *et al.*, 1973).

C. DETERMINATION OF YOLK AND FETUS AND ECTODERM, MESODERM, AND ENDODERM

The mouse egg cylinder is divided along its longitudinal axis into extra-embryonic and embryonic parts. Radially it is divided into endoderm, mesoderm, and ectoderm (Fig. 1b). It is now necessary to inquire if these regions are determined. It is likely that by the eighth day of pregnancy the extra-embryonic and embryonic parts have distinct and limited developmental fates and that longitudinal determination as occurred. The two halves of the egg cylinder differ in their capacity to form hemopoietic colonies (Moore and Metcalf, 1970). If yolk sacs from eighth-day embryos are cultured in isolation for 2 days, then it is found that they are able to form the cells of the erythroid series, megakaryocytes and granulocytes, when tested in an *in vitro* colony-forming assay. In contrast, eighth-day fetuses maintained in culture by themselves have neither hematopoietic cells in their vascular system nor the ability to form colonies when tested in the *in vitro* system. This would appear to be the only experiment that demonstrates a difference in determination between the cells of the yolk sac and the fetus early in development.

It is likely that the layers of the embryonic part of the egg cylinder are determined to form distinct parts of the adult mammal. The test of determination has been to dissect apart the layers and to study their development in extra-uterine sites. The development of the isolates in extra-uterine sites may not give precise information about the developmental capacity of the layers in the intact embryo; however, they indicate that different layers have undergone developmental restriction during the formation of the egg cylinder.

The ectoderm and endoderm of the two-layered embryonic part of the rat egg cylinder were separated after digestion by enzymes (Levak-Svajger and Levak-Svajger, 1971). Isolated ectoderm formed epidermis and neural tissue as expected; however, it also gave rise to normal mesoderm derivatives (muscle), and endoderm derivatives (intestine). In contrast to the multipotential ectoderm, the endoderm did not appear to grow.

As soon as the rat egg cylinder had become three layered, further developmental restrictions were found (Levak-Svajger et al., 1969). Again endoderm did not develop alone but, in combination with mesoderm, gut and respiratory epithelia were formed. Mesoderm alone only formed brown adipose tissue. Ectoderm from this three-layered stage usually developed into epidermis and neural tissue and only gave rise to the usual derivatives of the mesoderm.

The organization of the mouse egg cylinder may be similar to that of the rat although developmental restriction has not been studied in such detail. All that is known is that the ectoderm of the two-layered egg cylinder is capable of forming most of the tissue types of the fetus (Grobstein, 1951).

D. Studies on Induction

All further studies on mammalian development have been concerned with inductive events that occur after the tenth day of pregnancy (reviewed by Wolff, 1968). These experiments fall outside the scope of this review, except in so far as they illustrate earlier determinative events. For instance, the epithelium between the eleventh and the thirteenth days of pregnancy is divided up into regions that can be induced to form pancreas, submaxillary glands, and salivary glands. These regions are not interchangeable in the inductive systems, and the differences between them probably developed earlier than the development stage at which they were demonstrated. The mesenchyme that induces the formation of these glands may in some cases only be obtained from particular regions (e.g., submaxillary gland), whereas in other cases mesenchyme from several parts of the fetus can act as an inducer (e.g., pancreas). These studies, therefore, indicate that some regions of the epithelium and the mesenchyme have developed quite distinct properties by the tenth day of pregnancy. It remains to be formally demonstrated that these tissues are also distinctly determined.

VI. Conclusion

This review has been concerned with a single determinative event that occurs in a group of less than 100 cells. This event has probably been studied in more detail than comparable phenomena in other embryos. Despite this attention, the molecular basis of this determination remains completely unknown. It is probable that development after the blastocyst stage consists of a series of determinations similar in kind to this decision to form or not to form trophoblast.

ACKNOWLEDGMENTS

The authors of articles in *Current Topics in Developmental Biology* are asked to be controversial; Drs. Peter Barlow, Verne Chapman, Richard Gardner, and Mike Sherman assisted with ideas.

The research by the authors reviewed here was kindly supported by the Medical Research Council.

REFERENCES

Barker, J. E. (1968). *Develop. Biol.* 18, 14.
Barlow, P. W., and Sherman, M. I. (1972). *J. Embryol. Exp. Morphol.* 27, 447.

Barlow, P. W., Owen, D. A. J., and Graham, C. F. (1972). *J. Embryol. Exp. Morphol.* **27**, 431.

Bell, K. E., and Sherman, M. I. (1973) *Exp. Cell Res.* In Press.

Billington, W. D., Graham, C. F., and McLaren, A. (1968). *J. Embryol. Exp. Morphol.* **20**, 391.

Calarco, P. G., and Brown, E. H. (1969). *J. Exp. Zool.* **171**, 253.

Cerisola, H., and Izquierdo, L. (1969). *Arch. Biol. Med. Exp.* **6**, 10.

Child, C. M. (1941). "Patterns and Problems of Development." Univ. Chicago Press, Chicago, Illinois.

Dalcq, A. M. (1957). "Introduction to General Embryology." Oxford Univ. Press, London and New York.

Djaldetti, M., Bessler, H., and Rifkind, R. A. (1972). *Blood* **39**, 826.

Dunn, G. R., and Stevens, L. C. (1970). *J. Nat. Cancer Inst.* **44**, 99.

Enders, A. D., and Schlafke, S. J. (1965). *In* "Preimplantation Stages of Pregnancy" (G. E. W. Wolstenholme and M. O'Connor, eds.), p. 29. Churchill, London.

Fantoni, A., de la Chapelle, A., and Marks, P. A. (1969). *J. Biol. Chem.* **244**, 675.

Gardner, R. L. (1971). *Advan. Biosci.* **6**, 279.

Gardner, R. L. (1972). *J. Embryol. Exp. Morphol.* **28**, 279.

Gardner, R. L., Papaioannou, V. E., and Barton, S. C. (1973). *J. Embryol. Exp. Morphol.* In press.

Gilman, J. G., and Smithies, O. (1968). *Science* **160**, 885.

Graham, C. F. (1973). *In* "The cell cycle in development and differentiation" (M. J. Balls and F. S. Billett, eds.), p. 293. Cambridge Univ. Press, London and New York.

Grobstein, C. (1951). *J. Exp. Zool.* **116**, 501.

Gwatkin, R. B. L. (1966a). *Ann. N. Y. Acad. Sci.* **139**, 79.

Gwatkin, R. B. L. (1966b). *J. Cell. Physiol.* **68**, 335.

Hillman, N., Sherman, M. I., and Graham, C. F. (1972). *J. Embryol. Exp. Morphol.* **28**, 263.

Hsu, Y-C. (1972). *Nature (London)* **239**, 200.

Jenkinson, E. J., and Wilson, I. B. (1970). *Nature (London)* **228**, 776.

Kelly, S. J., and Graham, C. F. (1974). In preparation.

Kirby, D. R. S. (1965). *In* "Preimplantation Stages of Pregnancy" (G. E. W. Wolstenholme and M. O'Connor, eds.), p. 325. Churchill, London.

Kirby, D. R. S., Potts, D. H., and Wilson, I. B. (1967). *J. Embryol. Exp. Morphol.* **17**, 527.

Levak-Svajger, B., and Levak-Svajger, A. (1971). *Experientia* **27**, 683.

Levak-Svajger, B., Levak-Svajger, A., and Skreb, N. (1969). *Experientia* **25**, 1311.

Lin, T. P. (1969). *Nature (London)* **222**, 480.

McLaren, A. (1968). *In* "The Mammalian Oviduct" (E. S. E. Hafez and R. J. Blandau, eds.), p. 477. Univ. Chicago Press, Chicago, Illinois.

Mintz, B. (1962). *Amer. Zool.* **2**, 541 Abstr. 145.

Mintz, B. (1965). *In* "Preimplantation stages of pregnancy" (G. E. W. Wolstenholme and M. O'Connor, eds.), p. 194. Churchill, London.

Mintz, B. (1970). *Annu. Symp. Fund. Cancer Res., 23rd, 1969* p. 477.

Moore, M. A. S., and Metcalf, D. (1970). *Brit. J. Haematol.* **18**, 279.

Moore, N. W., Adams, C. E., and Rowson, L. E. A. (1968). *J. Reprod. Fert.* **17**, 527.

Mukherjee, A. B., and Cohen, M. M. (1970). *Nature (London)* **228**, 472.

Mullen, R. J., and Whitten, W. K. (1971). *J. Exp. Zool.* **178**, 165.

Mulnard, J. G. (1965). In "Preimplantation Stages of Pregnancy" (G. E. W. Wolstenholme and M. O'Connor, eds.), p. 123. Churchill, London.

Mulnard, J. G. (1971). Advan. Biosci. 6, 255.

New, D. A. T. (1971). Advan. Biosci. 6, 367.

Patton, D. E., Kirk, D. L., and Moscona, A. A. (1969). Exp. Cell Res. 54, 181.

Popp, R. A., and Popp, D. M. (1962). J. Hered. 53, 111.

Rodé, B., Damjanov, I., and Skreb, N. (1968). Bull. Sci., Cons. Acad. Sci. Arts R & F Yugoslavie, Sect. A 13, 304.

Ruddle, F. H., Shows, T. B., and Roderick, T. H. (1969). Genetics 62, 393.

Runner, M. N. (1947). Anat. Rec. 98, 1.

Seidel, F. (1960). Arch. Entwicklungsmech. Organismen. 152, 43.

Sherman, M. I. (1972a). Develop. Biol. 27, 337.

Sherman, M. I. (1972b). Exp. Cell Res. 75, 449.

Sherman, M. I., and Barlow, P. W. (1972). J. Reprod. Fert. 29, 123.

Sherman, M. I., and Chew, N. J. (1972). Proc. Nat. Acad. Sci. U.S. 69, 2551.

Solter, D., Damjanov, I., and Skreb, N. (1973). Z. Anat. Entwicklungsgesch. 139, 119.

Stern, M. S., and Wilson, I. B. (1972). J. Embryol. Exp. Morphol. 28, 247.

Stevens, L. (1970). Develop. Biol. 21, 364.

Tarkowski, A. K. (1959). Nature (London) 184, 1286.

Tarkowski, A. K. (1961). Nature (London) 190, 857.

Tarkowski, A. K., and Wroblewska, J. (1967). J. Embryol. Exp. Morphol. 18, 155.

Tuft, P. H., and Boving, B. G. (1970). J. Exp. Zool. 174, 165.

Whitten, W. K. (1971). Advan. Biosci. 6, 129.

Wilson, I. B., Bolton, E., and Cuttler, R. H. (1972). J. Embryol. Exp. Morphol. 27, 467.

Wolff, E. (1968). Cur. Top. Develop. Biol. 2, 247.

Wolpert, L. (1969). J. Theor. Biol. 25, 1.

CHAPTER 6

DIFFERENTIAL GENE ACTIVITY IN THE PRE- AND POSTIMPLANTATION MAMMALIAN EMBRYO

Robert B. Church and Gilbert A. Schultz

DIVISIONS OF MEDICAL BIOCHEMISTRY AND BIOLOGY,
FACULTY OF MEDICINE, UNIVERSITY OF CALGARY,
CALGARY, ALBERTA, CANADA

I. Introduction

In this chapter we would like to delineate some of the correlations between the appearance of the various classes of macromolecules and the anatomical features that develop during mammalian embryogenesis. Differential gene activity in the pre- and early postimplantation mammalian embryo results in the expression of certain parts of the genotypic potential to create a phenotypic form. The morphological development of an embryo has been characterized in terms of the ontogenetic landmarks for many years. A delineation of the pattern of ribonucleic acid (RNA) transcription during development would seem to be one of the first steps in any understanding of the regulation of gene action during embryogenesis. Unless otherwise noted, the work which we describe is limited to the pre- and postimplantation development of the mouse and rabbit. A more detailed review of the biochemistry of early mammalian development has been presented (Schultz and Church, 1973).

The biochemistry of embryogenesis in an increasing number of invertebrate and amphibian species has been described (Davidson, 1968; Flickinger, 1971). Corresponding studies in mammalian systems are hampered by the problem of obtaining sufficient preimplantation embryos, their extremely small size, and in the difficulties inherent in the culture of these preimplantation embryos. Nevertheless, considerable progress has been made in our understanding of the mechanisms of differential gene activity in the preimplantation and early postimplantation mammalian embryo in the past few years.

Pre- and postimplantation mammalian development has received more attention since the advent of intrauterine diagnosis of inborn errors of metabolism and karyotypic aberrations. The advent of prenatal diagnosis represents one of the most significant advances in the detection and prevention of congenital defects yet applied to the medical care of the human unborn (Milunsky and Littlefield, 1972). The genetic basis of congenital defects during the early phases of mammalian development have in the past been centered around the analysis of chromosomal abnormalties, since karyotypic anomalies are the commonest known cause of spontaneous abortions in man (Carr, 1971). These spontaneous abortions may be viewed as gross aberrations in the regulatory pattern of gene activity operating during embryonic development. Any interference with mechanisms that control differentation would seem to make the embryo subject to expulsion from the uterus.

The structure and functional characteristics of any particular cell in an organism is a reflection of the array of constituent proteins of that particular cell. Differentiation, therefore, may be defined as the process whereby cells of identical genetic constitution develop into phenotypically distinct entities expressing a characteristic pattern of gene activity. The differentiation process must involve a number of steps in the regulation of the synthesis of the characteristic biochemical patterns found in the different cells and tissues of an individual embryo. The exact mechanism by which the differential gene activity is regulated in mammalian development is unknown. The differential pattern of proteins observed in any type of cell probably reflects a dynamic equilibrium of a number of regulatory processes which act upon deoxyribonucleic acid (DNA) duplication, RNA transcription, and translation into proteins. The stability of any tissue may be governed by the susceptability of each or all regulatory mechanisms to intrinsic and extrinsic factors. In general, in differentiating mammalian cells there must exist control mechanisms capable of activating preferentially some of the genetic potential of the cell nucleus while, at the same time, repressing expression of other regions at different developmental stages or in different cell types during development of the organism. It is presumed that some genes involved in basic metabolic processes, such as protein and energy metabolism, DNA replication and repair, and membrane synthesis, will be active in many different cell types. Other genes contain the information for proteins that are characteristically unique to one cell type at a specific stage of development.

The control of cellular decision making at the level of gene transcription is universal, and there is a very large volume of literature about eukaryotic cells. The protein moieties that produce a distinct cellular phenotype and their regulation have been summarized (Rutter *et al.,* 1968; Moog, 1965). The genetic and biochemical evidence for changing patterns of gene activity during early mammalian development will be the subject of this article. The timing and onset of RNA synthesis in preimplantation embryos, the diversity of genetic information contained in RNA transcripts, and the relationship of these processes to other biochemical events in the embryo will be reviewed.

II. Genetic Expression during Preimplantation Development

Differential gene expression of genetic potential into any cellular phenotype requires the synthesis of messenger RNA (mRNA) molecules and their subsequent translation into protein. The programming of RNA transcription tells us when genes begin to act during early development. Most evidence to date suggests that the synthesis of nearly all classes of RNA commences shortly after fertilization. This conclusion is based on evidence obtained from studies of the mouse and rabbit; however, it may not be a general description of early gene activity for all mammals. A characteristic feature of all mammalian development, which is interposed between cleavage and implantation, is the formation of a blastocyst, whose structure is essentially similar in all mammals. However, there are differences in size and rate of cell proliferation from one species to another.

Different regions of the morula can be distinguished by their DNA labeling index and rate of cell proliferation (Graham, 1971). At the blastocyst stage the difference is more pronounced in cells of the trophoblast layer. Blastocyst differentiation results in the formation of the primary trophoblast and inner cell mass which are destined to become the placenta and fetus, respectively. Trophoblast differentiation in the mouse embryo is characterized by the formation of giant cells whose nuclei contain from 500 to 1000 times the haploid DNA content as a result of endomitosis (Chapman *et al.,* 1972). The increase in DNA content would not seem to be due to differential amplification of specific base sequences in the genome (Sherman *et al.,* 1972). The possibility of cell fusion has been eliminated by chimeric embryo experiments using the dimeric enzyme, glucose phosphate isomerase (GPI), as a marker (Chapman *et al.*, 1971; Gearhart and Mintz, 1972).

The data for differential RNA synthesis in the preimplantation mouse and rabbit embryo have come from *in vitro* studies. These involve the labeling of embryos with radioactive precursors of RNA or proteins and the subsequent observation of incorporation by radioautographic or biochemical methods. However, genetic tools have also been used in the analysis of gene expression in mouse embryos and some of these findings are discussed below. A critical review of nucleic acid metabolism in the preimplantation mammalian embryo has recently been prepared by Graham (1973).

A. RIBONUCLEIC ACID TRANSCRIPTION IN THE MOUSE

The synthesis of RNA in mouse embryos labeled *in vitro* with uridine-^{3}H can be detected from the 2-cell stage onward (Mintz, 1964; Monesi and Salfi, 1967; Woodland and Graham, 1969; Church, 1970; Knowland and Graham, 1972). Although the RNA synthesized at this stage has not been well characterized, analysis on sucrose gradients reveals the presence of both heterogeneous low molecular weight and high molecular weight RNA species (Woodland and Graham 1969; Church, 1970). Knowland and Graham (1972) have raised the possibility that ribosomal RNA (rRNA) synthesis may commence at the 2-cell stage. From the 4-cell stage onward, all major classes of RNA are synthesized in the mouse embryo.

Ribosomal RNA synthesis has been detected from the 4-cell stage onward by both chromatography on methylated albumin keiselguhr (MAK) columns and sucrose gradients (Woodland and Graham, 1969; Ellem and Gwatkin, 1968; Piko, 1970; Church, 1970). Radioautographical evidence showed a concentration of label over the nucleoli at the same stages of development (Mintz, 1964; Hillman and Tasca, 1969). The proportion of incorporation of labeled precursors going into rRNA species increases during development from the 8-cell stage onward (Ellem and Gwatkin, 1968). Piko (1970) has further shown that from the 8-cell embryo onward, short labeling periods label the 39 S region in a sucrose gradient, whereas, longer labeling periods show accumulation of radioactivity in the 28 S region. Since the radioactivity in the 39 S peak can be chased into the 28 S region in the presence of actinomycin D, at least some of the 39 S RNA would seem to be 28 S rRNA precursor.

As early as the 4-cell stage of development 4 S RNA is detectable in the mouse embryo (Woodland and Graham, 1969; Church, 1970; Ellem and Gwatkin, 1968; Piko, 1970). Much of the 4 S RNA synthesized in the 8-cell embryo seems to be transfer RNA (tRNA) since the 4 S

RNA has a characteristically high percentage of pseudouridylic acid, it can be methylated *in vivo*, and the incorporation of uridine does not represent end terminal (CCA) labeling of tRNA (Woodland and Graham, 1969).

The synthesis of heterogeneous RNA appears to have commenced by the 4-cell stage of development in the preimplantation mouse embryo (Church and Brown, 1972). Protein synthesis is detectable in early cleavage stages of mouse development (Monesi and Salfi, 1967; Tasca and Hillman, 1970). The inhibitory effects of low concentrations of actinomycin D on the cleavage of the mouse egg (Mintz, 1964; Thomson and Biggers, 1966) suggest that the mammalian embryo requires expression of the genetic information to continue development, which is in contrast to invertebrate and amphibian systems (Gross, 1968). Since an 85% reduction in uridine incorporation into RNA in the presence of actinomycin D results in only a 50% reduction of leucine-^{3}H into protein (Monesi *et al.*, 1970), about half of the protein synthesis in the embryo may be dependent on the continuing formation of mRNA and the other half may depend on much longer-lived mRNA. Alternatively, the effects of actinomycin D may be secondary and not a valid estimate of inhibition of RNA synthesis.

The information reviewed in the foregoing has shown that 4 S (tRNA), rRNA, and heterogeneous RNA synthesis is detectable at least as early as the 4-cell stage in mouse embryos. The rate of incorporation of uridine into RNA increases rapidly after the 8-cell stage and continues to rise throughout the development of the preimplantation mouse embryo (Monesi and Salfi, 1967; Ellem and Gwatkin, 1968; Woodland and Graham, 1969; Chuch, 1970; Piko, 1970). Complete summaries of RNA synthesis in the preimplantation mouse embryo have recently been presented by Graham (1973) and Schultz and Church (1973).

B. RIBONUCLEIC ACID TRANSCRIPTION IN THE RABBIT

Incorporation of uridine-^{3}H into acid-insoluble RNA in rabbit embryos *in vitro* has shown that there is no detectable incorporation in the unfertilized ova, but within 24 hours after coitus significant incorporation occurs (Manes, 1969). There is no net increase in RNA content per embryo, however, until 72 hours postcoitum at which time there is a marked acceleration of uridine incorporation. This correlates with the transformation of the morula into a blastocyst as the embryo leaves the oviduct and enters the uterus (Manes, 1969). The qualitative aspects of RNA synthesis in preimplantation rabbit embryos have been investigated by the electrophoretic separation of ^{3}H-labeled embryonic RNA on polyacrylamide gels (Manes, 1971). Ribonucleic acid molecules having migratory properties identical with those of tRNA are detectable from the 2-cell stage onward. Labeling of heterogeneous RNA is detectable from the 4-cell stage onward. The labeling of RNA species having the migratory properties of 28 S and 18 S rRNA was first detectable by 72 hours postcoitum (Manes, 1971). Ribonucleic acid that was isolated from purified ribosomes of rabbit embryos labeled *in vitro* with uridine-^{3}H at 200 μCi/ml for 4 hours showed some incorporation into 28 S and 18 S rRNA by the 16-cell stage (Schultz, Manes, and Hahn, unpublished results). The incorporation of label into RNA by stroma cells, which may be adhered to the mucin coat, has not been determined. The relative amount of uridine incorporated into rRNA at this stage of development is small, however, compared to that observed in the 72-hour blastocyst which contains approximately 128 cells. It would appear that the rabbit and mouse embryos both exhibit very early synthesis of presumptive tRNA but differ slightly in the timing of the onset of rRNA synthesis. Although rRNA synthesis is detectable by the 16-cell stage in rabbit embryos, it is not the major product of uridine incorporation until the 128-cell stage, whereas in the mouse embryo, rRNA is the major product of synthesis by the 8-cell stage.

Manes and Daniel (1969) have shown that protein synthesis is detectable during early cleavage stages of rabbit development. Heterogeneously labelling RNA species are also synthesized from the 2-cell stage onward (Manes, 1971). This finding provides indirect evidence that mRNA synthesis is occurring since high molecular weight heterogeneous RNA is thought to be the precursor to polysomal mRNA (Scherrer *et al.*, 1970; Darnell, 1968). Putative mRNA synthesis in rabbit embryos has been more directly demonstrated by Schultz *et al.* (1973a) by the assay of RNA molecules containing poly(A) sequences. These studies suggest that the synthesis of presumptive mRNA begins at least by the 16-cell stage in rabbit embryos. Synthesis of mRNA containing poly(A) is continued through blastocyst formation and maturation, and these RNA species have been shown to be present in both the heterogeneous RNA from nuclei and from polysomes in these early stages of rabbit development (Schultz *et al.*, 1973a).

The small differences in transcriptional patterns displayed by mouse and rabbit embryos may be related to morphological differences in the embryos. The rabbit ovum, for example, is about twice the diameter of the mouse ovum, cleaves more rapidly, reaches a morula stage of about 100 to 130 cells before cavitation begins, and retains its zona pellucida throughout the preimplantation period.

C. PROTEIN SYNTHESIS AND ENZYME ACTIVITY

Protein synthesis is detectable in the early cleavage stages of both mouse (Mintz, 1964; Monesi *et al.*, 1970) and rabbit (Manes and Daniel,

1969) embryos. It has not been shown whether this protein synthesis is dependent completely or only in part on *de novo* synthesis of mRNA molecules. Sensitivity to very low doses of actinomycin D (Mintz, 1964; Thomson and Biggers, 1966) suggests that immediate genetic activation may be required for normal mammalian development to proceed.

During the preimplantation period there is little change in total protein content, whereas enzyme activity can change dramatically. The activity of hypoxanthine–guanine phosphoribosyl transferase, adenine phosphoribosyl transferase, and hexokinase increases sixfold from the fertilized egg to the blastocyst stage (Brinster, 1968, 1971; Epstein, 1970). In contrast to this, glucose 6-phosphate dehydrogenase (Brinster, 1966), lactate dehydrogenase (Brinster, 1965a, 1967; Epstein *et al.*, 1969), guanine deaminase (Epstein *et al.*, 1971), and glucose phosphate isomerase (GPI) (Chapman *et al.*, 1971) have decreased activity in the blastocyst relative to the 1-cell embryo.

The normal development of the mouse blastocyst can be arrested *in utero* if the uterus has not been sensitized by estrogen. In this state of dormancy, DNA, RNA, and protein synthesis is drastically inhibited (McLaren, 1973) (see Fig. 4). These results imply that the mammalian blastocyst responds to its uterine environment in a very precise manner.

The patterns of changes in enzyme activities indicate independent control mechanisms probably reflecting, in part, the embryonic differential gene expression.

D. GENE ACTIVATION

Important questions in the study of genetic expression during mammalian development are concerned with the totipotency of the genetic information in each blastomere and the timing of expression of the paternal contribution to the zygotic genome.

The individual blastomes of the mammalian embryo appear to be totipotent up to the 8-cell stage (Tarkowski, 1959; Tarkowski and Wroblewka, 1969; Moore *et al.*, 1968). By the blastocyst stage, two cell types have formed: the outer trophoblast layer and the inner cell mass. These two populations have been shown to have restricted developmental capacities (Gardner, 1971, 1972). In mammalian embryos, there is a characteristic grouping of the inner embryonic cell mass to one side of the blastocyst cavity, leaving the flattened trophoblast cells in a peripheral configuration. Recent elegant studies determining the fate of specific blastomeres in mammalian embryos have been reported (Gardner, 1971, 1972; Graham, 1971, 1973; Hillman *et al.*, 1972; and Stern, 1972).

Parthenogenetically activated mouse eggs can develop normally to the blastocyst stage (Tarkowski *et al.*, 1970; Graham, 1970), suggesting that the paternal genome is not activated until blastocyst formation. Chapman *et al.* (1971) have used crosses of mouse lines that have electrophoretically distinguishable forms of glucose phosphate isomerase-1 (GPI-1) to show that the paternal form of this enzyme is first expressed in the late blastocyst. The paternal allele for isocitrate dehydrogenase is expressed by the ninth day of pregnancy (Epstein *et al.*, 1972).

Nesbitt and Gartler (1971) have shown that female mice heterozygous for Cattanach's translocation (Cattanach, 1962) have cells with an inactive normal X chromosome which can be distinguished from those cells with an inactive translocated X chromosome. They interpret their results to mean that X chromosome activation occurs in the late blastocyst stage before the determination of the primordial cell pools for the various tissues, within the inner cell embryonic mass.

The offspring of XO female mice suffer preimplantation mortality which may be specific for the embryos of OY karyotype (Morris, 1968). Further studies are required to establish if the mortality is actually a function of genetic failure due to the karyotype or not.

Most lethal mutations are expressed after implantation has occurred. One of the few mutations expressed prior to implantation is the t^{12}/t^{12} mutant. Embryos stop development at the 30-cell stage (Smith, 1956) for some, as yet, obscure reason. The yellow mutation also causes blastocyst arrest, but near the 50-cell stage of development. There is no evidence in either case for aberrant RNA transcriptional activity. Therefore, it would seem that systems such as the complex cell–cell interactions, mitchondrial metabolism and proliferation or maternal cytoplasmic contribution may be equally probable sites of mutant expression (Dyban, 1972).

Chimeric mice will be used in the future to study the possibilities of gene "rescue," to analyze the fate of different blastomeres during development, and to analyze the hypothesis that morulae cell position determines the specific pattern of gene activity that a cell is destined to follow.

III.   Ribonucleic Acid Transcriptional Complexity during Embryonic Development

A.   GENOME COMPLEXITY

The complexity or number of sequences in a genome is related to the genome size (Laird, 1971). The average mammalian cell nucleus contains approximately 6×10^{-12} gm of DNA. This amount of DNA is equivalent to about 4.5 to 5.0×10^9 nucleotide pairs (Mirsky and Ris, 1951; McCarthy, 1967). On the basis of the reassociation kinetics of sheared, single-stranded DNA isolated from higher organisms, it has been shown that the genome contains various classes of reiterated or repeated sequences as well as nonrepeated or single-copy DNA base sequences (Britten and Kohne, 1966, 1968).

The reassociation profiles of a number of different DNA's are shown in Fig. 1. The relationship between the second-order reassociation

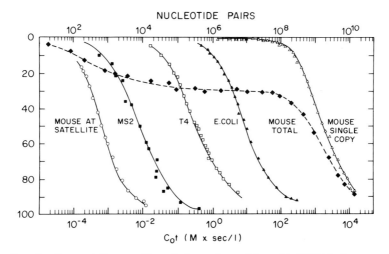

FIG. 1. Reassociation profiles of deoxyribonucleic acid (DNA) from various sources. Sheared, denatured mouse DNA at a concentration of 2 mg/ml was mixed with ³H-labeled single-copy DNA, which had previously been fractionated at C_0t 220, at a concentration of 1 µg/ml and with ¹⁴C-labeled *Escherichia coli* DNA at 10 µg/ml. The incubation reactions were carried out in 0.12 M sodium phosphate buffer, pH 6.8, at 60°C for increasing periods of time. The percentage reassociated DNA was determined by elution with phosphate buffer from hydroxyapatite. The AT-rich satellite fragments were isolated from total mouse DNA by CsCl centrifugation. The DNA preparations were sheared to 450–500 nucleotide fragments before being heat-denatured as described previously (Church, 1973). The MS-2 and T₄ nucleic acid reassociation kinetics are after Britten and Kohne (1968).

kinetics of any population of nucleotide sequences and the size of the genome is illustrated by the fact the *Escherichia coli* DNA, with about 1/750 the DNA content of mouse, reassociates approximately 750 times faster than do the nonrepeated sequences found in the mouse genome.

All mammalian genomes examined so far contain repeated DNA base sequences which make up between 10 and 60% of the total genome. The distinction between single copy and repeated sequences is, however, an operational definition since one theoretically should be able (under very stringent conditions) to prevent base pair mismatching so that each sequence behaves as a single-copy sequence (Church, 1973) unless sequences are identical in a family.

The mouse genome consists of three broad classes of reiteration frequency. A very rapidly renaturing fraction equal to between 6 and 9% of the genome reassociates 10^6 times faster than would be expected for sequences that are present only once in a genome the size of a mouse. Included within this very rapidly renaturing fraction is the AT-rich satellite found in CsCl ultracentrifugation studies. These sequences do not seem to be transcribed in any tissue or stage of development examined so far (Flamm et al., 1969) and have been shown to be primarily located within the centromere and telomere regions of the mouse chromosome (Pardue and Gall, 1969). They may be associated with the heterochromatic regions of the chromosome (Yasmineh and Yunis, 1969). These sequences have been separated into heavy and light strands on CsCl gradients by Walker (1969). The sequence analysis for this AT-rich satellite fraction suggests that the repeating unit has a corrected complexity of 140 base pairs (Sutton and McCallum, 1971), which is probably made up of short, mutated simple sequences. The apparent self-renaturation hairpin regions found within this fraction may be a functional-structural modification of the satellite DNA sequence which has a regulatory role (Church and Georgiev, 1973).

The rapidly reassociating DNA sequences constitute 20–25% of the mouse genome and reassociate at an average rate from a few to 100,000 times faster than would be expected. These sequences contribute the major portion of low C_0t RNA/DNA hybridization reactions.

The major group of DNA sequences in the mouse genome renature at a rate that is consistent with the second-order kinetics predicted for the mouse genome, assuming each sequence is present only once per haploid genome. These are termed the single-copy or nonrepeated DNA base sequences and constitute 60–70% of the genome (Fig. 1).

The RNA/DNA hybridization experiments are appealing to the developmental biologist for it is the only method that can be used to estimate the amount and the types of gene activity expressed during development. As a result, numerous studies have been carried out to estimate the extent of transcription of RNA from DNA base sequences in various mammalian cells. In the past, these studies have usually been based on experiments in which low concentrations of RNA sequences are hybridized with single-stranded DNA immobilized in agar or attached to nitrocellulose filters for short periods of time.

Due to low RNA concentrations, short reaction times, and the presence of DNA sequences represented by families of similar but not identical DNA sequences of varying repetition frequency, the RNA/DNA hybridization reactions with repetitive DNA base sequences rarely, if ever, display cistron specificity (Church and McCarthy, 1968). Therefore, complementary strands of the native duplex will seldom reassociate with each other since the probability of their reassociating with other members of the DNA base sequence family is greater (McCarthy and McConaughy, 1968). The reassociation criteria, namely, salt concentration, concentration of organic solvents, temperature, nucleic acid fragment size and reaction time, will determine the extent of DNA/RNA base sequence mismatching permitted within any reassociation reaction (Church, 1973). The extent of base pair mismatching can be measured by the thermal dissociation properties of the reassociation duplex. Estimates of the proportion of the genome active in different tissues utilizing repetitive RNA/DNA hybridization have been carried out for a large number of experimental mammalian systems (see Hahn and Church, 1970). Hybridization of RNA/DNA has also been used to discriminate the variable number of ribosomal cistrons associated with different dosages of nucleolar organizers in mutants of *Drosophila* (Ritossa and Spiegelman, 1965) and *Xenopus* (Wallace and Birnstiel, 1966). The use of nucleic acid hybridization analysis to show that the RNA synthesized *in vitro* using a chromatin template is not distinguishable from RNA synthesized *in vivo* (Paul and Gilmour, 1968; Smith *et al.*, 1969; Paul, 1970) also supports the discriminatory ability of the method. Competition experiments carried out by Church and McCarthy (1967a,b,) have shown that unlabeled RNA extracted from embryonic mouse liver, term embryo liver, and adult liver demonstrates remarkably large-scale alterations in the pattern of gene activity associated with tissue development.

Many other studies have been reported in the literature and, although difficult to interpret, they have revealed changes in the kinds or numbers of RNA transcripts made in cells in differing states of differentiation (Hahn and Church, 1970).

In recent years, advances in hybridization methodology have been made which also allowed the analysis of transcription from nonrepeated or single-copy DNA base sequences (Kohne, 1968; Bishop, 1972). Ribonucleic acid excess and DNA excess experiments with single-copy DNA have been used to estimate the amount of nonrepeated DNA transcribed in a variety of tissues of the mouse and rabbit, as well as in oocytes of *Xenopus* (Gelderman *et al.*, 1971; Hahn and Laird, 1971; Brown and Church, 1971, 1972; Schultz *et al.*, 1973b; Grouse *et al.*, 1972; Davidson and Hough, 1969, 1971).

The assay of transcriptional diversity from single-copy DNA base sequences may be more important in the assay of genetic activity during development than the assay of transcripts complementary to repeated DNA base sequences since about 65% of the heterogeneous nuclear RNA in L cells (Greenberg and Perry, 1971), rat liver (Melli *et al.*, 1971) and in rabbit blastocysts (Schultz *et al.*, 1973b) is transcribed from single-copy DNA base sequences. Extension of these experiments to heterogeneous RNA of polysomes revealed that 82% of the presumptive mRNA in L cells is transcribed from nonrepeated DNA base sequences (Greenberg and Perry, 1971).

B. RIBONUCLEIC ACID TRANSCRIPTION COMPLEMENTARY TO
   REPEATED DEOXYRIBONUCLEIC ACID SEQUENCES

Ribonucleic acid molecules isolated from *Xenopus* oocytes are complementary to 3.5% of the *Xenopus* DNA which reassociates by C_0t 50 (Hough and Davidson, 1972). Quantitatively, about 2 to 5% of the total oocyte RNA is complementary to these repetitive DNA base sequences. The exact number of different RNA transcripts represented in this fraction cannot be calculated because of the influence of base pair mismatching, the sequence family size, and transcript numbers on the RNA/DNA reassociation reaction (Church, 1973). The biological significance of the RNA transcripts complementary to repeated DNA is unknown. Qualitative population differences inherited in the embryo, which persist to blastulation, would seem to indicate an important functional role in early embryogenesis (Davidson *et al.*, 1966). The 2–5% of the total oocyte RNA complementary to repetitive sequences represents a much higher concentration of transcripts than do the 20×10^6 nucleotide pairs of single-copy DNA sequence transcripts present at this stage (Davidson and Hough, 1971).

In the preimplantation mouse embryo, Church (1970) has shown that approximately 5% of the RNA transcripts are complementary to repeated DNA sequences. Figure 2 illustrates an apparent increase in the extent of reaction of RNA transcripts with repeated mouse DNA sequences up to the blastocyst stage before leveling off for the rest of fetal development. These data are difficult to interpret since they may represent an increase in a number of relatively small repeated DNA sequence families being transcribed or a cross-reaction between RNA transcripts complementary to very large reiterated sequence families present in the genome. The fraction of RNA complementary to repetitive sequences cannot be calculated exactly because there is considerable variation in the concentration of individual RNA transcript populations and because there is base pair mismatching between reacting sequences.

An estimate of the repeated RNA transcripts in the rabbit is also shown in Fig. 2. The kinetics of this saturation-type experiment indicate that approximately 4% of the repeated DNA base sequences are capable

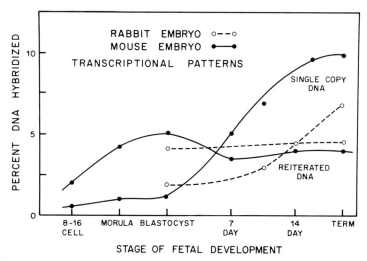

FIG. 2. Transcriptional complexity of ribonucleic acid (RNA) molecules complementary to repeated and single-copy deoxyribonucleic acid (DNA) base sequences at various stages of mouse and rabbit development. Labeled RNA isolated from whole embryos was incubated with filter-bound labeled repeated DNA base sequences. The repeated DNA base sequences were prepared from [14]C- or ^{3}H-labeled DNA, isolated from L cell or rabbit lung cells, which were sheared, heat denatured, and fractionated on hydroxyapatite with phosphate buffer. Rabbit and mouse DNA fragments were fractionated into single copy and repeated sequence after reassociation to C_0t 240 and 220, respectively. The diversity of transcription of RNA complementary to single-copy DNA was estimated by reacting a large excess of RNA with small amounts of labeled single-copy DNA fragments. The extent of reaction of ribonuclease-resistant duplex was assayed by hydroxyapatite chromatography. For complete experimental details, see Brown and Church (1972) and Schultz et al. (1973b).

of reacting with the RNA molecules present in the rabbit blastocyst. This is similar to the estimate obtained for the mouse blastocyst.

It should be kept in mind that because of the difficulty of obtaining sufficient amounts of material in the mouse, true saturation probably is not achieved, hence the "apparent saturation plateau" is representative of only those RNA transcripts that are in high concentration in the blastocyst. The problem of obtaining sufficient material may be helped by new techniques now available (Hinderstein, 1972).

Very large changes in the spectrum of RNA molecules complementary to the repetitive DNA sequences have been observed in various states of differentiation in many experimental systems. Differences in the spectrum of repeated RNA transcripts present in different tissues of the mouse were first reported by McCarthy and Hoyer (1964) and since that time have been demonstrated in various embryonic and differentiating systems (Church and Brown, 1972). In these experiments, RNA from a cell type in one state of differentiation is used to compete with RNA from a cell type in another state of differentiation for complementary sequences within the DNA of the genome. The analysis has shown that different families of repetitive DNA sequences are complementary to RNA populations found in various states of differentiation and at various stages of development.

Differences in the extent of repeated RNA transcript reactions with DNA have led Britten and Davidson (1969) and Georgiev (1969) to postulate models suggesting that the repeated DNA sequence transcripts may have a regulatory function in the control of cell differentiation. Genomic regulation of higher organisms involves families of repeated RNA transcripts which act as control mechanisms in differential gene activity. Although regulatory roles for repetitive transcripts have been suggested, at least some mRNA species originate from repeated DNA base sequences. Bishop *et al.* (1972) utilized the vast DNA excess hybridization procedure to demonstrate that the cistrons for the α and β chains of hemoglobin are present at a reiteration frequency of about 5 each. A much higher reiteration frequency is reported for the cistrons coding for histone mRNA (Kedes and Birnstiel, 1971). However, the majority of polysomal mRNA molecules seem to be derived from single-copy DNA sequences (Greenberg and Perry, 1971; Firtel *et al.*, 1972).

C. RIBONUCLEIC ACID TRANSCRIPTION COMPLEMENTARY TO SINGLE-COPY DEOXYRIBONUCLEIC ACID SEQUENCES

As shown in Fig. 1, about 60 to 70% of the genome consists of single-copy DNA sequences. The advantages of hybridization reactions utilizing single-copy DNA base sequences were quickly recognized. Most experiments use excess nonradioactive RNA in the presence of small amounts of radiocative single-copy DNA. Davidson and Hough (1971) used this procedure to estimate that the RNA prepared from the mature *Xenopus* oocyte was complementary to 0.7% of the single-copy DNA sequences present in the genome. This is equivalent to 4.5 genomes the size of *Escherichia coli* and represents sufficient genetic information for the translation of several thousand polypeptides. Utilizing single-copy DNA base sequences in mammalian tissues, Gelderman *et al.* (1971) demonstrated that about 12% of the single-copy DNA base sequences are present in newborn mouse RNA. Approximately 10% of the single-copy DNA is complementary to RNA from brain, and approximately 3% is complementary to RNA isolated from liver, spleen, and kidney of the adult mouse (Brown and Church, 1971; Hahn and Laird, 1971; Grouse *et al.*, 1972). These techniques demand nucleic acids of very great purity and proper controls must be included for any firm biological interpretation of the results of such experiments (Church, 1973). However, with good controls, bona fide RNA/DNA duplexes that exhibit thermal stabilities similar to DNA/DNA reassociation duplexes can result.

The extent of reaction of total mouse embryo RNA with repeated sequences of the genome increases from about 2 to 5% during the preimplantation stages of development and then plateaus at about 4% during the rest of embryonic development (Fig. 2). In contrast, total embryonic RNA, which is complementary to single-copy DNA sequences, shows a marked increase in the postimplantation period. Approximately 1% of the total single-copy DNA sequences form a duplex in the preimplantation stages of development which is followed by an increase in complexity of transcription to about 10% by parturition (Fig. 2) (Church and Brown, 1972). The estimates obtained for early stages of the mouse are based on the reaction of ^{3}H-labeled RNA with ^{14}C-labeled single-copy DNA in a formamide reaction mixture at 30°C for several weeks (Church, 1970). The rabbit blastocyst expands tremendously prior to implantation, and sufficient RNA can be obtained to provide the estimate that 1.8% of the genome is complementary to single-copy DNA. This is equal to about 60,000 base sequences 1000 nucleotides in length (Schultz *et al.*, 1973b) since the rabbit genome is comprised of about 4.5×10^9 base pairs (Vendrely and Vendrely, 1949) and 70% of the nuclear DNA is single copy.

In the mouse embryo, a marked increase in transcriptional complexity appears very shortly after implantation occurs (Fig. 2). It is difficult to obtain sufficient embryonic material totally free of contaminating extraembryonic membranes or decidual tissue before 7.5 days of pregnancy in the mouse. The value reported for 7-day embryos in Fig. 2 may, therefore, be an overestimate of true embryonic transcriptional activity. Therefore, the increase in complexity of transcription in the mouse may be similar to the pattern shown in the rabbit. The apparent differences between the mouse and rabbit may not be as great as indicated since differences in the length of the gestational period and in the rate of embryonic development may demand a faster utilization of the mouse genome. The data clearly show a quantitative increase in the number of single-copy DNA genes transcribed from the blastocyst through fetal development to parturition.

The complexity of transcription of the single-copy DNA base sequences in several organs during fetal and postnatal development of the mouse and rabbit are shown in Fig. 3. About 5% of the single-copy DNA base sequences are transcribed in the brain of the third trimester

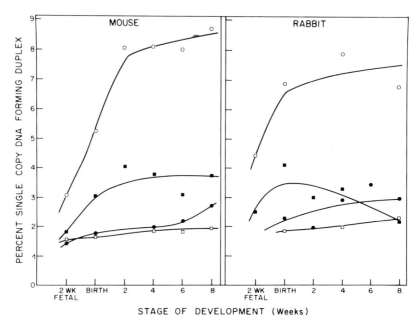

FIG. 3.   Complexity of ribonucleic acid (RNA) transcripts complementary to nonrepeated DNA sequences in various tissues during mouse and rabbit development. The RNA was isolated from brain (○), liver (■), spleen (●), and kidney (□) at the stages of development indicated and hybridized under saturating conditions with homologous ³H-labeled single-copy DNA. The values obtained represent the apparent saturation estimates for each RNA preparation at each stage of development. Complete technical details have been described (Brown and Church, 1972; Schultz *et al.*, 1973b).

fetus. Transcription in brain tissue rises to about 8% at parturition and continues to approximately 10% in the adult. In contrast, only about 2 to 3% of the single-copy DNA base sequences in liver, kidney, and spleen are transcribed in the newborn animal. The extent of RNA transcriptional complexity remains fairly constant between about 2.5 to 4.0% during development. The lower RNA transcriptional complexity in the rabbit may be related to the composition of the genome.

If the estimates for RNA transcription from different organs or between different stages of development of the same organ are about equal, it does not necessarily imply that these populations of RNA are very similar. Different fractions of the genome may be transcribed in each instance and only the quantitative diversity may be similar. Additive experiments in which RNA from newborn and adult liver were simultaneously hybridized to nonrepeated DNA provide an apparent saturation value of 3.5% compared with 2.5% for newborn liver RNA and 2.0%

for adult liver RNA. Therefore some RNA transcripts would seem to be common to the newborn and adult stage, whereas others are unique to certain stages of tissue development. The minimal additive effect observed for the reaction of newborn and adult brain RNA with nonrepeated DNA may indicate that most transcripts of nonrepeated DNA in the newborn brain are stable and are included in the spectrum present in the adult tissue or are continuously transcribed (Brown and Church, 1972). Similarly, Grouse et al. (1972) have done additive hybridization experiments with mixtures of liver and kidney RNA and liver and spleen RNA. In both cases, an apparent saturation plateau was obtained exceeding that obtained for RNA from either organ alone. Transcriptional overlap has also been demonstrated in the prenatal rabbit embryo (Schultz et al., 1973b).

Because of the long incubation times required for these hybridization reactions utilizing nonrepeated, DNA base sequences to reach saturation, RNA species of very low frequency in the cell may not be titrated (Church, 1973). Therefore, it is likely that the estimates of the diversity in transcription from single-copy DNA base sequences presented are minimal estimates. The large amount of potential information transcribed in the various tissues should not, however, be equated with an equivalent diversity in mRNA molecules since the majority of sequences are restricted to the cell nucleus. Heterogeneous nuclear RNA turns over in the nucleus and most of it never reaches the cytoplasm (Soeiro et al., 1968; Shearer and McCarthy, 1967; McCarthy et al., 1970). A variety of studies indicate that only about 8 to 10% of the total heterogeneous nuclear RNA is associated with poly(A) sequences (Schultz and Church, 1973). Although poly(A) is a good marker for putative mRNA species, it, unfortunately, fails to reveal the nonrandomness of selection of molecules for transport out of the nucleus (for review, see Schultz and Church, 1973).

The significance of the surprisingly high complexity of transcription in neural tissue cannot be meaningfully interpreted at this time. In the mouse, approximately 20% of the potential single-copy DNA sequences are transcribed. This is equivalent to 11% of the total genome and is equal to 300,000 genes coding for 300-chain length polypeptides. Homogeneous cell populations are required to determine the contribution that glial, neuronal, and other cell types make to the extent of genetic complexity found in brain tissue.

IV. Conclusions

The concept that all somatic cells of higher organisms contain the same genetic information is based upon nuclear transplantation experiments (Gurdon, 1962) and on the reiterated DNA/DNA–agar hybridization experiments carried out by McCarthy and Hoyer (1964). All cells of an organism probably contain a master copy of every DNA base sequence; however, there may be amplification of genes or reiteration of DNA base sequences in a particular differentiated cell line. For example, an erythrocyte may contain more hemoglobin cistrons than any other type of somatic cell, whereas, in some highly differentiated cell type, some base sequences may be absent from the genome. The conditions of the reiterated DNA/DNA hybridization studies carried out by McCarthy and Hoyer (1964) did not require specific enough base pairing to detect subtle changes in specific DNA base sequences between cell types. In fact, the L-cell line with its abnormal karyotype was not distinguishable from DNA isolated from somatic tissues of inbred mice. The mouse genome contains enough information for approximately 10^7 structural genes. Therefore, errors of much less than 1% in total base pairing analysis would still permit very large differences in DNA secondary structure and gene sequence to go undetected.

Although selective synthesis of small segments of the genome of higher animals has not been detected by radioaudiographic or by general pulse-labeling techniques, such a mechanism would seem to be a possible candidate for the regulation of gene activity. The best known example of such a mechanism is the amplification of the ribosomal RNA cistrons of amphibian oocytes (Brown and Dawid, 1968; Evans and Birnstiel 1968; Gall 1968; Vincent et al. 1968; Gall et al., 1969). Pavan and da Cunha (1969) have provided evidence that gene amplification also occurs within somatic cells of *Rhyncosciara*. Amplified ribosomal DNA sequences from *Xenopus* ovaries are not methylated, whereas the non-amplified ribosomal DNA sequences show 4.5% methylation (Dawid et al., 1970). These observations suggest that some functional specificity of methylation of DNA sequences may be involved in the regulation of selective amplification of ribosomal genes during oogenesis.

Deoxyribonucleic acid isolated from different stages of embryonic mouse liver development have been examined by differential elution chromatography from hydroxyapatite (Church and Georgiev, unpublished results). The results suggest that subtle changes occur in the secondary structure of native DNA during the various phases of cell proliferation. Four discrete populations of DNA sequences have been detected and their physical properties examined. The DNA isolated from mature liver behaves as a normal DNA duplex eluting from hydroxyapatite with greater than 0.27 M phosphate buffer. Deoxyribonucleic acid isolated from 10-day embryonic mouse liver contains DNA duplex in a form that elutes from hydroxyapatite at a lower phosphate molarity ($0.17\ M$) and exhibits an enhanced ability to bind to nitrocellulose filters.

Perhaps a common way for cells to react to a sudden demand for cell products is by the selective duplication of DNA sequences which, in turn, serve as a template in the synthesis of more RNA and subsequently more cell product.

Recently, suggestive evidence for amplification of ribosomal genes has also been reported during amphibian lens regeneration (Collins, 1972). It was found that 1.5 times more genes for rRNA are present in iris cells of a 7-day regenerating lens than in the normal iris, liver, or muscle cell. A 1.8-fold increase in rRNA genes in tissue culture hepatocytes has also been observed (Koch and Cruceanu, 1971). It is difficult, however, to visualize any important role for somatic two-fold amplification of rRNA cistrons since the ribosomal cistrons are already present in hundreds of copies in each cell unless a specific sequence is amplified.

Although very little evidence has accumulated for the special synthesis of selected portions of the genome involving either repeated or single-copy DNA base sequences, it is known that differences in the rate of total DNA synthesis exist in the preimplantation embryo (Graham, 1973). The importance of a further understanding of the influence of DNA duplication on RNA synthesis cannot be underestimated at this time. During the cleavage divisions the gradual decrease in the rate of cell division uncouples DNA and RNA synthesis. The relationship of the apparent high transcriptional activity of the repeated sequences in preimplantation development relative to single-copy transcription is not presently understood.

It is tempting to postulate a correlation between the extent of repeated RNA transcripts and the totipotency of early blastomeres. The morula position of a blastomere must somehow signal gene activity for the initial cell differentiation in mammalian development. Cells on the outside of the blastocyst are programmed so that they are unable to form part of the postimplantation fetus either as a group or as a single cell injected into another blastocyst, whereas the inner cells are unable to induce a decidua or continue development when introduced into the uterus of a pseudopregnant animal. Whether this apparent differentiation is the result of the differential activity of genes or of some positional cytoplasmic effect is not clear. If RNA synthesis is required for blastocyst differentiation, this requirement would seem to be a fairly nonspecific one. However, in the mouse, delayed implantation occurs if the uterus is not estrogen-sensitized. This means that the blastocyst is able to stop DNA synthesis and drastically inhibit RNA and protein synthesis for

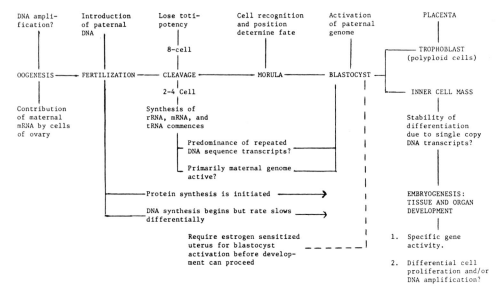

Fig. 4. Diagrammatic representation of the functional correlations between macromolecular synthesis and ontogenetic phenomena in early mouse development. rRNA, ribosomal ribonucleic acid; mRNA, messenger RNA; tRNA, transfer RNA; DNA, deoxyribonucleic acid.

a period of time before resuming full programmed development (Fig. 4).

The differences in the extent of RNA transcriptional complexity in the developing mouse and rabbit are not surprising since mammalian oocytes vary in size from about 60 μm in the mouse to 140 μm in the bovine. The preimplantation period and total gestation period vary tremendously between species. For example, in the mouse the gestation period is 21 days, of which the preimplantation period constitutes 5 days in comparison to the human in whom the gestation period is 270 days, with a preimplantation period of from 8 to 14 days. In the bovine with a gestation period of 275 to 290 days the preimplantation period lasts from 25 to 50 days. Preimplantation embryos stay in the fallopian tube for about 4 days in most species (Brinster, 1970). During preimplantation development, nutritional requirements and metabolism are similar in most mammals (Brinster, 1971). The protein synthesis that commences at the time of fertilization and the RNA synthesis that follows shortly thereafter are probably concerned with this basic metabolism.

The extent of the contribution of any maternal mRNA synthesized in the ovary to preimplantation gene activity is difficult to measure. The transcription occurring prior to blastocyst formation must be from the maternal portion of the genome since no true genetic mutant which has been shown to interfere specifically with gene activity prior to blastocyst formation has been identified. The transcription in the preblastocyst embryo might, therefore, be considered an extension of a maternal, somatic cell, gene activity pattern which commenced in the ovary.

A diagrammatic representation of the correlation between the appearance of ontogenetic phenomena during early mouse development and the synthesis of macromolecules is presented in Fig. 4. As we have pointed out in the foregoing, each species will probably have its own unique features in such a developmental program which can be superimposed upon the basic gene activity that is selectively conserved during evolution.

Current developments in the handling, manipulation, formation of chimeras, and storage (Whittingham *et al.*, 1972) of mammalian embryos will greatly enhance the rate at which our understanding of genetic activity during development will occur. Concurrent with our knowledge of the regulation of gene expression in the pre- and early postimplantation mammalian embryo will come a greater chance of ascertaining the basis of many birth defects in man.

ACKNOWLEDGMENTS

The authors would like to express their appreciation to Carol Holliday, Anne Vipond, and July Fleetham for their assistance during this project and to the National Research Council and Medical Research Council for operating grants.

REFERENCES

Bishop, J. O. (1972). *Biochem. J.* **126,** 171–185.
Bishop, J. O., Pemberton, R., and Baglioni, C. (1972). *Nature* (*London*) **235,** 231–234.
Brinster, R. L. (1965a). *Biochim. Biophys. Acta* **10,** 439–441.
Brinster, R. L. (1965b). *J. Exp. Zool.* **158,** 59–71.
Brinster, R. L. (1966). *Biochem. J.* **101,** 161–163.
Brinster, R. L. (1967). *Biochim. Biophys. Acta* **148,** 298–300.
Brinster, R. L. (1968). *Enzymologia* **34,** 304–308.
Brinster, R. L. (1970). *Biochem. Genet.* **4,** 669–676.
Brinster, R. L. (1971). *In* "The Biology of the Blastocyst" (R. J. Blandau, ed.), pp. 303–318. Univ. of Chicago Press, Chicago, Illinois.
Britten, R. J., and Davidson, E. H. (1969). *Science* **165,** 349–357.
Britten, R. J., and Kohne, D. E. (1966). *Carnegie Inst. Washington Yearb.* **65,** 73–88.
Britten, R. J., and Kohne, D. E. (1968). *Science* **161,** 529–532.
Brown, D. D., and Dawid, I. B. (1968). *Science* **160,** 272–280.
Brown, I. R., and Church, R. B. (1971). *Biochem. Biophys. Res. Commun.* **42,** 850–856.

Brown, I. R., and Church, R. B. (1972). *Develop. Biol.* **29**, 73–84.

Carr, D. H. (1971). *Annu. Rev. Genet.* **5**, 65–80.

Cattanach, B. M. (1962). *Genet. Res.* **3**, 487–490.

Chapman, V. M., Whitten, M. K., and Ruddle, F. H. (1971). *Develop. Biol.* **26**, 153–158.

Chapman, V. M., Ansell, J. D., and McLaren, A. (1972). *Develop. Biol.* **29**, 48–54.

Church, R. B. (1970). *In* "Congenital Malformations" (F. C. Fraser and V. A. McKusick, eds.), pp. 19–28. Excerpta Medica, New York.

Church, R. B. (1973). *In* "Molecular Techniques in Developmental Biology" (M. Chrispeels, ed.), pp. 223–301. Wiley, New York.

Church, R. B., and Brown, I. R. (1972). *In* "Results and Problems in Cell Differentiation" (H. Ursprung, ed.), Vol. 3, pp. 11–24. Springer-Verlag, Berlin and New York.

Church, R. B., and McCarthy, B. J. (1967a). *J. Mol. Biol.* **23**, 459–475.

Church, R. B., and McCarthy, B. J. (1967b). *J. Mol. Biol.* **23**, 476–486.

Church, R. B., and McCarthy, B. J. (1968). *Biochem. Genet.* **2**, 55–73.

Church, R. B., and Georgiev, G. P. (1973) *Mol. Biol. Rep.* **1**, 21–25.

Collins, J. N. (1972). *Biochemistry* **11**, 1259–1264.

Darnell, J. E. (1968). *Bacteriol. Rev.* **32**, 262–290.

Davidson, E. H. (1968). "Gene Activity in Early Development," pp. 247–346. Academic Press, New York.

Davidson, E. H., and Hough, B. R. (1969). *Proc. Nat. Acad. Sci. U. S.* **63**, 342–349.

Davidson, E. H., and Hough, B. R. (1971). *J. Mol. Biol.* **56**, 491–506.

Davidson, E. H., Crippa, M., Kramer, F. R., and Mirsky, A. E. (1966). *Proc. Nat. Acad. Sci. U. S.* **56**, 956–962.

Dawid, I. E., Brown, D. D., and Reeder, R. H. (1970). *J. Mol. Biol.* **51**, 341–360.

Dyban, D. (1972). Personal communication.

Ellem, K. A. O., and Gwatkin, R. B. L. (1968). *Develop. Biol.* **18**, 311–330.

Epstein, C. J. (1970). *J. Biol. Chem.* **245**, 3289–3294.

Epstein, C. J., Wegienka, E. A., and Smith, C. W. (1969). *Biochem. Genet.* **3**, 271–281.

Epstein, C. J., Daentl, D. L., Smith, S. A., and Krook, L. W. (1971). *Biol. Reprod.* **5**, 308–313.

Epstein, C. J., Weston, J. A., Whitten, W. K., and Russell, E. S. (1972). *Develop. Biol.* **27**, 430–433.

Evans, D., and Birnstiel, M. (1968). *Biochim. Biophys. Acta* **166**, 274–276.

Firtel, R. A., Jacobson, A., and Lodish, H. F. (1972). *Nature (London)* **239**, 225–228.

Flamm, W. G., Walker, P. M. B., and McCallum, M. (1969). *J. Mol. Biol.* **40**, 423–443.

Flickinger, R. A. (1971). *In* "Changing Synthesis in Development" (M. Runner, ed.), pp. 12–39. Academic Press, New York.

Gall, J. G. (1968). *Proc. Nat. Acad. Sci. U. S.* **60**, 553–560.

Gall, J. G., MacGregor, H. C., and Kidston, M. E. (1969). *Chromosoma* **26**, 169–187.

Gardner, R. L. (1971). *Advan. Biosci.* **6**, 279–296.

Gardner, R. L. (1972). *J. Embryol. Exp. Morphol.* **28**, 279–312.

Gearhart, J. T., and Mintz, B. (1972). *Develop. Biol.* **29**, 27–37.

Gelderman, A. H., Rake, A. V., and Britten, R. J. (1971). *Proc. Nat. Acad. Sci. U. S.* **68**, 172–176.

Georgiev, G. (1969). *J. Theor. Biol.* **25**, 473–490.

Graham, C. F. (1970). *Nature (London)* **226**, 165–167.

Graham, C. F. (1971). *Soc. Exp. Biol. Symp.* **25**, 371–378.

Graham, C. F. (1973). *In* "Regulation of Mammalian Reproduction" (S. Segal, R. Crozier, P. Corfman, and P. Condliffe, eds.), pp. 286–301. Thomas, Springfield, Illinois.

Greenberg, J. R., and Perry, R. P. (1971). *J. Cell Biol.* **50**, 774–786.

Gross, P. R. (1968). *Annu. Rev. Biochem.* **37**, 631–660.

Grouse, L., Chilton, M., and McCarthy, B. J. (1972). *Biochemistry* **11**, 798–805.

Gurdon, J. B. (1962). *Develop. Biol.* **4**, 256–269.

Hahn, W. E., and Church, R. B. (1970). *In* "Cell Differentiation" (O. A. Schjeide and J. de Vellis, eds.), pp. 119–140. Van Nostrand-Reinhold, Princeton, New Jersey.

Hahn, W. E., and Laird, C. D. (1971). *Science* **173**, 158–161.

Hillman, N. M., and Tasca, R. J. (1969). *Amer. J. Anat.* **126**, 151–174.

Hillman, N. M., Sherman, M. I., and Graham, C. (1972). *J. Embryol. Exp. Morphol.* **28**, 263–278.

Hinderstein, W., Kahn, A., and Koren, Z. (1972). *Int. J. Fert.* **17**, 72–74.

Hough, B. R., and Davidson, E. H. (1972). *J. Mol. Biol.* **70**, 491–509.

Kedes, L. H., and Birnstiel, M. L. (1971). *Nature (London)* **230**, 165–169.

Knowland, J., and Graham, C. (1972). *J. Embryol. Exp. Morphol.* **27**, 67–176.

Koch, J., and Cruceanu, A. Z. (1971). *Physiol. Chem.* **352**, 137–154.

Kohne, D. E. (1968). *Biophys. J.* **8**, 1104–1112.

Laird, C. D. (1971). *Chromosoma* **32**, 378–406.

McCarthy, B. J. (1967). *Bacteriol. Rev.* **31**, 215–229.

McCarthy, B. J., and Church, R. B. (1970). *Annu. Rev. Biochem.* **39**, 131–150.

McCarthy, B. J., and Hoyer, B. (1964). *Proc. Nat. Acad. Sci. U. S.* **52**, 915–920.

McCarthy, B. J., and McConaughy, B. L. (1968). *Biochem. Genet.* **2**, 37–53.

McCarthy, B. J., Shearer, R. W., and Church, R. B. (1970). *In* "Problems in Biology: RNA in Development" (E. W. Hanly, ed.), pp. 285–314. Univ. of Utah Press, Salt Lake City, Utah.

McLaren, A. (1973). *In* "Regulation of Mammalian Reproduction" (S. Segal, R. Crozier, P. Corfman, and P. Condliffe, eds.), pp. 321–326. Thomas, Springfield, Illinois.

Manes, C. (1969). *J. Exp. Zool.* **172**, 303–310.

Manes, C. (1971). *J. Exp. Zool.* **176**, 87–96.

Manes, C., and Daniel, J. C., Jr. (1969). *Exp. Cell Res.* **55**, 261–268.

Melli, M., Whitfield, C., Rao, K. V., Richardson, M., and Bishop, J. O. (1971). *Nature (London)* **231**, 8–12.

Milunsky, A., and Littlefield, J. W. (1972). *Annu. Rev. Med.* **23**, 57–76.

Mintz, B. (1964). *J. Exp. Zool.* **157**, 85–100.

Mintz, B. (1970). *Symp. Int. Soc. Cell Biol.* **9**, 15–42.

Mirsky, A. E., and Ris, H. (1951). *J. Gen. Physiol.* **34**, 451–462.

Monesi, V., and Salfi, V. (1967). *Exp. Cell Res.* **46**, 632–635.

Monesi, V., Molinaro, M., Spaletta, E., and Davioli, C. (1970). *Exp. Cell Res.* **59**, 197–206.

Moog, F. (1965). *In* "The Biochemistry of Animal Development" (R. Weber, ed.), Vol. 1, pp. 307–367. Academic Press, New York.

Moore, N. W., Adams, C. E., and Rowson, L. E. A. (1968). *J. Reprod. Fert.* **17**, 527–531.

Morris, T. (1968). *Genet. Res.* **12**, 125–136.

Nesbitt, M. N., and Gartler, S. M. (1971). *Annu. Rev. Genet.* **5**, 143–162.

Pardue, M. L., and Gall, J. G. (1969). *Proc. Nat. Acad. Sci. U. S.* **64**, 600–606.

Paul, J. (1970). *Curr. Top. Develop. Biol.* **5**, 317–352.

Paul, J., and Gilmour, R. S. (1968). *J. Mol. Biol.* **34**, 305–316.

Pavan, C., and da Cunha, A. B. (1969). *Genetics* **61** (*Suppl.*), 289–304.

Piko, L. (1970). *Develop. Biol.* **21**, 257–279.

Ritossa, F. M., and Spiegelman, S. (1965). *Proc. Nat. Acad. Sci. U. S.* **53**, 737–745.

Rutter, W. J., Clark, W. R., Kemp. J. D., Bradshaw, R. S., Sanders, T. G., and Ball, W. D. (1968). *In* "Epithelial–Mesenchymal Interactions," Halmemann Symp., 18th, (R. Fleischmajer, and R. E. Billingham, eds.), pp. 114–131. Williams & Wilkins, Baltimore, Maryland.

Scherrer, K., Spohr, G., Granboulan, G., Morel, C., Grosclaude, J., and Chezzi, C. (1970). *Cold Spring Harbor Symp. Quant. Biol.* **35**, 539–554.

Schultz, G. A., and Church, R. B. (1973). *In* "Biochemistry of Animal Development" (R. Weber, ed.), Vol. 3. Academic Press, New York.

Schultz, G. A., Manes, C., and Hahn, W. E. (1973a). *Develop. Biol.* **30**, 418–426.

Schultz, G. A., Manes, C., and Hahn, W. E. (1973b). *Biochem. Genet.* **9**, 247–259.

Shearer, R. W., and McCarthy, B. J. (1967). *Biochemistry* **6**, 283–289.

Sherman, M. I., McLaren, A., and Walker, P. M. B. (1972). *Nature* (*London*) **238**, 175–176.

Smith, D. M. (1956). *J. Endocrinol.* **41**, 17–29.

Smith, K. D., Church, R. B., and McCarthy, B. J. (1969). *Biochemistry* **8**, 4271–4277.

Soeiro, R., Vaughan, M. H., Warner, J. R., and Darnell, J. E. (1968). *J. Cell Biol.* **39**, 112–118.

Stern, M. S. (1972). *J. Embryol. Exp. Morphol.* **28**, 255–261.

Sutton, W. D., and McCallum, M. (1971). *Nature* (*London*) **232**, 83–84.

Tarkowski, A. K. (1959). *Nature* (*London*) **184**, 1286–1287.

Tarkowski, A. K., and Wroblewka, J. (1967). *J. Embryol. Exp. Morphol.* **18**, 155–180.

Tarkowski, A. K., Witkowska, A., and Nowicka, J. (1970). *Nature* (*London*) **226**, 162–165.

Tasca, R. J., and Hillman, N. (1970). *Nature* (*London*) **225**, 1022–1025.

Thomson, J. L., and Biggers, J. D. (1966). *Exp. Cell Res.* **41**, 411–427.

Vendrely, R., and Vendrely, C. (1949). *Experientia* **5**, 327–329.

Vincent, W. S., Halvarsen, H. O., Chen, H. R., and Shin, D. (1968). *Biol. Bull.* **135**, 441.

Walker, P. M. B. (1969). *Progr. Nucl. Acid. Res. Mol. Biol.* **9**, 301–342.

Wallace, H., and Birnstiel, M. L. (1966). *Biochim. Biophys. Acta* **114**, 296–310.

Whittingham, D. G., Leibo, S. P., and Mazur, P. (1972). *Science* **178**, 411–414.

Woodland, H. R., and Graham, C. F. (1969). *Nature* (*London*) **221**, 327–332.

Yasmineh, W. G., and Yunis, J. J. (1969). *Biochem. Biophys. Res. Commun.* **35**, 779–782.

CHAPTER 7

NEURONAL SPECIFICITY REVISITED

*R. K. Hunt and Marcus Jacobson**

DEPARTMENT OF ANATOMY AND THE INSTITUTE OF NEUROLOGICAL SCIENCES
UNIVERSITY OF PENNSYLVANIA MEDICAL SCHOOL, PHILADELPHIA, PENNSYLVANIA
AND THOMAS C. JENKINS DEPARTMENT OF BIOPHYSICS
THE JOHNS HOPKINS UNIVERSITY, BALTIMORE, MARYLAND

I. Introductory Essay

A. HISTORY OF THE THEORY

Neuronal specificity, like many other scientific concepts, originated as a daring novelty, gradually became accepted as a commonplace, and is now being challenged as an ancient and outmoded superstition. When a venerable scientific concept is perceived to be less than completely correct, there is frequently an overzealous reaction against it. In such cases there is a danger of rejecting the good indiscriminately with the bad. The temptation to reject the whole because of a flaw in one of its parts is most acute in the case of a complex concept such as neuronal

* *Present Address:* Department of Physiology and Biophysics, University of Miami, School of Medicine, Miami, Florida.

specificity, whose many aspects and levels of meaning may not all have become obsolete, but whose complexity makes retirement seem much easier than rehabilitation. Therefore, a critical definition and analysis of all aspects of the concept itself as well as a reconsideration of its history and methodology are essential. Expenditure of effort on such a critical exercise, rather than on more laboratory work, can be justified only because we agree that there "is much confusion at the present time in the study of the interconnexions between neurones in the vertebrate brain" (Gaze and Keating, 1972). The main sources of such confusion seem to be in the conceptualization and methodology rather than in the concept or theory of neuronal specificity itself.

Historically the concept of specificity arose during the past half-century. As a multiplicity of neuronal types were recognized, it was also realized that each type of nerve cell has invariant properties, highly predictable structural and functional relationships, a typical position within the multicellular pattern, and, most significantly, forms orderly and specific synaptic connections. Indeed, the concept of neuronal specificity has come to be applied most often to the regularity of neuronal architectonics: to the invariance with which neurons send their fibers out in particular directions, to branch and course in particular patterns, and to make connections selectively with particular target cells. Such pristine regularities inspire more than interest in developmental mechanics, for, as Vladimir Nabokov (1966) has put it: "There is, it would seem in the dimensional scale of the world a kind of delicate meeting place between imagination and knowledge, a point, arrived at by diminishing large things and enlarging small ones, that is intrinsically artistic."

By the early decades of this century, overwhelming evidence had been amassed to show that different types of neurons can be recognized by their invariant anatomical features and by their positions, their fiber pathways, and their synaptic connectivity. But opinions were sharply divided about the developmental mechanisms that brought the neurons together into selective synaptic associations. Various theories were proposed dealing with the orderly growth of nerve fibers and the selective formation of synaptic connections; chemotaxis, chemotropism, chemoaffinity, stereotropism, contact guidance, neurobiotaxis, stimulogenous fibrillation, and functional adaptation were some of the mechanisms that were suggested. It was thought that the growing nerve fiber or its presynaptic terminal selects the appropriate pathway and synaptic site by responding selectively to chemical, mechanical, or electrical signals. We shall not deal at length here with these theories because they have been discussed elsewhere (Harrison, 1935; Detwiler, 1936; Piatt, 1948,

Sperry, 1950, 1951a,b; Weiss, 1955; Jacobson, 1970b), and, because we are not attempting to write either a new history of theories nor a new theory of history. Rather, our main purposes are to define clearly the various meanings and connotations that may be given to the term *neuronal specificity* and to reconsider the experimental evidence and strategies that have been used to assay specificity.

> A major source of difficulty stems from the protean nature of the phenomena that show specificity. Weiss (1947) wrote: The frequency which such terms as specificity, selectivity, conformity, correspondence, etc., appears in biological literature is ample proof that they denote a universal and fundamental trait running like a common theme through all the manifestations of life. Yet, they are used with so many different shades of meaning and degrees of precision that it is impossible to tell whether the various phenomena to which they are applied bear a purely formal resemblance to each other, or whether there is essentially a single principle in back of them all.

Almost 20 years later, Gaze and Keating (1972) express a similar sentiment. They draw attention to "the vague and ill-defined terminology that has been used to discuss neuronal connections," and say that "Terms such as order, randomness and specificity have been commonly used; and it becomes more obvious with each paper published that each author is using a private language and the terms that he uses may mean one thing to him and another to someone else. These comments, of course, are equally true of us."

Much of the ambiguity, confusion, and fallacy in the literature of neuronal specificity has been the inevitable consequence of trying to accommodate too large and too diverse a body of phenomena within a single conceptual framework. Yet we find the concept of specificity too valuable to discard. Rather, we must apply a rigorous methodology for distinguishing one kind of specificity from another.

B. The Concept of Neuronal Specificity

Some of the difficulties have arisen because the concept of neuronal specificity has evolved historically on two levels. On one level it has arisen as a general theory concerned with the developmental mechanics of the nervous system, dealing particularly with the formation of nerve circuits and synaptic connections, and culminating in the chemoaffinity theory proposed by Sperry (1950, 1951b, 1963). On another level, the theory of neuronal specificity has evolved on a purely conceptual level as an abstract construct. The abstract construct is not explicitly defined, but it is implied in almost all attempts to describe how the brain develops, how it is structured, or how it functions. Therefore, we give the following short definition of the abstract construct of neuronal specificity: *a neuron is said to have specificity if it performs an operation the outcome of which is highly predictable and related to particular neuronal properties.* This definition neither places constraints on the physical nature of the properties and the ways in which they develop nor does it designate the operations or how they are performed. For example, the abstract construct has nothing to say about the nature of the position-dependent properties that may develop in any set of neurons (such as the population of retinal cells or tectal cells) nor does it indicate how such properties may be expressed during morphogenesis of neuronal circuits and connections (e.g., retinotectal connections). The actual mechanisms have to be determined empirically for each set of neurons, and empirical criteria (morphological, functional, or biochemical) must be found for assigning neurons to a particular set. Further consideration of the kinds of specific neuronal properties and operations will be deferred to the end of this paper, but it suffices here to point out that properties and operations may be acquired by each individual neuron either with or without reference to the other neurons in its set (i.e., either in a contextual mode or in a noncontextual mode). We believe that difficulties stem from the failure to make a clear distinction between these two modes of development of neuronal specificity. Other difficulties seem to have arisen as a result of the numerous shades of meaning that may be given to the concept of specificity, and from the many grades of specificity that nerve cells may, in principle, exhibit. At one extreme, specificity means a necessary or obligatory characteristic always exhibited by an individual nerve cell, whereas at the other extreme, it denotes a mere facultative tendency, preference, or predisposition displayed under some, but not all, conditions. In addition to these grades of specificity, one has to consider its exclusivity or inclusivity. The specificity, whether obligatory or merely facultative, may belong exclusively to an individual neuron or it may be shared by many as an inclusive property of a neuron set.

We return, now, to consider the general theory of neuronal specificity proposed by Sperry (1950, 1951a,b, 1963). The theory holds that the self-assembly of neuronal circuits is brought about as a result of selective biochemical affinities and disaffinities between nerve cells. Historically, the theory arose in reaction to the view, prevalent in the 1930s, that use and experience organized adaptive circuits out of initially equipotential neuronal networks. Sperry's hypothesis (Sperry, 1963), in his own words,

> suggested that the patterning of synaptic connections in the nerve centers, including those refined details of network organization heretofore ascribed

mainly to functional molding in various forms, must be handled instead by the growth mechanism directly, independently of function, and with very strict selectivity governing synaptic formation from the beginning. The establishment and maintenance of synaptic association were conceived to be regulated by highly specific cytochemical affinities that arise systematically among the different types of neurons involved via self-differentiation, induction through terminal contact, and embryonic gradient affects.

The evidence for this theory has been reviewed in five articles by Sperry (1950, 1951a,b, 1963, 1965) and we shall not presume to summarize his summary. We think it important to emphasize that, although Sperry's neuronal specificity theory was his solution of the nature–nurture problem, it sprang directly out of embryological concepts and owes a particular debt to the concept of tissue affinity and cellular adhesion as morphogenetic mechanisms (Holtfreter, 1939). Neurobiology has a way of lagging behind the rest of biology in the development of its concepts and its theories. Consider, for example, why the neuron theory enunciated in 1891 should have been delayed so long after the cell theory was proposed in 1838, or why the theory of neuronal chemoaffinity should have been developed such a long time after Holtfreter's 1939 paper showing that cytoaffinity is a basic mechanism of assembly of cells into tissues.

We shall not take up the theme of the nature-nurture controversy in this paper. It suffices to say that, although some "fine tuning" of certain synaptic connections may be brought about by function and experience, all the evidence shows that differentiation and morphogenesis of the main neural circuits is largely completed in the prefunctional stage of ontogeny and that the main developmental processes, including nerve cell proliferation, migration, outgrowth of nerve fibers, and the patterning of their terminal connections are not influenced by learning. Our concern will largely be with the problem of cell and developmental biology that have been raised by Sperry's theory.

Although Sperry's theory has left many questions open, it clearly states that the self-assembly of neuronal circuits results from intercellular recognition, which is, in turn, based upon cytochemical specificities that are a distinctive property acquired by the indiviual neuron* as a result of cellular differentiation. It is alco clear that Sperry conceived of these properties as being distributed in a systematic manner—not discontinuously but in a graded way through neuronal populations. For example, he says (Sperry, 1950):

---

* This means that an individual neuron has a specific property but it neither implies that the property is held exclusively by one neuron nor that it is independent of the presence of other neurons.

the over-all process of differentiation is presumed to follow a tree-like pattern, as a rule, with the gross subdivision being set off first and these, in turn, successively subdividing to produce increasing refinement. As a result, the chemical properties of the individual neuron elements, as finally determined, are not haphazardly arranged but exhibit systematic familial relationships reflecting rather closely the functional relations.

Sperry has repeatedly emphasized that the specificities are distributed in a fieldlike way within the nerve cell population. Considering the particular case of the visual system, he (Sperry, 1950) says:

> The optic fibers differ from one another in quality according to the particular locus of the retina in which the ganglion cells are located. The retina apparently undergoes a polarized, field-like differentiation during development, which brings about local specification of the ganglion cells and their optic axons. The functional relations established by the optic fibers in the brain centers are patterned in a systematic manner on the basis of this refined specificity.

Sperry's theory meets the requirements that a good theory should "proceed from some *simple, new, and powerful idea*" (Popper, 1962), and in its generality neither puts constraints on the biochemical mechanisms of neuronal specificity nor on the modes of its origin and expression during development. It is surprising, therefore, that Gaze and Keating (1972) have rejected Sperry's theory in advancing the notion that:

> reconnections formed by a given retinal ganglion cell depend not only on the retinal situation of that ganglion cell and the tectal situation of a tectal cell, but also on the extent of the retinal fiber complement projecting to the tectum and the extent of the tectum available. We have called this type of mechanism "systems-matching" to emphasize its difference from the selective and exclusive cell-to-cell specificity explicit in the chemoaffinity hypothesis.

Apparently they have not perceived how the neuron could acquire and hold an individual biochemical specificity which could be related to its context within the total system, but it is to their credit that they were first to champion the view that the total system should not be neglected. But, as we have shown in the foregoing, neither Sperry's theory nor the abstract construct of neuronal specificity put constraints on the nature of the specific neuronal properties or the specific neuronal operations, either or both of which may be either noncontextual or contextual ("systems-matching" seems to be a particular case of the latter). We are prepared to consider systems matching as an unsystematic attempt to define a limited aspect of neuronal specificity, but it patently fails to grasp the problem of specificity analytically and comprehensively in all its aspects. Perhaps that is why it is likely to be misconstrued as an *alternative* to Sperry's theory, as when for example, in a recent editorial comment on systems matching [*Nature* (*London*), Vol. 236, April 7, 1972] it is bluntly stated that "it now seems clear that Sperry's original concept of strict neuronal specificity cannot be retained."

This statement reveals a misconception of the scope of Sperry's chemoaffinity theory, restricting it arbitrarily to a single mode of specificity and excluding other modes in which the position at which an individually specified neuron forms a connection may vary according to the context in which the connection is formed. This statement also shows inadequate appreciation of the limitations of the experimental tests of Sperry's theory. When we come to examine the experimental evidence and the means that have been employed to obtain it, we shall find the evidence insufficient and the means intrinsically incapable of discovering the so-called rules governing the formation of neuronal connections or of showing whether the rules are contextual or noncontextual. Finally, one cannot disregard differences in the mode of specificity that different classes of neurons may display (for example, large motor neurons versus small interneurons), nor should one fail to appreciate that there are greater differences between different types of neurons (Purkinje cells versus retinal ganglion cells, for example) than there are likely to be between different individual neurons of the same type. It is to these levels of neuronal specificity that we now turn.

C. LEVELS OF SPECIFICITY

According to the chemoaffinity theory, the main criterion of neuronal specificity is the selective formation of synaptic connections: a specificity that is expressed on at least two levels, namely with regard to the *types* of neurons that associate selectively and with respect to their *positions* in the cell population. The selective association between particular types of nerve cells is an expression of *neuronal phenotypic specificity*. In addition, a presynaptic axonal terminal may select a postsynaptic target and form synaptic connections at a particular position within the cell population and thus express its *locus specificity*. With the visual system of the frog as an example, we have defined locus specificity as the specific property of the individual retinal ganglion cell that predisposes it to form tectal connections selectively at a particular position in the the retinotectal map (Hunt and Jacobson, 1972b).

Considering phenotypic specificity, we adopt many criteria for taxonomic classification of neurons and for assigning a particular neuron to a specific type. The distinctive and invariant features that identify a neuronal phenotype include cell form, position, alignment, direction of outgrowth and form of dendrites and axon, trajectory of axonal growth, relationship to neuroglial cells, and synaptic association with other types of neurons (Hamburger, 1960). Recognition of phenotypic specificity is possible only if each type of neuron exhibits these aspects of its specificity and shows a tendency to conform to its type during normal development as well as under a variety of experimental conditions. Such invariance is most obvious in the case of the large neurons with long axons (principal neurons, "macroneurons") which are the first to develop in each part of the nervous system and which are easily identified in all individuals of the same species. That phenotypic specificity is less well-documented for the small neurons (granule cells, "microneurons") may reflect the morphological lability of these cells and their susceptibility to modification by external influences (Altman, 1967, Jacobson, 1969, 1970a,b, 1973). Alternately, the variability usually attributed to small interneurons may be more apparent than real, reflecting (1) variable morphology but invariant biochemical properties or (2) variability that is more conspicuous, but not greater, in small neurons than it is in large neurons. This difficulty may not be overcome until biochemical assays are invented to characterize the specific profile of each type of neuron. Research on neuronal specificity has been confined almost entirely to the large neurons, not only because their normal phenotypic invariance provides a base line upon which the effects of experimental manipulations can be measured but also because of the ease of access to their cell bodies and axons and the possibility of assaying their synaptic connectivity. The populations of large nerve cells whose long axons comprise the main nerve pathways are spatially organized in such a way that the topography of the cell bodies is mirrored in the topography of their axonal projections and connections. When the spatial distribution of cell bodies and axon terminals is mapped anatomically and electrophysiologically in such systems, the invariant order in the relative positions of the neurons provides a measure of their specificities. The locus specificity is denoted by the position that the neuron occupies and at which it forms connections, and the phenotypic specificity is indicated by the types of neurons that associate synaptically at any given position.*

---

* The separate expression of locus specificity and phenotypic specificity is shown in the organization of the sensory projection zones in the brain in which cells are arranged as vertical columns in the tectum (Székely, 1971) and in the cerebral cortex (Mountcastle, 1957; Hubel, and Wiessel, 1972). A particular locus in the retina projects to a single column, which is composed of several types of neurons, but which all appear to share the same locus specificity. Different functional types of retinal ganglion cells are found in the frog (Maturana et al., 1960), and each type expresses its phenotypic specificity by projecting to a different level in the tectum and, apparently, synapsing selectively with different types of tectal cells. Another example of independent expression of phenotypic and locus specificity is found in the cerebellum of the "reeler" mutant mouse, in which connections are

Research in this field has been dominated by the problem of the spatial organization of the visual system, which "has become, in a sense, a battleground on which the opposing misconceptions of the intrinsic organization of the brain have been tested" (Polyak, 1941). To a large extent, therefore, our critique will be focused on experiments that have attempted to discover the rules that govern development of a spatially organized neuronal projection from the eye to the brain.

II. Theory of the Methodology

A. LIMITATIONS OF VISUAL PROJECTION MAPPING

A major technical advance in the field of neuronal specificity occurred with the application of electrophysiological techniques in the late 1950s. Two groups of investigators, working on the distribution and response characteristics of visual input to the frog's optic tectum, extended their studies to include frogs in which the optic nerve had been cut and allowed to regenerate. Those pioneering experiments (Gaze, 1959; Maturana et al., 1959) provided the first direct evidence in support of Sperry's inference that the severed optic fibers returned to the tectum in their proper retinotopic order.

Over the past 15 years, as the hardware of electrophysiological recording have improved, the verbal descriptions of what it does have become more and more vague and misleading. The technical limitations have become obscured by the citation of 10-year-old papers. Words with subtly different meanings have been gradually bent into synonymy and, by a sort of conceptual synecdoche, oscilloscope traces and crackling noises over a loudspeaker have become ganglion cell synapses; optic evoked potentials have become "fixed place specificities" and "sliding retinotectal connections"; visuotectal projections have become retinotectal connections. What has emerged for the developmental biologist who is not also a neurophysiologist is a series of blurred images, which provide neither the clear (if simplified) overview that could lead him through the jungle of electrode impedances, response latencies, single unit analyses nor the kind of rigorous theoretical framework that would enable him to evaluate critically experimental results on his own. More damaging still has been the effect on the field itself. Even as the data and the methods of obtaining them have become more reliable, the interpretation of the data and the status of the recording paradigm have become progressively more tenuous.

---

formed selectively between the proper types of nerve cells although the cells are severely malpositioned (Rakic and Sidman, 1972).

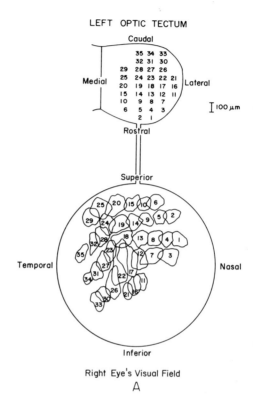

FIG. 1. Normal projection of right eye's visual field onto the left optic tectum in the adult clawed frog, *Xenopus laevis*, assayed in a normal juvenile animal. Numbers on the tectum indicate positions of a microelectrode during the projection assay. For each numbered position in the tectum, an enclosed and correspondingly numbered region of the visual field is shown (A), such that the visual field area represents the "effective stimulus area" for an electrode at the numbered tectal locus. A small spot of light anywhere within the enclosed numbered area, but nowhere else in the visual field, evoked potentials in the electrode at the corresponding tectal position.

The remainder of this section aspires to bring the recording techniques once again under critical scrutiny and to reexamine the strengths and limitations of the whole recording paradigm as an assay system for the study of neuronal specificity. (In the Appendix we consider the nature of the raw data, its physical limitations, the ways in which it is obtained, and how it is represented in the published results.)

B. VISUOTECTAL PROJECTION AS AN ASSAY OF RETINOTECTAL CONNECTIVITY

The electrophysiological technique delineates the projection of the visual field onto the optic tectum (Fig. 1). The legitimacy of interpreting

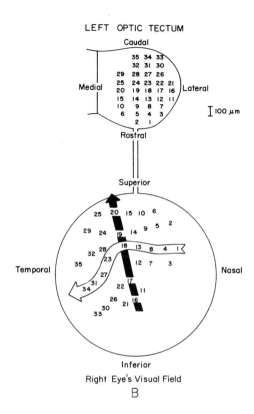

In the second diagram (B), only the "maximum stimulus position" in the visual field (i.e., that site in the effective stimulus area that gives the greatest response) is shown (by the number) and arrows have been added to help visualize the axial organization of the map. The methods by which visual projections are obtained and the conventions for their representation are discussed in detail in Appendix A.

such data on *visuo*tectal *projections* in terms of *retino*tectal connections is limited at best and rests upon two assumptions that must be validated in every new experimental setting. The first assumption, which permits the transformation of *visual* projection to *retinal* projection, postulates a point-to-point topographic relationship between a stimulus position in the visual field and its image on the retina (even though there is inversion of the image). This may be a reasonable assumption in normal adult frogs. But in experimental animals, a number of pathological conditions resulting in aberrations of the image are possible in which the assumption would not hold, among them: (1) defects in the lens or pupil or shape of the eyeball, e.g., malformations resulting from anoxia and surgical derangement at embryonic stages, (2) cataracts and scratches or scars on the cornea, (3) cloudiness of the vitreous, (4) optical aberrations or other abnormalities characteristic of the immature state, especially in larvae, and (5) abnormalities in the *intraretinal* connections, which normally "channel" the visual information from particular localized groups of photoreceptors to the specific ganglion cells in their immediate area. In fact, all these abnormalities have at some time been observed or strongly suspected in the course of our work; yet some workers insist on attributing abnormalities in the precision or organization of the visual projection to aberrant behavior on the part of the growing optic fibers (Gaze and Jacobson, 1963a; Gaze *et al.*, 1972).

The second assumption is that the tectal responses originate from part of a retinotectal synapse. In fact, the source of the potentials we record has never been demonstrated directly; and historically the bias to any one source has rested entirely on the strength of indirect arguments designed to exclude other sources. For instance, the response characteristics of the elements we record (e.g., whether they respond to light "on" or light "off" and whether they give a single action potential or a "burst") are identical to those found when the electrode probes the optic nerve itself, but very different from those observed when the electrode probes the deep, cellular layers of the tectum (Lettvin *et al.*, 1959; Maturana *et al.*, 1960). Thus, it has been inferred that we record from the optic nerve fibers in the tectum. Similarly, since the optic nerve fibers course across the tectal surface en route to their destination in the retinotectal map, the empirical observation of retinotopy in our experiments has led to the inference that we cannot be recording from optic fibers coursing past the electrode but only from their terminal arborizations (Maturana *et al.*, 1960; Gaze and Jacobson, 1963a,b; George, 1970). Biophysical considerations plus histological findings have supported this assumption in normal adult frogs (Lázár and Székely, 1967, 1969; Potter, 1969, 1972).

But over the years, terminal arborization has been translated into "presynaptic terminal." Like the first assumption, this extrapolation is legitimate in normal adult animals, where ultrastructural studies have failed to show optic fibers passing out of the tectum or ending blindly on the tectal surface. All fibers plunge into the superficial layers and form synaptic relations with tectal neurons, although it is not known whether all such synapses are functional or equally efficient. In the regenerating animal or the immature one, there are no data on the fate of optic nerve fibers in the tectum. Thus, the so-called terminal arborization might be a sessile nerve tip, growth cone, presynaptic element in a nonfunctional synapse, or presynaptic element in a functional synpase.

In short, the visuotectal *projection* of an experimental or immature animal cannot be translated into a pattern of synaptic *connections*. Nor are any retinotectal connections necessarily present or functional if present. Nor can the projections be used to analyze the rules governing the formation of specific neuronal connections. These aims can only be met by assaying beyond the synapse by special techniques (Skarf, 1973; Hunt, 1974; Skarf and Jacobson, 1974), and by testing the visuomotor behavior of the frog, for example, its ability to locate a small lure and follow the direction of its movement in visual space. No single test is entirely satisfactory, but several used in combination may provide reasonably reliable information about the connectivity pattern. It is especially worth noting that visuomotor behavioral tests may be a sensitive assay of functional circuits, and have, in most cases, given results that are in agreement with the electrophysiological visuotectal projection. The visuomotor behavior of our animals has allowed us to predict the result of the eletrophysiological recording in the great majority of cases. There are cases in which visuomotor behavior is mediated by diencephalic visual centers (Muntz, 1962) and optokinetic reflexes persist in the absence of the tectum (Székely, 1971; Mark and Feldman, 1972). Hence, the presence of visuomotor behavior assures us that the eye has made functional synaptic connections in the brain, but it does not allow localization of the position of such connections.

In summary, it is probably reasonable in normal adult animals to interpret visuotectal projection data in terms of retinotectal connections; but in experimental animals, larvae and immature froglets, controls are necessary to validate the assumptions that (*1*) the visual field projects in visuotopic, point-to-point fashion onto the retina and that (*2*) the electrode is recording from optic nerve fiber terminals that have formed synaptic connections with tectal neurons in the vicinity.

C. VISUOTECTAL MAPPING AS AN ASSAY OF LOCUS SPECIFICITY

Visuotectal projection also has severe limitations as an assay of the position dependent properties of retinal ganglion cells. Those of us who use this technique to assay ganglion cells properties (cf. Jacobson and Hunt, 1973a) must recognize its limited applicability and must accept severe limitations upon the kinds of questions the technique can hope to answer. For example, we must give up all hope of monitoring changes in the properties of ganglion cells during their differentiation in the embryo, for the only phase in the ganglion cell's life that is accessible with this technique is that which occurs after the arrival of optic axons in the tectum (Chung *et al.*, 1972). We must likewise forego all prospects of studying the effects of pharmacological agents on the differentiating ganglion cells if these agents also produce abnormalities in the eye as a functioning organ. That is, without normal photoreceptors, inter-retinal circuits, visual optics, and pathways from the eye to the brain, the technique is useless as a specific assay of ganglion cell locus speci-ficities.

An even more fundamental limitation concerns the problem of how the spatial pattern of optic nerve fiber terminals relates to specific prop-erties of retinal ganglion cells in different positions in the retina. For neither the concept of neuronal specificity nor Sperry's chemoaffinity theory (Sperry, 1945, 1951b) demand that one particular termination site in the tectum reflect one particular ganglion cell locus specificity in an if-and-only-if relationship. Indeed, many different specificity values, arranged in different patterns in the retina, could in principle generate a single pattern of fiber terminations in the tectum; and, conversely, a particular property or groups of properties at some position in the retina might, under different conditions, be expressed in the selection of several different tectal termination sites.

In short, without knowing the mechanisms of *expression* of the gan-glion cell locus specificities, the visuotectal map cannot be used to deduce precisely which locus specificities are present in the retina as a whole or at any particular retinal position. What the assay *can* provide, however, is information about how locus specificities at one retinal position differ from those found at other retinal positions. Thus, the main limitation of the technique is that, in an experimental eye, it cannot assay the range of the properties or tell whether the set of properties is complete, re-duced, or augmented. But it can provide information about the relative order with which the set of properties has been spatially laid out in the retina.

If, for instance, the set of properties in the normal retina is (1,2,3,4,5, 6,7,8,9,10), the assay might not be able to distinguish the normal set of properties from a set with a larger (0,2,4,6,8,...,18) or smaller (2, 2.5, 3, 3.5, 4,...,6.5) or different (11,12,13,14,...,20) range, or from a set in which random deletions (1,2,4,5,7,9,10) or block deletions (1,2,6,7,8,9,10) have been made. But the assay can be expected to distinguish any of the foregoing sets from sets in which the order of properties had been inverted (10,9,8,7,6,5,4,3,2,1,) or partially inverted (1,2,3,9,8,7,6,5,4,10) or redupli-cated (1,2,3,4,5,5,4,3,2,1). The assay should also be able to show whether two groups of retinal cells terminating in the same tectum possess the same or different locus specificities (see page 222).

In summary, the assay, at best, permits a partial characterization of the set of locus specificities in the eye; in many cases, this may be no more than relative information about the disposition of these properties across the retinal population. It may be sufficient to permit correlation between a direction of disposition of these properties and the previous orientational history of an eye, which has been surgically translocated or reoriented during development. Also, it may even be possible to change the orientation of the eye systematically, using the visual projection map to obtain enough information about the final set of locus specificities to make inferences about the times and conditions of its origins. However, it may be extremely risky, as will be shown, to try to correlate discontinuities and continuities in the retinal fiber projection to the tectum with a history of deletion or amplification of parts of the retino-tectal system.

In the previous section we stressed the limitations of visuotectal projection mapping as an assay of retinotectal connections. By comparison, we believe that use of this technique to examine ganglion cell properties in the retina, despite the grave limitations involved here as well, is a much more fruitful and open-ended approach. Presynaptic recording seems inevitably doomed to failure as an assay of retinotectal connectivity. However, even a *partial* characterization of the properties, limited though it may be, is something to be built upon. One can identify what is *not* known about the set of locus specificities and attempt to develop special methods directed at these particular gaps in our knowledge. Moreover, one can use the partial characterizations in limited ways, to study, for example, the origins of the locus specificities during development (Jacobson and Hunt, 1973a).

D. SOME CONSTRUCTS

The visuotectal projection itself is an abstraction, not a biological entity. It merely depicts the correspondence between visual space and the space delimited by the ostensible margins of the tectum (tectal space). Therefore, the aim of a biological analysis is not to determine the rules for correspondence between loci in the two spaces, but to determine the mechanisms of interconnection of retinal ganglion cells and tectal cells. Thus, inferring rules for predicting correspondences between loci in the two spaces is an abstraction and may be biologically meaningless. For a single correspondence pattern between two spaces may be mediated by many different combinations of cellular properties, functions, and operations.

The difficulty in making biologically meaningful interpretations is illustrated by the following example. Suppose we depict visual space as a system of 100 loci (10 × 10), each designated by an ordered pair of coordinates. Now, suppose that tectal space is similarly divided into ten rows of 10 loci, also designated by an ordered pair of coordinates, and that an electrode tip is positioned at tectal locus (3,5). In the normal animal, we observe that a small spot of light can excite the electrode only when the light is positioned at locus (3,5) in visual space. We infer that, in the normal animal, this light falls on a particular locus in the retina, which we arbitrary call locus (3,5) of the retina, and excites a particular retinal element there. We further infer that this particular element, in the normal animal, possesses a particular property (locus specificity) which has directed its axon, at some time during normal development, to a termination site near our electrode tip. Lastly, we infer that near our electrode lies a particular tectal element, which also has a particular property (locus specificity), and on which our retinal element has formed a retinotectal synapse.

We now repeat the recording procedure on an experimental animal, again positioning the electrode at locus (3,5) of tectal space, only to find that we cannot excite the electrode with a light at locus (3,5) in visual space. Instead, the electrode is excited when the light is positioned at locus (6,4) in visual space. How can this observation be interpreted in biologically meaningful terms? In fact, there are several possible ways in which our experimental animal might differ from the normal case, including (1) retinal locus (3,5) contains a different element; (2) retinal locus (3,5) contains the same element, but its property is different; (3) retinal locus (3,5) contains the same element with the same property, but the property was expressed differently in the development of the experimental animal [this change in expression might have involved (3a) formation of a synapse at a different site in the tectum or (3b) selection of a different termination site without formation of any connection in the tectum]; (4) tectal locus (3,5) contains a different element; (5) tectal locus (3,5) contains the same element but the property of the element is different; and (6) tectal locus (3,5) contains the same element with the same property, but the property was expressed in a different way in the development of the experimental animal; or (7) any combination of cases 1 to 6. That additional possibilities exist follows from the discussion of the technical limitations of the recording method: as a result of optical defects, light at locus (3,5) of visual space might not fall on retinal locus (3,5), and abnormalties in intraretinal circuits may cause light falling at retinal locus (3,5) to excite elements elsewhere in the retina.

There are, then, at least four possible categories of cellular response by which the retinotectal system can effect a change in the projection of visual field onto optic tectum. *Cell deployment* can be altered, by means of specific patterns of cell proliferation, migration, and/or death. Specific *cellular properties,* such as locus specificities of the individual retinal ganglion cells, may be altered in the absence of histogenetic or degenerative changes. Specific *cellular operations,* such as those involved in the selection of a locus for terminal arborization, may be altered independently of any changes in the cells or their properties, but without a synapse forming at the atypical tectal locus. Finally, *synaptic selectivity* itself may be altered, resulting in the formation of a retinotectal synapse between two neurons whose locus specificities are such that they would not have become connected in the normal animal. That cells should exhibit a sensitivity to the state of the system as a whole may reflect a phenomenon called *contextuality,* which is frequently encountered in complex systems whose elements exhibit specificity. Adapted to the elements in the retinotectal system, contextuality can be defined as follows.

A specific property of an element (cell) is contextual if it is a function of, not only the identifying characteristics of the particular element, but also of the *total set* of elements present in the system. Thus, a contextual property (e.g., the locus specificity of a given ganglion cell) can be predicted by knowing both the identity of the element (e.g., which ganglion cell, as determined by retinal position, history of origin, and migration) and the state of the system as regards the other elements present (e.g., census of all ganglion cells and tectal cells capable of receiving their synapses). Likewise a specific operation (e.g., locus selection by a given optic fiber) is contextual when the outcome of the operation is a function of not only the identity and property of the particular element(s) in question but also on the total set of elements and properties involved in similar transactions in the same system (e.g., all retinal cells, all tectal cells capable of receiving their synapses, and all their specificities). In principle, any property or operation of an element in a complex system may be contextual. Moreover in open systems in which elements are being added or deleted over time (e.g., by cell birth or cell death in the retina and tectum), it is possible for the deployment of the elements to be contextual as well. In this last case, the identity of the deployed cell is determined on the basis of its characteristic properties *other* than locus specificity (e.g., time and site of birth or mode of migration) and evaluated against the cell's position in the array (e.g., ganglion cell's position in the retina). That is, when cell deployment is contextual, the identity of a given cell as determined by the characteristics just described cannot be predicted solely on the basis of the cell's position but requires additional information about the state of the system when cell deployment processes were taking place.

The concept of contextuality, then, can be developed into constructs which make it possible to confront, classify, and categorize a whole range of cellular phenomena which exhibit specificity but which also show the influence of experimental intervention. In the extreme, certain such phenomena may intuitively seem highly variable, even capricious. Indeed, much of the conceptual confusion and negative publicity that have come to attend the theory of neuronal specificity can be attributed to the failure to recognize the difference between contextuality and randomness, and on the erroneous interpretation of contextual phenomena as being nonspecific or less specific than previously supposed. Because the distinction cannot be overemphasized, we have chosen to consider directly a number of points.

1. Most basically, there is nothing unspecific, random, loose, stochastic, or approximate about contextual systems—contextuality and specificity preside over different domains. They do not vary systematically with one another; although both may come in degrees, absolute specificity is possible in completely contextual systems. Hence, within any single context, the properties and operations of a given cell can be absolutely invariant and predictable. At the cellular level, then, contextuality is not a euphemism for, nor is it to be confused with, randomness, imprecision, or lack of specificity. Rather, contextuality and noncontextuality —of cell deployment, properties, operations, and connectivity itself— define, in their various possible combinations, the kinds of cellular responses that experimental intervention can potentially evoke in systems exhibiting cellular specificity.

2. Contextuality is in no way incompatible with Sperry's theory (Sperry, 1951a,b), which is a theory of normal development (although studies on surgically deranged animals may have helped to inspire it) and not a theory of the behavior of neurons in artificial environments. Thus, surgically created contexts never faced by normal retinal ganglion cells and tectal cells may have only limited relevance for the theory. Moreover, although the theory postulates a cytochemical mechanism for synaptogenesis, the proposal is advanced in descriptive biological terms. Broad outlines of "fieldlike differentiation" in the retina, giving rise to "graded and continuous" differences among the fibers, make no suppositions about whether cells will change their properties when half the retina is ablated or whether a particular chemoaffinity between two cells will lead to a stable and functional synapse under all possible conditions of surgical derangement. These points are important, surely; but the theory simply does not address them.

3. Nothing presented thus far precludes the possibility of real variability, randomness, or "looseness" of constraints in neuronal systems. Nor does it minimize the importance of addressing experiments to this

question. In fact, an understanding of the *precision* of locus specificity mechanisms is a prerequisite not only to an evaluation of the usefulness and limitations of the theory but also to an appreciation of the kind of cellular and molecular forces that must be invoked to explain their operation. Our point, however, is that the precision of locus specificity must be evaluated with an entirely different set of constructs, derived not from systems theory but from target theory.

Accordingly, it is both appropriate and important to ask whether, in all identically treated animals (or in the same animal in repeated trials) an optic fiber with a given locus specificity will "hit" a particular tectal locus 100% of the time. If not, it is important to determine the percentage of "misses" and the fates of fibers which fail to hit. Do they die without forming a synapse or die after forming an abortive synapse (*error elimination*)? Or do they proceed nevertheless to form a synapse and then disengage from it, and/or try again to hit the original target locus (*error correction*)? Moreover, if an errant fiber terminates or synapses at an atypical tectal locus, is this site determined on a purely stochastic basis (all-or-none specificity) or does locus specificity impart to the neuron a second and third choice of targets or postsynaptic cells (hierarchical specificity).*

In short, the constructs presented earlier (contextuality) encourage analysis of the precision of locus specificity, but they also direct approaches to the problem to their proper experimental arena. The solution to the precision problem lies in comparing the properties and activities of individual neurons, not in different surgically deranged settings or insurgically deranged vs. normal animals, but rather in repetitive trials in the same animals or in many instances of a single experimental context.

4. Of the four categories of contextuality presented on p. 218, only the fourth entails the compatibility of pre- and postsynaptic cells. When cells or their properties are contextual, for example, there is no change in the criteria for compatibility between two "marriagable" neurons, those binary combinations of pre- and postsynaptic cell specificities that

---

* These arguments can be extended to consider the true variability in all four categories previously considered: cell deployment, cell proprties, cell operations, and synaptic selectivity. However, we are less concerned here with developing additional constructs for analyzing real variability than we are with contrasting categories of nonspecific cellular responses (or responses with limited specificity) with categories of contextual but specific cellular responses. There has been no rigorous analysis of precision of locus specificity mechanisms in the visual system or of the variability of events in retinotectal circuit wiring (see, however, Macagno *et al.*, 1973; LoPresti *et al.*, 1973).

define chemoaffinity and permit a synapse to form between the two cells. Only the position of the "pair" that meets the particular combinatorial criteria is changed. Similarly, if specific operations involved in locus selection are contextual, and a given locus is selected without a synapse forming there, again the combinatorial criteria have not changed.

Only in the last case, wherein synaptic selectivity itself is contextual, does a synapse form between two neurons whose locus specificities do not conform to one of the standard combinations found among the pairs of connected cells in the normal animal. Even this, however, with its important implications for synaptogenetic mechanisms, is not inconsistent with the general concept or specific theory of neuronal specificity. For the new combination of pre- and postsynaptic cell specificities may itself define an invariant criterion for synaptogenesis in this particular experimental context.

5. *A priori,* there is no way of predicting whether a given system (e.g., the retinotectal system of a lower vertebrate) will exhibit contextual cell deployment, cell properties, cell operations, or selectivity. Simply demonstrating that the system responds to some experimental intervention by showing changes in the correspondence of visual and tectal space is not a biological answer; it is merely an enticement. Even a direct demonstration of contextuality in one of the four cellular functions is only a partial answer. The full answer must include the contingencies under which contextuality occurs, and the rules for contextual expression. This information is essential for understanding neurogenetic plasticity, for predicting the behavior of a given cell in a context previously unseen, as well as for isolating the mechanisms underlying the context-dependent and context-independent aspects of neuronal differentiation and morphogenesis. Moreover, until the full answer is obtained, we must adopt a conservative posture experimentally, when using the visuotectal projection as an assay for the set of locus specificities in the retina. At best, we may reliably infer only limited information about how cells in one part of the retina compare to those in the other (e.g., direction of the axes about which locus specificities are organized). In order to obtain more information, special procedures must be employed. The competitive innervation assay is one such special procedure.

In principle, this assay examines the visuotectal projections of two eyes that have innervated a single tectum, thus standardizing the innervation field (one set). If one of the eyes is a normal eye, it can serve as a "standard" itself, against which the experimental eye can be evaluated. In the general case, where part of the tectum is shared by fibers from the two eyes, and other parts of the tectum are solely occupied by fibers from one eye or the other, it is possible to obtain quantitative information about the set of specificities in the experimental eye. This information includes (1) an empirical value for the *near end of the range* of specificities, based on the boundary of the test fiber population within the normal eye's map; (2) an empirical value for the *rate of change in locus specificity* per millimicron of retina in the experimental eye, based on the regression of the two fiber populations across the shared tectal region; and (3) estimated value for the *far end of the range* of locus specificities in the experimental retina, extrapolated from data of *1* and *2*. A specific case, in which the unshared tectal area approaches zero and the normal and test eye (here an eye previously cultured *in vitro*) project in register to the entire tectum is shown in Fig. 6 (Section IV). Some applications of the competitive innervation assay have been presented elsewhere (Jacobson and Hunt, 1973a; Hunt and Jacobson, 1974a), and a mathematical treatment of the general case will be published shortly (Hunt, 1974).

Thus far, the competitive innervation assay is still in the development stages. We have shown that all three eyes in a three-eyed frog can undergo normal histogenesis. However, we are still working to eliminate problems with resorption of the third eye, fusion of the two eyes on the same side, and failure of one of the two eyes to connect with the tectum. Nevertheless, from more than forty successful cases mapped to date, it is clear that the competitive innervation assay will be of great help in characterizing the set of locus specificities in an experimental eye. Moreover, until the question and character of contextuality in this system have been settled, such competitive innervation assays are an absolute requirement before distortions (expansions, compressions) of the visuotectal projection can be interpreted in terms of meaningful cellular events.

III. Research Results Reconsidered

A. TRADITIONAL RESEARCH STRATEGIES

The oscilloscopes had scarcely cooled following the first direct probes of the tectum after regeneration of the frog's optic nerve fibers (Gaze, 1959; Lettvin *et al.*, 1959), when two main strategies for research began to evolve that were to monopolize experimental activity to the present day. The first approach involved assaying the visual projection to the tectum following the surgical creation of a "retinotectal size disparity" (Gaze, 1970), an experimental procedure conceived by Attardi and Sperry (1960, 1963), developed and championed by Gaze and collaborators (Gaze *et al.*, 1963, 1965; Gaze and Sharma, 1970; Gaze, 1970; Jacobson and Gaze, 1965; Sharma, 1967, 1972a,b,c; Gaze *et al.*,

1971; Feldman *et al.*, 1971), and consummated by Yoon (1971, 1972a,b). The second approach involved examination of the intermediate stages of the regeneration process as well as the normal development of the retinotectal system (Jacobson, 1961a,b; Gaze and Jacobson, 1963a; Jacobson and Gaze, 1965; Gaze and Keating, 1970a,b; Keating and Gaze, 1970; Cronly-Dillon, 1968; Horder, 1971, 1974; Chung *et al.*, 1972; Gaze *et al.*, 1972). Before turning to the two main avenues of research then, let us briefly consider five experiments that provided information on some rather different points.

One such experiment demonstrated that the embryonic development of the retinotectal map can occur in the absence of the normal sequential protracted program of optic fiber arrivals in the tectum (Hunt and Jacobson, 1972a, 1973c). The authors sequestered an embryonic *Xenopus* eye on the side of the body (stage 32) for a month or 6 weeks starting in early embryonic life, before the eye had formed any connections with the brain. On reimplantation into the right orbit, in place of the host's own right eye, the sequestered eye developed orderly visuotectal projections, good visuomotor responses (Hunt and Jacobson, 1972a), and functional retino*tectal* synapses (Hunt and Jacobson, 1974b). In a complementary study, Feldman *et al.* (1971) removed one eye in *Xenopus* embryos before the contralateral tectum had received input from it; after metamorphosis, they deflected the optic nerve from the remaining eye to innervate the "virgin" tectum for the first time with the result that a normal visuotectal projection was formed.

Before these interesting results can be considered complete, it will be necessary to perform two control experiments: (*1*) control mapping of the "virgin" tectum before deflecting the optic nerve into it to assure that it was not connected directly to the ipsilateral eye as frequently happens after embryonic eye removal or eye surgery (if that had occurred, the tectum was not as virgin as had been assumed) (Hunt and Jacobson, 1974b; Hirsch and Jacobson, 1973); and (*2*) recording postsynaptically from tectal neurons to determine whether functional optic connections formed with the neurons of the virgin tectum.

That retinotectal fibers need not follow a particular path from eye to brain (and need not approach the tectum from a particular direction) in order to generate a retinotopic map was shown in two additional experiments. Hibbard (1967) grafted eyes in *Xenopus* tadpoles so that the optic nerve fibers grew into the brain via the *oculomotor* nerve root. As frogs, these animals showed good visual acuity and spatial localization, suggesting a retinotopic pattern of central connections; and histological methods revealed that the optic fibers had indeed reached the tectum from this unusual approach. Recently, Sharma (1972d) grafted

Rana pipiens eyes on the dorsal midline over the tectum and mapped the visual field projections in four frogs in which the eye survived and sent optic fibers down to the tectum through the ventricle. Although no *connection* patterns could be inferred since neither postsynaptic recording nor behavioral testing was done, the visual field of the ectopic eye clearly projected retinotopically onto the tectum.

Recently several investigators have followed the approach of Sharma (1967) in examining the visuotectal projection after rotation of pieces of tectum and regeneration of the optic nerve. In both adult goldfish (Sharma, 1967; Sharma and Gaze, 1971; Yoon, 1973) and *Xenopus* froglets (Levine and Jacobson, 1974), normal visuotectal projections were reestablished when the piece of tectum was reimplanted in normal anatomical orientation. When the tectal fragment was reimplanted in 180-degree rotated orientation, the regenerated projection of the central field onto the tectal graft was inverted in both axes, while the peripheral visual field positions projected normally to the unoperated areas (Yoon, 1973; Levine and Jacobson, 1974). Zero-degree rotated implants gave different results in the two species. Levine and Jacobson's frogs exhibited 90-degree rotated projection of central field positions onto the implant, within a normal projection of peripheral field positions onto unoperated tectal regions. Sharma and Gaze's fish showed a more continuous visuotectal projection with a smooth "rippling" of the map axes through the central field—an observation which is presently uninterpretable but is reminiscent of findings on insects (Lawrence, 1971; Lawrence *et al.*, 1972). In general, though, the results suggest that tectal cells also have developed position-dependent locus specificities (Sperry, 1951b), but retinotectal synapses and tectal output remain to be studied.

These special approaches notwithstanding, most of the research on the expression of locus specificity in the retinotectal system can be classified as either size disparity experiments, which will be reviewed shortly, or time course experiments to which we now turn.

B. TIME COURSE EXPERIMENTS

Analysis of intermediate states as well as the initial and final state, important in principle, is indispensable in studies on developmental processes; in practice the approach suffered until recently from the difficulty of recording the same animal on more than one occasion. Thus, results have frequently been subject to criticisms that too few animals were used and that it is hazardous to reconstruct dynamic processes in a single animal from static observations made on many animals. Only Yoon (1971, 1972a,b) has squarely met this criticism by making repeated visual projection assays in the same animals. In addition, the experimenters have occasionally pushed the visual projection assay beyond its technical limitations. Thus, it is difficult to interpret the visual projection data obtained from frogs assayed only a few weeks or months after optic nerve section, before restoration of a normal visual projection (Jacobson, 1961a). For example, the disorganized projections (a postulated early intermediate stage) might reflect a disorganized pattern of optic nerve terminals as the authors suggest (Jacobson, 1961a,b; Gaze and Jacobson, 1963a; Gaze and Keating, 1970b) or it might reflect (1) optical abnormalities, (2) abnormalities in retinal function as a result of circulatory or other disturbances, or (3) lower recording threshold in fibers of passage in the tectum of the regenerating animals. No anatomical controls or optic nerve recordings were done to control for these possibilities. Some animals in the series studied by Gaze and Jacobson (1963a) showed organization of the visual projection in the mediolateral axis of the tectum, but not in the anteroposterior axis. This result might reflect a later intermediate state of incomplete fiber sorting, as the authors suggest, but it might be interpreted in another way: the result might have been produced by recording potentials from fibers of passage in the presence of a completely sorted fiber population.

It is also unclear as to whether retinotectal synapses are present in these frogs exhibiting abnormal visual projections early in regeneration of the optic nerve and, if so, whether they exist at inappropriate loci as well as at appropriate loci (even if the latter comprise only a few fibers that accidently reached the appropriate site prior to sorting). Nor was this crucial question settled in the recent, more detailed reexamination of optic nerve regeneration in adult frogs (Gaze and Keating, 1970a,b; Keating and Gaze, 1970). Examination of the ipsilateral visuotectal projection (which with reservations made on p. 243 confirms retinotectal connectivity) and of the depths of termination of optic nerve fibers of the four phenotypic classes was confined to the late postoperative animals in which the projection assay had revealed a normal retinotectal map. Thus, assuming for the moment (and this is by no means certain) that the disorganized visuotectal projections, seen shortly after surgery, really do reflect intermediate stages of fiber-sorting (Gaze and Jacobson, 1963a), we remain ignorant of whether synapses are turning over during the sorting process, are formed only after sorting is completed (and thus at the appropriate tectal loci only), or are formed only at the appropriate loci but whenever the fiber arrives there (during the sorting process). Nor do we know whether the operations of selecting the correct depth in the tectum (a function of phenotypic specificity) and of selecting the correct tectal locus proceed independently of one another.

One additional paper has attracted particular attention and merits careful scrutiny because its data is both particularly promising and particularly vulnerable to overinterpretation and unwarranted inference. A landmark study by Gaze et al. (1972) examined the visual projections in 137 Xenopus laevis tadpoles at various larval stages. This fascinating paper provides the first real evidence for early larval expression of position-dependent properties by the ganglion cells (see in the following) and shows that ganglion cells at the retinal margin, arising in later larval life, express locus specificity as soon as their axons first become detectable in the tectum. In addition, the development of techniques for recording from little tadpoles less than 2 weeks old is a major technical advance. At the same time, however, the paper serves as the "Who's Who" in omitted controls and overinterpreted results. One could not have objected if Gaze et al. (1972) had presented their results with the caution displayed in their earlier report (Chung et al., 1972).

The findings emphasized by Gaze et al. are that the normal "adult retinotectal projection, seen first at metamorphosis, is very different from the projection found at larval stages. In very young tadpoles, the projection is chaotic in the front part of the tectum while the back part of the tectum is electrically silent (Fig. 2). From the end of the early larval period to metamorphosis, the larval projection shows a normal order of visual field positions but highly abnormal spacings between them becoming more normal as metamorphosis approaches. Gaze et al. (1972) observe visuotectal projections but present their results in terms of retinotectal projections, framing their conclusions in terms of retinotectal connections. They conclude that the retinal fibers (1) randomly innervate the front of the tectum in early larval life and branch extensively therein but refrain from entering the back of the tectum until much later; (2) the optic fibers quickly sort out into the correct retinotopic order but maintain abnormal (and inconsistent) metrics as a result of the disparate modes of growth in the retina [radial growth, according to Straznicky and Gaze (1971)] and the tectum [linear growth, front to back, according to Straznicky and Gaze (1972)]; and (3) the optic fibers ultimately take up their final positions after having shifted their tectal connections continually throughout development. Although such "sliding connections" (Gaze, 1970) may well be hypothesized, to infer their existence from these observations is to go well beyond the evidence.

In point of fact, no controls were performed to validate either of the two assumptions on which the visual-to-retinal and projection-to-connection extrapolation may be justified (see critique of methodology, p. 212). That the young tadpole has a refined optical system (in water or air) and a point-to-point projection of visual field on to retina has never

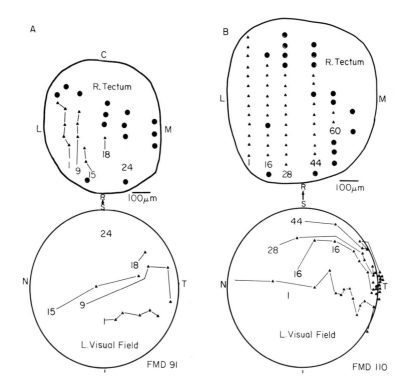

Fig. 2. Projection of the left visual field on the right optic tectum in *Xenopus* tadpoles, (A) at developmental stages 49 and (B) at stage 57, corresponding with 12 and 41 days of age. The triangles indicate electrode positions in the tectum at which electrical activity was recorded when a stimulus was at the corresponding position in the visual field. Circles indicate electrode positions at which no responses to visual stimulation could be recorded. The significance of these results are discussed in the text. (From Gaze *et al.*, 1972.)

been determined; nor is the degree of precision of the intraretinal connections known for early *Xenopus* larvae. The visual function of these animals is not so demanding as to *require* precise optics or precise retinal circuits. Moreover, there is no compelling evidence that a single retinotectal connection, functional or nonfunctional, exists in *Xenopus laevis* prior to metamorphic climax when intertectal fiber activity can first be evoked. [Indeed, the formation of *retino*tectal connections could be the limiting step in the detection of visually evoked *tecto*tectal fiber potentials (Beazeley *et al.*, 1972).] The tadpole's vision could be subserved entirely by other visual centers as has been demonstrated already for the optokinetic response (Székely, 1971; Mark and Feldman, 1972). Finally, the absence of optically evoked electrical activity at the back of the tectum does not necessarily mean that there are no fibers there— the fibers may be electrically silent, injured during surgery, cut off from their blood supply, etc.

To sum up, the application of correlative anatomical methods and/or recording from the optic nerve (Cronly-Dillon, 1968) as well as post-synaptic recording (Skarf, 1973) are a necessary supplement to the technical accomplishment of recording the visuotectal projection in tadpoles. At present, the technique has provided preliminary evidence for a relatively early expression of position-dependent properties in the life of the retinal ganglion cell and no solid evidence whatever for gradual fiber sorting or sliding retinotectal connections or continual synaptic turnover during development.

There is little conclusive information, then, on the intermediate stages in the development of the normal retinotectal map, either in the unoperated embryo or in the adult with optic nerve transection. Whether locus specificity is expressed in the optic nerve or only in the tectum, whether it involves fiber–fiber interactions as well as fiber–cell interactions, whether fiber growth across the tectal surface is random or "destination-bound," whether branching is extensive or limited, whether or not cells that make erroneous connections are eliminated by synaptic turnover or cell turnover, all these questions remain to be rigorously analyzed in future laboratory work.

It will also be imperative, if cellular mechanisms are to be elucidated, to obtain more reliable data on the production and destruction of retinal ganglion cells as well as on the tectal cells with which they connect during the embryonic development of the retinotectal map and during its restoration after optic nerve section. For instance, we know nothing whatever about the number of cells that die during optic nerve regeneration, the number replaced, and the mode of replacement, nor about the number of optic fibers that complete the journey to the tectum.

Similarly, recent radioautographic studies by Straznicky and Gaze (1971, 1972) have been used to revitalize the classic view that the retina and tectum have different modes of growth (radial in retina, linear in tectum) and to focus considerable attention (Gaze et al., 1972; Gaze and Keating, 1972) on the topological problems this creates for development and maintenance of a map. However, the radioautography failed to (1) include controls for differential accessibility or permeability to the isotope (thymidine-^{3}H) or (2) justify its sweeping assumptions about the absence of differential or extensive cell death in development of these structures (cf. Glücksmann, 1951, 1965; Hughes, 1961; Prestige, 1967a,b, 1970; Cowan and Wenger, 1967). Likewise, the integration of these radioautographic results with those derived from the visual projection assay of developing tadpoles (Gaze *et al.*, 1972) has proceeded without considering changes in the eccentric position of the frog's optic nerve head and changes in the geometry of the tectum during development. Both these points are crucial to the problem of relating the centers of the labeling patterns in retina and tectum to the centers of the visual projection map.

C.   RETINOTECTAL SIZE DISPARITIES IN ADULTS

The strategy of creating retinotectal size disparities was adopted from Attardi and Sperry (1963), who had used histological methods to examine the retinotectal projection, following hemiretinal ablation and section of the residual optic nerve, in young adult goldfish. Their silver-stained material showed that the residual optic fiber population passed over the part of the tectum which had previously been innervated by the ablated hemiretina; instead, only the appropriate half of the tectum was innervated. Since then, several investigators have performed many variations on this theme, in which the visual projection was assayed electrophysiologically following deletion or amplification of specific regions of retina or tectum. Jacobson and Gaze (1965) used visuotectal mapping to confirm that half an optic fiber population, challenged to reinnervate an intact adult goldfish tectum, terminates within the appropriate half of the available tectum. When the rostral, caudal, medial or lateral half of the tectum was removed in conjunction with optic nerve section in *Xenopus* larvae (Straznicky *et al.*, 1971a) or adults (Straznicky, 1973) or in adult *Hyla* (Meyer and Sperry, 1973), the residual tectum was reinnervated by only the appropriate half retina and showed no innervation by fibers previously connected to the ablated half. Contrasting the consistent findings of noncontextual regeneration in these systems, half-tectum experiments in goldfish have yielded conflicting results.

Jacobson and Gaze (1965) found that when the medial or lateral half of the tectum was ablated at the time of optic nerve section, these fish regenerated a *partial* visual projection; the regions of the visual field that had previously projected to the ablated tectal region appeared not to project anywhere on the remaining part of the tectum—a result similar to and antedating the findings on half-tectum frogs.

A complementary study by Gaze and Sharma (1970) yielded different results: when visual projections of goldfish were assayed after regeneration of the entire retina into a *rostral* half-tectum, the entire visual field projected, in visuotopic order, to the remaining half-tectum.

These rather different results were at first reconciled by assuming that "axial differences" exist in the adult goldfish tectum, such that the projection is more elastic in the rostrocaudal axis of the tectum than in the mediolateral axis (Sharma, 1967; Gaze and Sharma, 1970; Gaze, 1970). It should be emphasized, however, that neither of the two series of experiments provided (1) evidence that the regenerated optic nerve fibers had formed synaptic connections in the residual half-tecta or that the pattern of the projection reflected the pattern of such connections; or (2) radioautographic controls to eliminate the possibility of massive cell replacement in the half-tecta in response to surgery (such processes, particularly important in Sharma's results might have gone undetected by conventional histology).

These limitations also apply to the studies of Yoon (1971), who found evidence of compressibility of the whole visual field into part of the tectum *in both tectal axes*. His evidence for "biaxial plasticity" derived from somewhat different experimental procedures (extirpation of quarter-tecta) from those of Jacobson and Gaze (1965). In other experiments (Yoon, 1972a), the compression of the entire retinotectal projection into the rostral or caudal half of the tectum was shown to be reversible. When the incision in the split tectum healed or when the inserted gelatin barrier dissolved, the optic fibers gradually extended across the surgical incision and "expanded" the projection to its normal metrics (Fig. 3). Lastly, Yoon (1972b) performed a sequential surgical treatment on several fish, with the final result that the nasal half of the visual field (surviving after temporal hemiretinal ablation) projected onto the *rostral* half-tectum (surviving after caudal hemitectal ablation), a mismatch relative to the regional correspondence found in the normal visual projection (temporal field:caudal tectum). Again, however, the presynaptic recording method precluded the acquisition of important data on the relationships between optic fibers and tectal cells during the expansion and compression of the projection. Do the fibers form connections at their original connection sites and then continually exchange these connections for new ones during the compression or expansion of the map? Or do they connect once and then disconnect until the complete expansion–compression has occurred? Or, another alternative, do they delay the formation of connections until the final configuration is obtained? Indeed, it is presently impossible to rule out any of these alternatives.

Yoon's experiments provide elegant evidence for the existence of adaptive plasticity in the retinotectal mapping mechanisms. By recording sequentially from the same fish, he was able to show conclusively that the compression–expansion sequence was a real sequence, thus elevating the standard of acceptability for "time series" experiments as well. Not

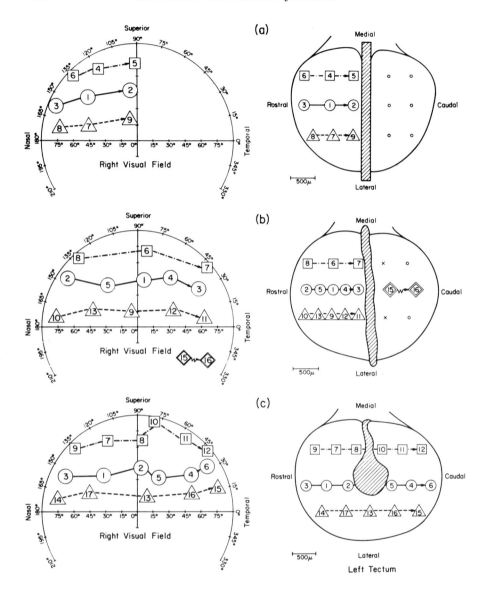

FIG. 3.   Restoration of a normal visuotectal projection in an adult goldfish after its previous compression, induced by insertion of an absorbable gelatin barrier into the tectum. (a) Control, mapped just after insertion of barrier; (b) mapped 67 days later, showing the compression; (c) mapped 184 days after insertion of the absorbable barrier, showing restoration of a normal visuotectal projection. (From Yoon, 1972b.)

least, his reversibility criteria and use of split rather than bludgeoned tecta strongly suggest, although they do not prove, that massive cellular replacement did not occur in the tecta of his fish.

D. RETINOTECTAL SIZE DISPARITIES IN EMBRYOS

That massive histogenetic responses did not occur also remains to be demonstrated in the *Xenopus* compound eye system, now entering its twelfth year of analysis (Gaze *et al.*, 1963, 1965, 1970; Straznicky *et al.*, 1971; Feldman and Gaze, 1972). The basic technique, the recombination of embryonic eye fragments to form morphologically whole eyes, was developed by Székely (1954) and is routinely performed at early tailbud stages (30–32) of *Xenopus* before the optic nerve fibers grow out of the eye (Gaze *et al.*, 1963, 1965, 1970; Gaze, 1970; Straznicky *et al.*, 1971; Feldman and Gaze, 1972).

The "double-nasal" or NN eyes were prepared by replacing the temporal half of the right eye of a stage 30–32 host embryo, with the nasal half of a left eye taken from a donor embryo of the same stage. The two nasal halves fused over several hours, forming a morphologically whole eye. After metamorphosis, the visual projection of the compound eye was examined in the adult. As expected, each electrode position in the tectum received input from two visual field positions, symmetrically disposed about the vertical meridian (Fig. 4). Unexpectedly, however, each half of the visual field projected across the entire rostrocaudal extent of the tectum, not merely across the caudal part of the tectum normally innervated by the nasal region of the retina (Gaze *et al.*, 1963, 1965; confirmed by Hunt and Jacobson, 1974b).

Likewise, Gaze *et al.* (1963) made TT eyes by replacing the nasal half of a stage 30–32 right eye with the temporal half of the left eye of a donor embryo. When the visual projection was examined in adult life, both halves of the visual field again projected to the entire tectum. This observation has also been confirmed (Straznicky *et al.*, 1971; Hunt and Jacobson, 1974b). "Double ventral" eyes have been prepared (Gaze *et al.*, 1970); in these the visuotectal projection showed mirror symmetry about the horizontal meridian, each half of the visual field appeared to project over the entire surface of the tectum. Likewise, "double-dorsal" eyes have been attempted, but the absence of a choroid fissure in these compound eyes prevented development of the optic nerve. However, the remaining discussion concerns only NN and TT eyes.

In 1965, Gaze and collaborators confirmed and extended their earlier observations, and attempted to assess the "normality" of the tectum innervated by the compound eye. Yet, the demonstration of doubling of the retinotectal magnification factor (Jacobson, 1962) and

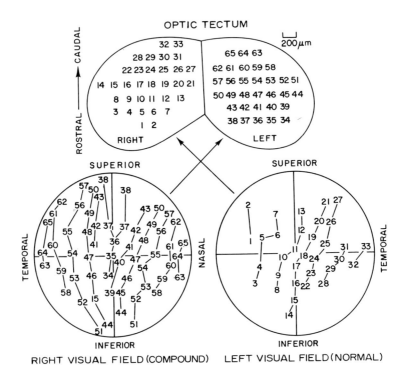

FIG. 4. Map of the retinotectal projection from the normal left visual field to the right optic tectum and from the compound, right visual field to the left optic tectum. Each point in the projection from the compound visual field is reduplicated symmetrically about the vertical meridian so that the nasal and the temporal half of the field each projects to the entire tectum (from Gaze, Jacobson, and Székely, 1965).

of relatively normal ipsilateral projection from the NN and TT eyes failed to provide compelling evidence that the tectum innervated by the compound eye was normal. More recently, then, Straznicky *et al.* (1971) uncrossed the optic chiasmata in newly metamorphosed *Xenopus* that had been reared from embryos with one NN or TT eye. Upon electrophysiological examination 6 months later, the frogs showed a "compound projection" from the compound eye to the tectum that had developed in association with the unoperated eye, and the authors claimed to find a "normal" projection from the unoperated eye to the tectum that had developed in association with the *compound* eye. They concluded that both tecta contained a normal set of tectal locus specificities, but they admitted the possibility that the halves of the compound eye might not be true "half-eyes." To examine cell production in compound eyes, Feldman and Gaze (1972) prepared eight *Xenopus* embryos with one

NN eye at stage 32, injected them with tritiated thymidine at stage 47, fixed them 24 hours later, and made radioautographs of sections through the eye. They noted silver grains at the margin of the eye and no silver grains at the "fusion site" between the two halves.

The significance of these results must be evaluated against several backdrops: the technical limitations of the recording method and the theoretical constructs discussed in the previous sections; the theory of neuronal specificity; and the most fruitful directions for future research. Although the authors' interpretation have varied somewhat over the years, the focal point of all interpretations has been the observation that the *whole* tectum receives visual projection from each *half* of the visual field of the compound eye.

In considering these observations, it is reasonable to assume, first, that the compound visual projection derives from a compound retinal projection (it is difficult to envisage an optical defect producing such a projection artifact, although a simple anatomical control could remove any residual doubt), and second, that at least some retinotectal synapses develop from the compound eye (based on the presence of the ipsilateral visuotectal projection). However, it is unclear whether the *pattern* of fiber terminals inferred from the visuotectal projection reflects in any way the pattern of retinotectal connections, especially as (1) the ipsilateral projection of the compound eye is *not compound* but is nearly normal, and (2) information on the visually guided behavior of *Xenopus* with compound eyes is conspicuously lacking after 12 years of study. It bears repeating that, in the absence of behavioral perimetry tests and/or detailed mapping postsynaptically in the tectum, conclusions about connectivity are premature.

Nevertheless, interpretations of the compound eye experiments have made two assumptions. First, a compound pattern of synaptic interconnections has been assumed to link each half-retina with the whole tectum. Second, the system being analyzed has been thought to hold the answer to the question, How are the synaptic "slots" in the normal tectum filled when it is innervated by an optic nerve containing no fibers with "nasal specificities," for example, and twice the normal number of fibers with "temporal specificities"? With the question so loaded, it is not surprising that a single answer, namely, "with considerable elasticity," has reappeared, in various guises in all the publications on the subject. The problem, as we have tried to argue, is that the map of correspondence between visual space and tectal space may have nothing to do with the "rules for formation of retinotectal connections"; that changes in this map can result, not only from elastic rules but also from changes in cell deployment, cell properties, or cellular operations not involving synaptogenesis; and that rules for connectivity or even for locus selection (without regard to whether a functional connection develops at a selected locus) can only be inferred from systems in which these other variables have been controlled.

At present, such controls are lacking in the *Xenopus* compound eye system. Feldman and Gaze (1972), for example, thought it very unlikely that each half of the compound eye undergoes "retinal pattern regulation," which they define as "the production of a full scale of 'specificity' values along half the normal axis." As we have already seen, however, there are more ways to alter the correspondence between visual and tectal space than just altering cellular deployment. Moreover, there is no published evidence on the nature of retinotectal projections from compound eyes in animals less than 6 months postmetamorphosis: therefore *continuous* changes of any kind remain to be demonstrated. These radioautographic studies also fail to provide evidence that (1) tritiated thymidine gets into all the cells; (2) compound eyes have normal patterns of cell *migration;* (3) compound eyes have normal pattern of cell *death;* (4) cell division at the site of fusion between the two halves does not occur at stages other than stage 47; (5) the eyes in these experiments were physiological compound eyes (i.e., control mapping was not done); or (6) TT eyes, not included in these experiments, show mitotic patterns similar to NN eyes. Nor are these reservations allayed by the recent demonstration that if one fragment of a compound eye is prelabeled with tritiated thymidine, label is still confined to that half of the compound eye at stages 35–39; and small grafts of labeled retinal cells do not migrate or disperse across the retina (Horder and Spitzer, 1973).

Similarly, the intriguing results of Straznicky *et al.* (1971) are limited by the absence of (1) control mapping of visual projections prior to uncrossing the chiasma to show that the normal eye had not initially innervated both tecta (Hunt and Jacobson, 1974b; Jacobson and Hirsch, 1973); (2) demonstration that synaptic connections developed after chiasma uncrossing, between the eyes and the tecta which they were forced to innervate; (3) controls for alterations in cell deployment or all properties during the 6-month delay between the surgery and mapping; or (4) an adequate explanation of the major abnormalities of the so-called "normal" projections from the unoperated eye onto the tecta which had developed in association with the compound eye.

We have stated our preferences for using the visual projection to characterize partially the set of locus specificity in the retina. This view leads one to approach eye fragment experiments in a different light, emphasizing the question of whether the fragment of an embryonic eye will possess (or give rise to) the same partial set of locus specificities to which it will give rise in the corresponding region of an intact embryonic eye. Thus, the compound eye of choice is a combination of fragments with predictable *differences* in their partial sets of locus specificities.

Thus, we were led to perform several variations on the standard NN eye procedure of Gaze *et al.* (1963, 1965). In a separate experiment, we replaced the temporal half of the host's right eye with (*1*) a stage 32 ventral half eye making an NV compound eye, or (*2*) a stage 32 temporal half of a left eye making an N_RT_L compound eye, or (*3*) a stage 32 temporal half of a sibling right eye, making an N_RT_R compound eye, or (*4*) the same temporal half just removed from the host; in other cases, we simply bisected the eye and let the two halves heal without removing the temporal piece at all (Hunt and Jacobson, 1973b; Jacobson and Hunt, 1973b).

Assuming that each fragment went on to generate the partial set of locus specificities found in that region of the normal intact eye, the NV eye should develop as follows. Each half of the adult eye should contain a nasoventral quarterset of locus specificities, and one unique quarterset apiece (nasodorsal in the N half, temperoventral in the V half). Thus part of the tectum should be shared by fibers from both halves of the retina, with the corresponding regions of the visual field projecting in register to it, whereas other tectal regions should be solely occupied by fibers from one or another half of the eye. In the remaining four (N_RT_L, N_RT_R, etc.) cases the two halves of the adult retina should contain mutually exclusive half-sets of locus specificities (one temporal, the other nasal), which should project to completely different regions of the tectum.

Quite to the contrary, the predicted result was not obtained in most cases (Hunt and Jacobson, 1973b; Jacobson and Hunt, 1973b). Instead, both halves of the visual field projected, in register, to the entire tectum, as in the case of the original NN eye. This was observed in all the NV eyes (Fig. 5A), all the N_RT_L eyes (Fig. 5B), most of the N_RT_R eyes, and in a few cases where the autograft was replaced or where the eye was simply bisected and allowed to heal. (The remainder of these latter types showed normal visuotectal projection.) Although these animals gave evidence of functional retinotectal connections, based on recording ipsilateral visual responses (Hunt and Jacobson, 1973b), it is not clear whether the pattern of fiber terminals accurately reflects the pattern of retinotectal synapses.

The results permit our rather circumscribed conclusion that "when different parts of eye primordia from early pre-optic-nerve stages are fused, each piece in such a reconstructed eye does not generate ganglion

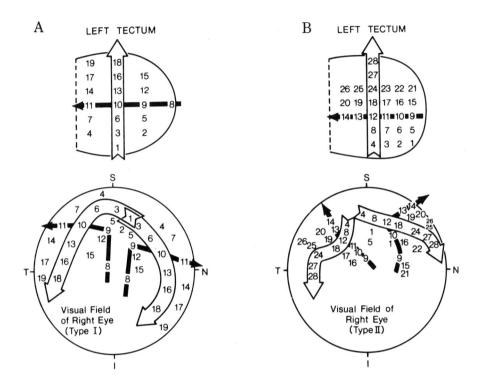

FIG. 5. (A) Visuotectal projection of the right eye in *Xenopus* in which the temporal half has been removed and replaced by a ventral half (Type I). (B) Visuotectal projection of the right eye in which the temporal half of the right eye has been removed and replaced by the temporal half of the left eye (Type II). Each number in the visual field shows the position of the stimulus that optimally evoked potentials recorded by an electrode at the position shown by the same number on the tectum. The smallest distance between tectal electrode positions is 100 μm. (From Hunt and Jacobson, 1973b.)

cells with the partial-set of locus specificities normally arising from that region of the intact eye" (Hunt and Jacobson, 1973b).

In terms of cellular mechanisms, however, many crucial distinctions and unresolved questions have been lost in the circumlocution of the stated conclusion. First, experimental proof is lacking for the underlying assumption that the grafted T or V half-eye rudiments contain the precursors for all the cells in the temporal or ventral regions of the normal adult eye (see, also, Gaze, 1970) or for all the cells residing in the temporal region of our adult NV or NT compound eyes. Nor is it clear whether the *nasal* region of the adult NV or NT eyes contains a normal nasal half-set of locus specificities or an abnormal set (e.g., a whole set or a completely different set). This can only be settled by special procedures such as the competitive innervation assay described on p. 222. Finally, it is unclear whether the unexpected properties of cells in the *temporal* region of the NV or NT eye reflect contextual cell deployment, or contextual cell properties, or some form of "reprogramming" of one fragment by the other. These alternatives will have to be considered more carefully in other experiments, perhaps by examining the patterns of cell production and migration and death among the progeny of the two fragments or by direct examination of the possibility of reprogramming in experiments featuring short-term combination of fragments followed by their independent growth.*

The results of the NV and NT compound eye experiments permit only the following two conclusions: first, the locus specificities found in the nasal and temporal regions of the NV and NT adult retina are virtually identical to one another, both in range and in spatial disposition; second, in the case of the temporal region, the axial relationships could not have been predicted on the basis of what is found (1) in the temporal region of a normal adult eye, or (2) in the temporal region of an adult left eye, or (3) in the ventral region of an adult eye, or (4) after transplantation of temporal or ventral half-eye rudiments in the formation of conventional TT or VV eyes.

Thus our results (Hunt and Jacobson, 1973b; Jacobson and Hunt, 1973b) merely raised the specter of "retinal regulation" as defined by Feldman and Gaze (1972; see also p. 236 in the preceding), as a mechanism for explaining the NN and TT compound eye results. That is, it is clearly possible, by one mechanism or another, to get an altered

---

* In this connection, it is worth noting that half-eye experiments have already providing promising results. After ablation of the nasal or temporal half of a stage 31–32 primordium, the resulting fragment (termed *nasal remains* or *temporal remains*) ultimately became a normal-looking adult eye whose visual projections could be mapped electrophysiologically. Such animals usually showed a normal visuotectal projection, similar to that found in unoperated animals and to that shown in Fig. 1; but a few animals of each type showed a compound projection similar to that found in the homologous compound eye (e.g., nasal remains resembled NN, temporal remains resembled TT).

These unpublished observations by Straznicky, Keating, and Gaze were cautiously introduced by Gaze (1970), but other authors (e.g., Wolpert, 1971) have interpreted these results in terms of "regeneration" and "pattern reduplication" of partial embryonic fields. Although we have confirmed the observations of Straznicky and collaborators, it is premature to draw conclusions about regeneration or reduplication without further characterizing the range of locus specificities in these eyes (Hunt and Jacobson, 1974b) and determining whether abnormalities in these ganglion cell properties resulted from contextual cell deployment or contextual cell properties.

pattern of locus specificity in compound eyes which does not correlate strictly with the history of the fragments. But our experiments do not serve as controls for the NN and TT compound eye experiments either, for the latter can only be accomplished by special techniques applied to those specific cases. This will entail the use of the competitive innervation assay, either in three-eyed frogs (Jacobson and Hunt, 1973a) or in animals with partially uncrossed optic chiasmata (Straznicky et al., 1971) controlled for nonrandom input to the two tecta.

Over the years since the first compound eye experiments, in considering the interpretation of size disparity experiments, particularly as regards the theory of neuronal specificity (Sperry, 1945, 1951b), one notes a progressive disorganization—beginning with the disembodiment of theory from method and ending with the disembodiment of theory from theory. Thus, the "gradient hypothesis" of Gaze et al. (1963), although totally speculative as regards the experimental results, was, nevertheless, an internally consistent script with distinct and well-defined parts for all the players. The cells were deployed normally, their position-dependent properties (specificities) were stable and graded across the topography of the retina, and the retinotectal connections assembled according to a clearly articulated rule: the fibers, arranged according to their specificities, from "most temporal" to "least temporal," filled up the available tectal synaptic sites from most anterior to most posterior. Moreover, the hypothesis was presented as an affirmation and slight extension of the "graded and continuous" set of ganglion cell properties explicitly stated in Sperry's theory of neuronal specificity (Sperry, 1951a,b).

In contrast, the system-matching concept currently being emphasized (Gaze and Keating, 1972), although it also implies a looseness of constraints operating in the assembly of retinotectal connections (and must also respect the fact that the data supporting it are no more compelling now than in 1963), is much more vague and uncertain in casting the various players. It is not clear whether systems matching accommodates or stands in contrast to changes in cells or cell properties or changes in cellular operations short of synapse formation. Moreover, it has been entirely misconstrued in many circles as an *alternative* to Sperry's theory.

In fact, systems matching might be both appropriate and useful as a general term for a class of phenomena, in which fiber projections adapt to creation of size disparities by varying the metrics of the projection while retaining its topological features. In such a case, however, systems matching must be appreciated as a classification for a kind of phenomenon whose mechanisms are to be elucidated later and must not be misconstrued as a theory, hypothesis, explanation, or mechanism.

In summary, to survey this area of research from our point of historical advantage, it now seems that Attardi and Sperry (1963) opened a Pandora's box by performing an experiment to test whether, in the context of a surgically deranged retinotectal system, the optic nerve fiber would pass over "vacant slots" and select the same synaptic locus as it does in the normal animal. Perhaps because Sperry was also the author of the theory of neuronal specificity this strategy gradually became detached from its limited purposes in the Attardi and Sperry (1963) paper. Thus, the strategy of "creating retinotectal size disparities" (Gaze, 1970) and the existence of "fixed place specificities" (Gaze et al., 1963, 1965; Jacobson and Gaze, 1965) came to be regarded as the critical test of the validity of Sperry's theory and of neuronal specificity.

We have tried to develop the theme that both these assumptions are wrong. On the latter point, the theory of neuronal specificity, and the abstract concept of specificity as well, do not require that a cell with a particular locus specificity *always*, under all possible surgically deranged contexts, connect at a single fixed place in the brain. On the former point, the methods do not allow one to infer, from a change in the correspondence of visual space and tectal space, that the original specificity had been expressed in the formation of what would normally be a completely inappropriate connection. It is equally plausible, in the absence of appropriate controls, that fiber terminations do not reflect functional connections, or that the original specificity had been replaced by a different specificity on the same cell, or the original cell had been replaced by a different cell.

IV. Summary: Toward a Cell Biology of Neuronal Specificity

Cell biologists who have followed us with increasing irritation down the tortuous paths of criticism and abstraction may not be aware that we too would have preferred to bring them the latest word on biochemical mechanisms in neuronal specificity. But, unfortunately, the biochemical aspects of this problem could have been reviewed in less than one page. Some readers might well have preferred this, believing that the interim application of the limited techniques that are presently available is a futile phenomenological exercise; but we strenuously dispute this view. We justify a vigorous critical analysis of the research of the past decade on four counts. First, biochemical strategies, when they are eventually used, will have to be based on whatever firm foundations have been built by behavioral, embryological, and neurophysiological studies that have gone before. It is thus worth assessing the value of these earlier studies to define what is proven and what is disproven; what is probable and what is improbable; what is possible and what is impossible. Second, that some aspects of neuronal specificity may remain refractory to direct physicochemical analysis for some time necessitates a careful reappraisal of how the limited techniques and approaches currently available, might best be employed. Third, it is important to try to single out those phenomena that appear to have the greatest biological relevance and appear to be most worth pursuing. Finally, we must try to isolate these phenomena from whatever biases and overinterpretations might have accompanied their initial discoveries so that they may be approached with as few misconceptions as possible.

It is clear that much useful information can be obtained from visual projection mapping if its technical limitations are recognized and if it is modified to examine, more directly, the properties of retinal cells and the states of nerve fiber terminals in the tectum. The visuotectal projection map is related to cellular properties by a long series of extrapolations, and, even under the best experimental conditions the map must be interpreted cautiously.

Acknowledgment of the many interpretive difficulties in visuotectal mapping experiments, as well as the translation of concept and strategy from the medium of geometry to that of cellular biology, will as a first step require a reworking of much of the research that has gone before. In some instances, the visual projection mapping method will have to be modified slightly or dramatically; but in many instances, only the experimental design may need to be expanded or reworked.

If, for example, we are to benefit from the work already done on animals with surgically created retinotectal size disparities (Gaze, 1970), it will be necessary to examine whether and how the response of the retinotectal system in these animals changes with time. In the split-tectum goldfish, Yoon (1971, 1972a,b) found that the expansion and compression of the visuotectal projection was a gradual process. It may now be possible to improve these pioneering studies (in the repetitive recording from the same fish) to obtain visual projection maps of higher resolution (<100 mμ) from the intermediate stages in the expansion–compression processes.

An exciting result of Sharma (1972a) further emphasizes the importance of respecting the regenerating visual projection as a dynamic system. He examined the visuotectal projection of adult goldfish at two different intervals after optic nerve cut and removal of a large chunk of central optic tectum. Animals mapped a few weeks after surgery had regenerated visual projection, but lacked any representation of the central visual field positions normally projecting to the (ablated) central tectum. Other animals mapped months after surgery, however, showed complete representation of the visual field onto the residual fringes of the experimental tectum. At present many questions remain. (Can the results be confirmed in single fish mapped twice? Do synapses form with tectal neurons after the first stage of regeneration, the second, neither, or both? If the nerve were cut a second time, after either the first or second stage had been completed, would the re-regeneration also be a two-stage process?) Nevertheless, even these preliminary results raise the possibility that the noncontextual regeneration observed by Jacobson and Gaze (1965) and the contextual responses to surgical derangement reported more recently (Sharma, 1967; Gaze and Sharma, 1970; Sharma, 1972a; Yoon, 1971, 1972a,b) may reflect *different stages of a single dynamic process* in the regeneration of goldfish visuotectal projection. Future work must address the question of what constitutes a final state (equilibrium configuration) and what are merely intermediates. Obtaining a cell biological answer will require that we not only distinguish the various phases of synaptogenesis (cell deployment, properties, operations involved in locus selection, and synaptic selectivity) and evaluate their contextuality but also dissociate the kinetic from the thermodynamic parameters in each phase (and evaluate *their* contextuality). In brief, what is easiest for the neuron, in the short run, may not be the most stable, in the long run.

Time series experiments will also have to be repeated on the initial development of retinotectal connections in normal tadpoles and juvenile frogs (Gaze *et al.*, 1972) as well as their restoration following optic nerve section in otherwise normal adult frogs (Jacobson, 1961a; Gaze and Jacobson, 1963a; Gaze and Keating, 1970a,b). In these experiments, however, mapping the distribution of terminal arborizations of optic nerve fibers will have to be supplemented by assaying beyond the synapse by special electrophysiological methods. Indeed, such postsynaptic recording will be usefully applied to the intermediate stages of map compression and expansion in split-tectum goldfish (Yoon, 1971, 1972a,b) and goldfish with chunks of tectum removed (Sharma, 1972a).

Mapping of the ipsilateral projections (believed to be relayed through the contralateral tectum and thus to provide evidence of functional retinotectal connections in the *contralateral* tectum; see p. 215 in the foregoing) is simple and straightforward but limited by the fact that (*1*) only parts of the visual field is represented ipsilaterally; (*2*) we know little of the anatomical pathway mediating the ipsilateral projections; and (*3*) it remains to be demonstrated how accurately the *pattern* of ipsilateral visuotectal projection reflects the pattern of retinotectal synapses in the contralateral tectum (cf. Gaze *et al.*, 1969; Jacobson and Hirsch, 1973). Recording binocularly driven units (Skarf, 1973; Skarf and Jacobson,

1974) is limited by the grave difficulty of finding such units (two to five units in one frog is excellent) and by their large receptive fields. These drawbacks, although failing to prevent demonstrations that connections are present, make a postsynaptic map exceedingly difficult to obtain.

One possible solution to this dilemma may be provided by the "three-eyed frog," whose virtues as a competitive innervation assay of the set of locus specificities in the retina have been extolled elsewhere (Jacobson and Hunt, 1973a; also see the following and p. 223). A heretofore unmentioned virtue of these animals is that individual retinal ganglion cells arborize over a large volume of tectum and presumably synapse upon at least several tectal neurons. Thus, the three-eyed frog, with two "contralateral eyes" on the right side, should possess many cells that are simultaneously receiving synaptic input from optic fibers from two contralateral eyes. Binocularity thus serves as a marker indicating that the unit is postsynaptic to optic nerve fibers (a unit excitable through two different eyes cannot possibly be an optic nerve fiber). The artificially created "binocular" units of the three-eyed frogs should be numerous and easily detected, thereby greatly simplifying the task of obtaining a postsynaptic map.

The limitations of neuronal specificity, concept and theory, also ought to be reinvestigated. How far can the concept of specificity (in the explicit theory) be extended, without a conflict with empirical observations or a loss of its usefulness. Having seen that contextual changes in specific neuronal properties or behaviors are not to be mistaken for evidence of randomness, variability, or nonspecificity, we must then face the virtual dearth of rigorous data on the precision with which neurons exhibit specificity in the formation of retinotectal connections. Nor can this deficiency be remedied without at least two kinds of experiments. The first entails a rigorous examination of the fate of individual retinal ganglion cells (as regards a specific cellular property or function) during repetitive synaptogenetic "trials" under a constant set of conditions (e.g., repetitive regeneration in the same animal or in observations on many different individuals with as nearly identical histories as possible). Careful monitoring throughout the process of synatogenesis will assure detection of cells that ultimately die or become nonfunctional; outcomes of the successive trials can be evaluated in accordance with conventional target theory. Some progress has recently been made in other systems (Jensen and Nichols, 1972; Macagno et al., 1973; LoPresti et al., 1973; Sklar and Hunt, 1973).

The second series of experiments on the limitations of neuronal specificity involves an analysis of the role of function in the fine control of synaptogenesis in the retinotectal system. Ample evidence can be adduced to show that the *general pattern* of retinotopic projection can develop in animals reared in the dark, raised with one eye rotated, or having regenerated visual connections following optic nerve section in larval or adult life. That the fine structure of the arborization, the depth distribution of terminals (and presumably the phenotype of postsynaptic neurons) for the various ganglion cell phenotypes, the efficiency of retinotectal synapses, and the quantitative aspects of fiber–cell relations in the tectum are all normal in animals raised in the dark or with rotated eyes remains to be shown. That function may participate in the fine-tuning of synaptic architecture has been suggested in experiments on higher visual circuits of many species (see Gaze, 1970; Jacobson, 1970b; Mark and Feldman, 1972).

In summary, the task which is most pressing and to which the visual projection mapping techniques can most readily contribute is to bolster the data on the preparations already described, particularly to give the existing observations a firm cellular basis. Not the least of the many facets of this task is the analysis of contextuality exhibited by animals with partially ablated retina or tectum, split tectum, and ablation or recombination of embryonic eye rudiments. Do these results reflect contextual cell deployment, cell properties, cellular operations in fiber growth and locus selection, or the actual contingencies in the pre- and postsynaptic cell membranes which subserve synaptic selectivity? In all likelihood, a multilevel analysis may have to be applied to each preparation. Comprehensive radioautographic studies of cell production, migration, and death hold the key to separating the contextuality of *cell deployment* from the remaining three categories. But they must transcend the limitations of previous work (Jacobson, 1968b; Hollyfield, 1971; Straznicky and Gaze, 1971, 1972; Feldman and Gaze, 1972) both in controls and in scope. Next, postsynaptic recording holds the key to isolating the third category of contextual response: contextuality of specific cellular operations involved in locus selection, but without synapse formation. In this instance, the use of three-eyed frogs to amplify the number and detectability of binocular units may prove the method of choice. Finally, special competitive innervation assays, in which the set of locus specificities in the retina is the dependent variable and other parameters have been standardized, can distinguish systems exhibiting contextual cell deployment or properties from those in which contextuality attends specific cellular operations or synaptic selectivity itself (Fig. 6). Then, having given the previously recorded geometrical transformations a biological meaning, a basis in specific parameters of cellular response, it should be possible to determine the conditions under which these critical parameters exhibit contextuality and the mechanisms by

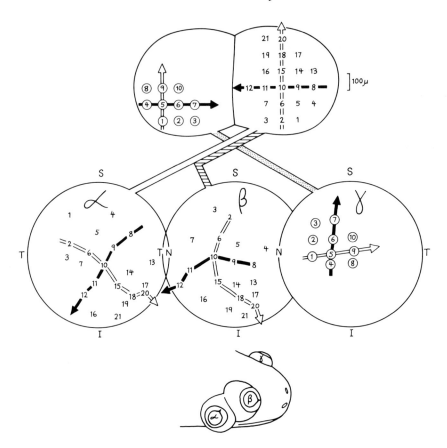

FIG. 6. Competitive innervation assay, as illustrated in the three-eyed frog, which compares the set of locus specificities in an experimental retina with that in a normal retina. In this particular animal, the posterior eye on the right side was grown *in vitro* for 4 days from stage 22, before fixation of retinal axes; the anterior right eye was a normal eye of a stage 38 donor. Both eyes were placed together in the right orbit of a stage 40 host; 6 weeks later, following metamorphosis, the visual projections of both eyes to the same left tectum were mapped. That both eyes project *in register to the entire tectum* shows that a normal set of specificities had developed in the experimental eye.

which the cells accommodate a change in context (Jacobson and Hunt, 1973a).

An entirely different and somewhat bolder approach to the study of cellular mechanisms in neuronal specificity involves the attempt at direct analysis of cytochemical properties and affinities of retinal and tectal neurons. In this regard, some headway has been made by S. Roth and his co-workers (Roth, 1968; Roth *et al.*, 1971; Barbera *et al.*, 1973), who have focused on the chicken embryonic retina which has many more cells at comparable stages of differentiation and morphogenesis. They have challenged cells, dissociated from specific quadrants of embryonic retina, to adhere to tectal fragments or "collecting aggregates of tectal cells" derived from regions of tectum normally innervated by the given retinal quadrant ("matching" elements) or from regions of tectum not normally innervated by the retinal quadrant being tested ("nonmatching" elements). Preliminary results indicate that the *probability of formation of a cellular adhesion* (number of adhered retinal cells per minute over short intervals of 30 minutes or less) is significantly higher between matching elements than between nonmatching ones (Barbera *et al.*, 1973). Although the authors emphasize its preliminary natυre at present, this assay offers particular promise for rapid and efficient analysis of cellular chemoaffinity in the embryonic retinotectal system. If it survives the appropriate controls, it will certainly facilitate analysis of the biochemical substrates of locus specificity through the use of inhibitors, analogs, and other chemical probes.

Hopefully, the intercellular adhesion assay of Roth's group (Roth *et al.*, 1971; Barbera *et al.*, 1973) will prove to be only one of many cell biological techniques to be applied to the study of neuronal specificity. Additional optimism attends the recent development of tissue culture systems that support retinogenesis in the early amphibian eye primordium (Hunt *et al.*, 1973) and allow retinotectal connections to develop from the cultured eye (Hunt and Jacobson, 1972b, 1973a; Jacobson and Hunt, 1973a,b). This assay, although discouragingly slow and complicated, has the advantage of examining not only the presence of locus specificities but their spatial distribution across the retina as well. Moreover it offers prospects, by disrupting the early "polarities" around which the set of locus specificities is spatially organized in the retina, of producing adult "specificityless" retinas for biochemical analysis.

A final area for experimental cell research in the analysis of neuronal specificity in the retinotectal system concerns the mechanisms by which the individual retinal ganglion cells, at particular positions in the retina, *acquire* particular locus specificities, as well as the mechanisms underlying the differentiation of the ganglion cell phenotype(s) as a whole. On the latter point very little is known. The first ganglion cells are born during the early tailbud stages, around the time of axial specification in the eye rudiment, send out axons in a few hours, and innervate the tectum shortly thereafter (Herrick, 1941; Stone, 1944, 1960; Jacobson, 1968b; Straznicky and Gaze, 1971; Bergey *et al.*, 1973). Other ganglion cells are gradually added to the frog retina throughout larval and into adult life, many at the ciliary margin (Glücksmann, 1940; Hollyfield, 1968, 1971; Straznicky and Gaze, 1971). However, there is some evidence to suggest, and no controls to rule out, the possibility that additional ganglion cells arise *in situ* in more central regions of the retina (Hollyfield, 1971).

In a study that requires reinvestigation with previously omitted controls (see p. 229), Jacobson (1968b) analyzed the uptake of tritiated thymidine by retinal precursor cells in embryonic *Xenopus laevis.* After chronic exposure to the isotope, commencing at different larval stages, the morphologically differentiated retina was examined with respect to label distributions in the cells. The first stage at which 100% labeling of the retinal cell population was no longer possible (stage 29), *all of the unlabeled cells* in the morphologically differentiated retina (e.g., stage 42) were ganglion cells. Thus, at a minimum, the mitosis of origin of retinal ganglion cells must either produce two ganglion cells or one ganglion and one precursor cell; it cannot generate one ganglion cell and another postmitotic neuron of a different retinal phenotype (cf. Holtzer, 1970). This conclusion has received additional support from recent studies on the effects of the thymidine analog, 5-bromodeoxyuridine, on the emergence of retinal neuron phenotypes in *Xenopus laevis* embryos (Bergey *et al.*, 1973; Hunt *et al.*, 1973).

Studies on the origins of locus specificity in the ganglion cells have uniformly focused on early programming events in the optic bulge, optic vesicle, and optic cup stages, e.g., stages 20–32 of *Xenopus* (Stone, 1944, 1960; Székely, 1964; DeLong and Coulombre, 1965; Jacobson, 1967a,b, 1968a, Hunt and Jacobson, 1972a,b, 1973a, 1974a; Jacobson and Hunt, 1973a,b; Hunt, 1973; Jacobson *et al.*, 1973). These experiments have not been reviewed here. First, they are too numerous simply to append to the many experiments already considered; second, these experiments relate to the general embryological tradition of Harrison (1933, 1935) and his students (Swett, 1937; Detwiler, 1936; Piatt, 1948) on early patterns of spatial differentiation in organ rudiments; finally, to evaluate critically this work would require a separate and detailed analysis of an additional body of theory, of technical aspects and limitations, of potential artifacts and misinterpretations, and background literature on limb and ear rudiments (cf. Wolpert, 1969, 1971). However, this work has recently been summarized in popular form (Jacobson and Hunt, 1973a), and a critical reconsideration of the limitations of the work and of the kind of approaches it employs is in preparation.

For the present, it need only be said that the set of locus specificities in the adult retina is spatially organized about two orthogonal reference axes that are fixed early in the embryo. These axes are present from post-neural tube stages, but only become irreversible in the intact eye at tailbud stage 30–32, many hours later. This time of axial specification coincides with the cessation of uptake of tritiated thymidine in the central region of the retina, and with the disappearance of certain intercellular junctions from this region (Dixon and Cronly-Dillon, 1972; Duda and Jacobson, 1973).

The problem with this limited focus on a 5-hour critical period in the early embryo is that it restricts one's vision to the *establishment of a developmental program* at the tissue level at the expense of the execution of particular parts of the program at the level of individual cell differentiations. Because we operate on the embryo but only assay the locus specificities in the adult or late premetamorphic eye, we do not know when the final set of locus specificities develops [although according to our interpretations, the experiments of Gaze *et al.* (1972) indicate that the retinal locus specificities have developed before the optic nerve fibers arrive in the tectum during embryonic and early larval life]. In short, at stage 31 when the retina contains about 500 ganglion cells, the locus specificities are determined not only for the cells that are present at that early stage but for all the retinal ganglion cells (about 500,000) that will ultimately develop in the adult eye (Jacobson and Hunt, 1973a).

More direct approaches will be needed to determine the mechanisms by which individual ganglion cells acquire information about their precise role in the program set down during the early tailbud stages. In this regard we conclude by proposing two models for development of locus specificities in retinal and tectal cell populations: locus specificity is generated in the first model by cellular interactions and in the second model by transmission of a signal from the stem cells to their progeny. In the cellular interaction model (A), the stem cell (M) does not possess locus specificity itself and is not concerned with providing nascent nerve cells with locus specificity. It serves only to generate neurons of the correct *cellular phenotype;* this neuron (X) is initially without locus specificity itself, but it then interacts with the nearest specified neuron (n) and so develops the locus specificity appropriate to its position in the array ($n + 1$). This process is then repeated

$$1.2.3 \ldots n. \ (M)$$
$$\downarrow$$
$$\text{mitosis}$$
$$\downarrow$$
$$1.2.3 \ldots n. \ (X) \ (M') \qquad\qquad (A)$$
$$\downarrow$$
$$\text{interaction}$$
$$\downarrow$$
$$1.2.3 \ldots n. \ n + 1 \ (M')$$

Thus, in the cellular interaction model, all the stem cells (e.g., involved in ganglion cell production at the ciliary margin) are qualitatively identical in space and time, as are the newly emerging neurons that lack locus specificity at first. In contrast, in the differential mitosis model (B), specificities are inherited directly by neurons from the stem cells that generate them:

$$1.2.3 \dots n. \ (M^n)$$
$$\downarrow$$
$$\text{mitosis}$$
$$\downarrow$$
$$1.2.3 \dots n. \ n + 1. \ (M^{n-1}) \tag{B}$$
$$\downarrow$$
$$\text{mitosis}$$
$$\downarrow$$
$$1.2.3 \dots n. \ n + 1. \ n + 2 \ (M^{n-2})$$

There are probably many ways of testing these models, three of which are suggested here: (1) inhibition of cellular interaction but not of mitosis should block model (A) but not model (B); (2) retinal stem cells may be cloned and the specificities of their progeny may be assayed by challenging them to connect with the tectum or by measuring the adhesion of such cells to various parts of the tectum (Roth, 1968; Roth et al., 1971; Barbera et al., 1973); (3) destruction of specific stem cells or of the orderly schedule of position-dependent cell production will produce a deficit in the pattern of retinotectal connections in model (B) but not in model (A). In other words, (A) regulates completely and (B) does not regulate at all.

In some preliminary experiments, in which stem cells have been destroyed chemically (fluorodeoxyuridine treatment), mechanically, or by irradiation, in Xenopus retina at stages 38–42, cell production and growth of the retina abruptly ceased. After several weeks, these eyes had reconstituted stem cells and resumed growth. Some of these eyes never attained normal size by the time of mapping, but the small eye, nevertheless, projected normally to the tectum without apparent deficits in the visuotectal map. In other cases, the eye recovered to attain its normal size and to form a retinotectal projection. In both instances, when the eye was disoriented at the time of treatment (e.g., rotated through 180°), the visuotectal projection that ultimately developed was orderly but inverted, indicating that the set of specificities in the recovered eye was spatially deployed according to the original program set down in the tailbud embryo (Hunt and Holtzer, 1973). Important competitive innervation assays have not been completed on the small eyes that only partially recovered from growth suppression (see pp. 223 and 244; Fig. 6); until these assays are completed, it will be impossible to determine whether the small eyes have a restricted or a normal adult range of locus specificities in their reduced ganglion cell population. It has been shown that the completely recovered growth-suppressed eyes project in register with a normal eye to the same tectum, indicating that the eye has recovered to develop a normal set of locus specificities (Jacobson and Hunt, 1973a; Hunt and Holtzer, 1973).

In summary, neuronal specificity is alive and well, both the explicit theory of Sperry (1951a,b) and the general concept as revealed by electrophysiological analysis of the retinotectal system of lower vertebrates. Recent criticism of the theory (e.g., Gaze and Keating, 1972) has largely mistaken contextuality for a lack of specificity, has been hampered by the many levels of meaning that have come to be associated with the term "neuronal specificity," and has failed to respect the technical limitations of the visuotectal projection mapping methods. Our purposes in writing this review were numerous, but three stand out. We believe that no understanding of the cellular basis of neuronal specificity is possible without a serious reconsideration of methodology. The aim has been to provide the general embryologist and the cell developmental biology specialist with the tools for critical evaluation of results of past and future experiments on this system, identifying possible sources of artifact and overinterpretation, and suggesting some technical remedies. A second purpose, rather subordinated to the other two, has been to apply the critical tools and the concepts behind them to a body of experimental work, much of which is thereby revealed to be wrongly interpreted, inadequately controlled, and in a few instances poorly conceived. On the other hand, the same and related work has frequently turned up provocative results which, if inadequately controlled or otherwise uninterpretable now, could be transformed into clear-cut results wih unambiguous implications about the properties and behavior of developing neural cells. In short, much of the existing work holds the promise of becoming the firm phenomenological base for future work; and we have stressed its limitations only so that they might be easily identified, remedied, and transcended in the near future.

Lastly and most importantly, we have reconsidered the whole concept and theory of neuronal specificity in the hope of tracing its history, identifying and clarifying its ambiguities, evaluating its present position of controversy, and finding its most appropriate and comfortable conceptual framework. Before criticizing the theory again we should perhaps evaluate its past and future usefulness, as well as its consonance or dissonance with our intuitions. For theories, even when they are right, are never equal to the phenomena that inspire them. So too, the theory of neuronal specificity is, at best, only a partial depiction of some aspects of the development of specific neuronal connections. The many details it omits and the questions it fails to address form the constants and coefficients in the equation that relates the theory to biological reality.

APPENDIX

A. Sample Experiment

With its tecta surgically laid bare, the frog lies immobilized upon a platform. Its eye is 33 cm from the arc of a projection perimeter, upon which small spots of light, or black discs, can be moved to any position within the eye's visual field. Each tectum, which receives the optic fibers from the contralateral eye, is a hemispheric structure of 1 to 2 mm in diameter; but only the most dorsal two-thirds is exposed and directly accessible to an electrode lowered from above. By means of micromanipulators, the microelectrode is placed at a precisely defined locus on the tectal surface (± 10 mμ) and is lowered into the tectum to a designated depth (± 20 mμ). Using a 1-cm visual stimulus, we locate all areas in the visual field (usually one) from which the stimulus evokes action potentials in the electrode. These action potentials, which we call *the response*, are displayed on an oscilloscope and can be heard over a loudspeaker. Generally, the response derives from many cellular elements firing simultaneously in the superficial tectal layers, 1–200 mμ from the surface. Occasionally, however, the response arises entirely from one cellular element, whose properties can be analyzed (Maturana *et al.*, 1960).

Using the smallest stimulus capable of evoking a response, we then map out the entire *effective stimulus area* in the visual field from which this small stimulus (e.g., 2 mm) will evoke a response. In normal adult frogs, these effective stimulus areas may be only 10–20° in diameter; but they may reach 40–50° in surgically treated adults (Gaze and Jacobson, 1963a; Cronly-Dillon, 1968; Hunt and Jacobson, 1973d) and up to 60° or more in normal *Xenopus* tadpoles (Gaze *et al.*, 1972). Then according to various conventions, a *central point* is determined within the effective stimulus area and designated with a number. We determine the locus evoking the maximum audible response; other criteria that might be used include the geometric center of the effective stimulus area or the locus for stimulating the most prominent single unit or obtaining the minimum latency. Choice of convention may be unimportant in normal adults, but may be of great significance when using a single numbered point to denote a huge effective stimulus area (Gaze and Jacobson, 1963a; Gaze *et al.*, 1972).

Then the electrode is systematically moved in 100-mμ steps across the tectum, repeating the aforementioned procedures at each tectal position. The resulting raw data are shown in Fig. 1A denoting the topographical relationship between the effective stimulus areas in the visual field and the corresponding electrode positions on the tectum. Generally, however, the results are reported showing only the center points of the various effective stimulus areas each denoted by a number (Fig. 1B).

This is the so-called contralateral or direct retinotectal projection better called the *contralateral visuotectal projection* (see in the following). Whenever, the foregoing procedures are applied to normal adult frogs and fish, a point-to-point visuotopic projection of visual field onto tectum is obtained. There is also a projection from each eye onto the ipsilateral tectum, which arrives there indirectly after first synapsing in the contralateral side of the brain.

B. LIMITS OF RESOLUTION

In the froglet, two electrode positions (100 mμ apart) on the tectum are separated by 8 to 10 neuron diameters; the arc separating the corresponding stimulus positions subtends 4–8 ganglion cell diameters on the retina (Jacobson, 1962, 1968a). Thus the mapping technique is not sensitive enough to detect local errors in the order of optic fiber termination, if these errors involve fiber translocations of four or less loci in the fiber array. Moreover, it should be stressed that the conventional mode of representation of the results (Fig. 1B) misleadingly suggests that successive visual field positions are contiguous but discontinuous. In actual fact, the effective stimulus areas overlap to some extent in the normal animal and overlap to an even greater extent in experimental animals, with effective stimulus areas reaching 40° or more in some transplanted eyes and 90° or more in very young frog larvae (Gaze *et al.*, 1972; Hunt, 1974).

The recording technique, as described, most often detects the electrical activity of many cellular elements in the general vicinity of the electrode. With minor modifications, however, we can selectively record the optic evoked electrical activity of individual cellular elements, such as the terminal arborization of a single retinal ganglion cell axon. Although this approach is much more time-consuming (making it difficult to obtain projection data on large numbers of frogs), it can provide information about the nature of the fiber–cell relationships in the tectum which is simply unobtainable with the usual techniques.

For instance, the effective stimulus areas of electrode positions in the conventional assay may be larger or smaller than normal in a given experimental animal. However, while this provides some measurement of reliability in locating the optimum locus (the *number* in the projection diagram, Fig. 1B), it cannot be interpreted at the cellular level. Indeed, *enlarged receptive fields,* as such oversized effective stimulus areas are usually termed (Gaze and Jacobson, 1963a; Gaze et al., 1972; Cronly-Dillon, 1968), could result from (1) increased branching by the individual optic fiber, (2) increased "scatter" across the tectum of different fibers from a single retinal locus, or (3) abnormal optics or intra-retinal circuits in the eye. On the other hand, if the receptive fields of individual optic nerve fibers are also determined, by single-cell recording procedure, this information may permit the interpretation of the data obtained with the usual technique of recording from many cells at once (Cronly-Dillon, 1968). Thus, if the sizes of the effective response areas of individual cells are normal, for example, the possibility of optical or intraretinal abnormalities can be reasonably dismissed.

Finally, it should be noted that our recording technique determines the visual field position (dependent variable) projecting to a given tectal locus (independent variable). This tends to foster conceptual confusion, for it runs counter to the usual mental picture of where in the tectum a given retinal ganglion cell will send its axon. It also makes for horribly indirect measurements of parameters such as amount of branching of optic nerve terminals in the tectum or the amounts of "scatter" or local disorder of optic terminals. A much more direct method, as yet unapplied to developing or regenerating systems, involves a double-probe method developed by George (1970). He presented visual stimuli or direct stimulation of the optic nerve in adult frogs, whose tectum had been penetrated by *two* electrodes. By determining how far apart he could separate the electrode and still record from the same optic fiber terminal, he obtained estimates of the size of the terminal arborizations which correspond with their histological appearance (Potter, 1969, 1972). The Class III fibers of Maturana et al. (1960), from which it is easiest to record electrical potentials, arborize over 150 mµ mediolaterally and 50 mµ anteroposteriorly. These observations provide both an intriguing method which might be fruitfully applied to developing, regenerating, or surgically deranged retinotectal systems, and additional arguments against trying to reduce the limits of resolution of the visual projection assay by recording at 50-mµ rather than at 100-mµ intervals on the tectum.

C. ERRONEOUS DATA

The probability of obtaining an orderly retinotectal map of 20 to 40 positions by chance is infinitesimal, but erroneous points in the experimental map can result from errors in performance of recording procedure.

The pretectal region, for instance, receives some visual input (Knapp *et al.*, 1965; Lázár and Székely, 1969; Scalia, 1972), and the effective stimulus areas for evoking pretectal responses do not form a proper extension of the retinotectal map. Thus, pretectal positions may be improperly included in the tectal map, especially in cases where the anterior boundary of the tectum is not clearly demarcated.

A second source of error involves attributing the optic evoked potential *to the wrong eye*. For in frogs, the visual fields of the right and left eyes overlap frontally and superiorly (producing a binocular field of view), so that even though the perimeter is *centered* about the frog's *right* eye, the *left* eye can also "see" many of these same positions on the perimeters (Gaze and Jacobson, 1962). In normal animals, the left eye sends *indirect* visual projections ultimately terminating in the left (ipsilateral) tectum (Gaze and Jacobson, 1963b; Fite, 1969; Keating and Gaze, 1970; Skarf, 1973), and experimental animals may develop chiasmatic defects producing direct optic fiber input to the ipsilateral tectum (Hirsch and Jacobson, 1973; Jacobson and Hirsch, 1973). Thus, it is of paramount importance that the normal left eye be completely occluded when mapping the projection of the visual field of the experimental right eye to the left tectum. If this is not done, visual field positions corresponding to stimulation areas for the normal eye may be erroneously included in the experimental map.

In summary, accidental recording from the pretectal region may create the illusion that single retinal points are projecting to two different tectal points; and it follows that when such a pattern is observed in the laboratory, special controls are necessary (e.g., independent determination of anterior tectal border based on *inter*tectal projections). Conversely, accidental recording through the wrong eye may create the illusion that a single tectal locus is receiving input from two distinct points on the experimental retina; when such a pattern is observed, special controls are required (e.g., showing that both responses are extinguished when the *experimental* eye is covered).

REFERENCES

Altman, J. (1967). *In* "The Neurosciences. A Study Program" (G. Quarton, T. Melnechuk, and F. O. Schmitt, eds.), pp. 723–743. Rockefeller Univ. Press, New York.

Attardi, D. G., and Sperry, R. W. (1960). *Physiologist* **3**, 12.

Attardi, D. G., and Sperry, R. W. (1963). *Exp. Neurol.* **7**, 46.

Barbera, A., Marchase, R., and Roth, S. (1973). *Proc. Nat. Acad. Sci. U.S.* **70**, 2482.

Beazley, L., Keating, M. J., and Gaze, R. M. (1972). *Vision Res.* **12**, 407.

Bergey, G., Hunt, R. K., and Holtzer, H. (1973). *Anat. Rec.* **175**, 271.

Chung, S. M., Gaze, R. M., and Keating, M. J. (1972). *J. Physiol. (London)* **222**, 37P.

Cowan, W. M., and Wenger, E. (1967). *J. Exp. Zool.* **164,** 267.

Cronly-Dillon, J. (1968). *J. Neurophysiol.* **31,** 410.

DeLong, G. R., and Coulombre, A. J. (1965). *Exp. Neurol.* **13,** 351.

Detwiler, S. (1936). "Neuroembryology. An Experimental Study." Macmillan, New York.

Dixon, J., and Cronly-Dillon, J. (1972). *J. Embryol. Exp. Morphol.*

Duda, M., and Jacobson, M. (1973). In preparation.

Feldman, J. D., and Gaze, R. M. (1972). *J. Embryol. Exp. Morphol.* **27,** 381.

Feldman, J. D., Gaze, R. M., and Keating, M. J. (1971). *Exp. Brain Res.* (*Berlin*) **14,** 16.

Fisher, S., and Jacobson, M. (1970). *Z. Zellforsch. MiRrosk. Anat.* **104,** 165.

Fite, K. V. (1969). *Exp. Neurol.* **24,** 475.

Gaze, R. M. (1959). *Quart. J. Exp. Physiol. Cog. Med. Sci.* **44,** 290.

Gaze, R. M. (1970). "The Formation of Nerve Connections." Academic Press, New York.

Gaze, R. M., and Jacobson, M. (1962). *Quart. J. Exp. Physiol. Cog. Med. Sci.* **47,** 273.

Gaze, R. M., and Jacobson, M. (1963a). *Proc. Roy. Soc., Ser. B.* **157,** 420.

Gaze, R. M., and Jacobson, M. (1963b). *J. Physiol.* (*London*) **169,** 1P.

Gaze, R. M., and Keating, M. J. (1970a). *Brain Res.* **21,** 207.

Gaze, R. M., and Keating, M. J. (1970b). *Brain Res.* **21,** 183.

Gaze, R. M., and Keating, M. J. (1972). *Nature* (*London*) **237,** 375.

Gaze, R. M., and Sharma, S. (1970). *Exp. Brain Res.* (*Berlin*) **10,** 171.

Gaze, R. M., Jacobson, M., and Székely, G. (1963). *J. Physiol* (*London*) **165,** 484.

Gaze, R. M., Jacobson, M., and Székely, G. (1965). *J. Physiol.* (*London*) **176,** 409.

Gaze, R. M., Keating, M. J., Székely, G., and Beazley, L. (1970). *Proc. Roy. Soc., Ser. B.* **175,** 107.

Gaze, R. M., Keating, M. J., and Straznicky, K. (1971). *J. Physiol.* (*London*) **214,** 37P.

Gaze, R. M., Chung, S. H., and Keating, M. J. (1972). *Nature* (*London*), *New Biol.* **236,** 133.

George, S. (1970). Ph.D. Thesis, The Johns Hopkins University, Baltimore, Maryland.

Glücksmann, A. (1940). *Brit. J. Ophthalmol.* **24,** 153.

Glücksmann, A. (1951). *Biol. Rev. Cambridge Phil. Soc.* **26,** 59.

Glücksmann, A. (1965). *Arch. Biol.* **76,** 419.

Hamburger, V. (1960). *J. Cell. Comp. Physiol.* **60,** Suppl. 1, 81.

Harrison, R. G. (1933). *Amer. Natur.* **67,** 306.

Harrison, R. G. (1935). *Proc. Roy. Soc., Ser. B.* **118,** 155.

Harrison, R. G., (1945). *Trans. Conn. Acad. Arts Sci.* **36,** 277.

Herrick, C. J. (1941). *J. Comp. Neurol.* **74,** 473.

Hibbard, E. (1967). *Exp. Neurol.* **19,** 350.

Hirsch, H. V. B., and Jacobson, M. (1973). *Brain Res.* **49,** 67.

Hollyfield, J. G. (1968). *Develop. Biol.* **18,** 164.

Hollyfield, J. G. (1971). *Develop. Biol.* **24,** 264.

Holtfreter, J. (1939). *Arch. Exp. Zellforsch. Besonders Gewebezuecht.* **23,** 169.

Holtzer, H. (1970). *Symp. Cell Biol.* **9,** 69.

Horder, T. (1971). *J. Physiol.* (*London*) **217,** 53P.

Horder, T. (1974). *Physiol. Rev.* In press.

Horder, T. J., and Spitzer, J. L. (1973). *J. Physiol.* (*London*) **233,** 33P.

Horrige, G. A., and Meinertzhagen, I. A. (1970). *Proc. Roy. Soc., Ser. B.* **175**, 69.

Hubel, D. H., and Wiesel, T. N. (1972). *J. Comp. Neurol.* **146**, 421.

Hughes, E. (1961). *J. Embryol. Exp. Morphol.* **9**, 269.

Hunt, R. K. (1973). Submitted for review.

Hunt, R. K., and Holtzer, H. (1973). In preparation.

Hunt, R. K., and Jacobson, M. (1972a). *Proc. Nat. Acad. Sci. U.S.* **69**, 780.

Hunt, R. K., and Jacobson, M. (1972b). *Proc. Nat. Acad. Sci. U.S.* **69**, 2860.

Hunt, R. K., and Jacobson, M. (1973a). *Proc. Nat. Acad. Sci. U.S.* **70**, 509.

Hunt, R. K., and Jacobson, M. (1973b). *Science* **180**, 509.

Hunt, R. K., and Jacobson, M. (1974a) *Proc. Nat. Acad. Sci. U.S.* In press.

Hunt, R. K., and Jacobson, M. (1974b). In preparation.

Hunt, R. K., Bergey, G. K., and Holtzer, H. (1973). Submitted for review.

Jacobson, M. (1961a). *J. Physiol. (London)* **157**, 27P.

Jacobson, M. (1961b). *Proc. Roy. Soc. Edinburgh* **28**, 131.

Jacobson, M. (1962). *Quart. J. Exp. Physiol. Cog. Med. Sci.* **47**, 170.

Jacobson, M. (1967a). *Science* **155**, 1106.

Jacobson, M. (1967b). *In* "Major Problems in Developmental Biology" (M. Locke, ed.), pp. 339–383. Academic Press, New York.

Jacobson, M. (1968a). *Develop. Biol.* **17**, 202.

Jacobson, M. (1968b). *Develop. Biol.* **17**, 219.

Jacobson, M. (1969). *Science* **163**, 543.

Jacobson, M. (1970a). *In* "The Neurosciences: Second Study Program" (F. O. Schmitt, ed.), pp. 116–129. Rockefeller Univ. Press, New York.

Jacobson, M. (1970b). "Developmental Neurobiology." Holt, New York.

Jacobson, M. (1973). *In* "Studies on the Development of Behavior and the Nervous System" (G. Gottlieb, ed.). Academic Press, New York.

Jacobson, M., and Gaze, R. M. (1965). *Exp. Neurol.* **13**, 418.

Jacobson, M., and Hirsch, H. V. B. (1973). *Brain Res.* **49**, 47.

Jacobson, M., and Hunt, R. K. (1973a). *Sci. Amer.* **228**, 26.

Jacobson, M., and Hunt, R. K. (1973b). In preparation.

Jacobson, M., Hirsch, H. V. B., Duda, M., and Hunt, R. K. (1973). Submitted for publication.

Jansen, J. K. S., and Nicholls, J. G. (1972). *Nat. Acad. Sci. U.S.* **69**, 636.

Keating, M. J., and Gaze, R. M. (1970). *Quart. J. Exp. Physiol. Cog. Med. Sci.* **55**, 284.

Knapp, H., Scalia, F., and Riss, W. (1965). *Acta Neurol. Scand.* **41**, 325.

Lawrence, P. A. (1970). *Advan. Insect Physiol.* **7**, 197.

Lawrence, P. A., Crick, F. H. C., and Monro, M. (1972). *J. Cell Sci.* **11**, 815.

Lázár, G., and Székely, G. (1967). *J. Hirnforsch.* **9**, 329.

Lázár, G., and Székely, G. (1969). *Brain Res.* **16**, 1.

Lettvin, J. Y., Maturana, H. R., McCulloch, W. S., and Pitts, W. H. (1959). *Proc. Inst. Radio Eng. N.Y.* **47**, 1940.

Levine, R., and Jacobson, M. (1974). Submitted for review.

LoPresti, V., Macagno, E. R., and Levinthal, C. (1973). *Proc. Nat. Acad. Sci. U.S.* **70**, 433.

Macagno, E. R., LoPresti, V., and Levinthal, C. (1973). *Proc. Nat. Acad. Sci. U.S.* **70**, 57.

Mark, R. F., and Feldman, J. (1972). *Invest. Ophthalmol.* **11**, 402.

Maturana, H. R. (1959). *Nature (London)* **183**, 1406.

Maturana, H. R., Lettvin, J. Y., McCulloch, W. S., and Pitts, W. H. (1959). *Science* **130,** 1709.

Maturana, H. R., Lettvin, J. Y., McCulloch, W. S., and Pitts, W. H. (1960). *J. Gen. Physiol. Suppl.* **43,** 129.

Metcalf, D. (1966). "The Thymus." Springer-Verlag, Berlin and New York.

Meyer, R., and Sperry, R. W. (1973). *Exp. Neurol.* **40,** 525.

Mountcastle, V. B. (1957). *J. Neurophysiol.* **20,** 408.

Muntz, W. R. A. (1962). *J. Neurophysiol.* **25,** 699.

Nabokov, V. (1966). "Speak, Memory." Putnam, New York.

Piatt, J. (1948). *Biol. Rev. Cambridge Phil. Soc.* **23,** 1.

Polyak, S. L. (1941). "The Retina," p. 437. Univ. of Chicago Press, Chicago, Illinois.

Popper, K. (1962). "Conjectures and Refutations: The Growth of Scientific Knowledge," p. 241. Routledge & Kegan Paul Ltd., London.

Potter, H. D. (1969). *J. Comp. Neurol.* **136,** 203.

Potter, H. D. (1972). *J. Comp. Neurol.* **144,** 269.

Prestige, M. C. (1967a). *J. Embryol. Exp. Morphol.* **17,** 453.

Prestige, M. C. (1967b). *J. Embryol. Exp. Morphol.* **18,** 359.

Prestige, M. C. (1970). *In* "The Neurosciences: Second Study Program" (F. O. Schmitt, ed.), pp. 73–82. Rockefeller Univ. Press, New York.

Rakic, P., and Sidman, R. L. (1972). *J. Neuropathol. Exp. Neurol.* **31,** 192.

Roth, S. (1968). *Develop. Biol.* **18,** 602.

Roth, S., McGuire, E., and Roseman, S. (1971). *J. Cell. Biol.* **51,** 525.

Scalia, F. (1972). *J. Comp. Neurol.* **145,** 223.

Sharma, S. C. (1967). Ph.D. Thesis, Edinburgh University.

Sharma, S. C. (1972a). *Proc. Nat. Acad. Sci. U.S.* **69,** 2637.

Sharma, S. C. (1972b). *Exp. Neurol.* **34,** 171.

Sharma, S. C. (1972c). *Exp. Neurol.* **35,** 358.

Sharma, S. C. (1972d). *Nature (London) New Biol.* **238,** 286.

Sharma, S. C., and Gaze, R. M. (1971). *Arch. Biol. Ilal.* **109,** 357.

Skarf, B. (1973). *Brain Res.* In press.

Skarf, B., and Jacobson, M. (1974). *Exp. Neurol.* In press.

Sklar, J., and Hunt, R. K. (1973). *Proc. Nat. Acad. Sci. U.S.* **70.** In press.

Smart, I. (1961). *J. Comp. Neurol.* **116,** 325.

Sperry, R. W. (1945). *J. Neurophysiol.* **8,** 15.

Sperry, R. W. (1950). *In* "Genetic Neurology" (P. Weiss, ed.), pp. 232–239. Univ. of Chicago Press, Chicago, Illinois.

Sperry, R. W. (1951a). *In* "Handbook of Experimental Psychology" (S. S. Stevens, ed.), pp. 236–280. Wiley, New York.

Sperry, R. W. (1951b). *Growth, Symp.* **10,** 63.

Sperry, R. W. (1963). *Proc. Nat. Acad. Sci. U.S.* **50,** 703.

Sperry, R. W. (1965). *In* "Organogenesis" (R. L. Dehaan and H. Ursprung, eds.), pp. 161–186. Holt, New York.

Stone, L. S. (1944). *Proc. Soc. Exp. Biol. Med.* **57,** 13.

Stone, L. S. (1960). *J. Exp. Zool.* **145,** 85.

Straznicky, K. (1973). *J. Embryol. Exp. Morphol.* **29,** 397.

Straznicky, K., and Gaze, R. M. (1971). *J. Embryol. Exp. Morphol.* **26,** 67.

Straznicky, K., and Gaze, R. M. (1972). *J. Embryol. Exp. Morphol.* **28,** 87.

Straznicky, K., Gaze, R. M., and Keating, M. J. (1971). *J. Embryol. Exp. Morphol.* **26,** 523.

Straznicky, K., Gaze, R. M., and Keating, M. J. (1971a). *Proc. Int. Union Physiol. Sci.* **9,** 540.

Straznicky, K., Keating, M. J., and Gaze, R. M. (1974). *J. Embryol. Exp. Morphol.* In press.

Swett, F. H. (1937). *Quart. Rev. Biol.* **12,** 322.

Székely, G. (1954). *Acta Physiol. Acad. Sci. Hung.* **6,** Suppl. 18.

Székely, G. (1971). *Vision. Res. Suppl.* **3,** 269.

Weiss, P. (1947). *Yale J. Biol. Med.* **19,** 235.

Weiss, P. (1955). *In* "Analysis of Development" (B. H. Willier, P. Weiss, and V. Hamburger, eds.), pp. 346–401. Saunders, Philadelphia, Pennsylvania.

Wolpert, L. (1969). *J. Theoret. Biol.* **25,** 1.

Wolpert, L. (1971). *Curr. Topics Develop. Biol.* **6,** 183.

Yoon, M. (1971). *Exp. Neurol.* **33,** 395.

Yoon, M. (1972a). *Exp. Neurol.* **35,** 565.

Yoon, M. (1972b). *Exp. Neurol.* **37,** 451.

Yoon, M. (1973). *J. Physiol. (London)* **233,** 575.

SUBJECT INDEX

A

Alkaline phosphatase, in trophoblast differentiation, 172–173
Antibody, production of, DNA replication as prerequisite for, 28–33

B

Blastocysts, of mammalian embryos, manipulation studies on, 173
Bromodeoxyuridine
    as differentiation inhibitor, 92–94
    effects on cartilage, 118–125

C

Cartilage
    BUdR effects on, 118–125
    chondroitin sulfate synthesis and, 106–109
    collagen of, 109–110
    culture of, 111–112
    definition of, 104
    differentiation of, 103–149
    formation by somites, 112–114
    glycosaminoglycans of, 105–106
    in vitro studies on, 110–118
Chondrogenesis, of limbs, 114–118
Chondroitin sulfate, biosynthesis of, 106–109
Collagen, synthesis of, 109–110

D

Differentiation, in early mammalian embryo, 151–178
Dimethylformamide, effects on erythroleukemic cells, 92–94
Dimethyl sulfoxide
    effects on erythroleukemic cells, 84–92
    inhibition of, 92–94
DNA
    replication of, as prerequisite for antibody production, 28–33
    RNA transcriptional activity in embryonic development, 190–192
Drosophila imaginal discs
    cellular determination in, 41–58
    defect experiments, 48–49

evidence for, 45–48
    genetic mosaics, 55–57
    mutants, 50–55
    transplantation experiments, 49–50
specification and pattern formation in, 58–79

E

Embryo
    differential gene activity in, 179–202
    in preimplantation development, 181–186
    RNA transcription in, 186–195
    mammalian, differentiation of, 151–178
    emancipation from female reproductive tract, 152–155
    induction studies, 176
    inner cell mass derivatives, 173–176
    in preimplantation embryo, 155–170
Erythroleukemic cells, murine-virus induced
    differentiation in, 81–101
    enhancement of, 84–92
    iron metabolism, hemoglobin synthesis and, 83–84

G

Genes, differential activity of, in mammalian embryo, 179–202
Glycosaminoglycans, of cartilage, 105–106

H

Hemoglobin synthesis, in erythroleukemic cells, 83–84

I

Imaginal discs
    of *Drosophila*, cellular determination and pattern formation in, 41–79
    general features of, 42–45
Immune reactivity, induction of, 33–35
Immunogenic signals
    cell receptors for, 5–8
        for carrier determinants, 6–8
        nature of, 24–27
    lymphocyte reception of, 1–39